THE MODERN
HOME PHYSICIAN

A COMPLETE GUIDE TO THE ATTAINMENT AND PRESERVATION OF HEALTH

BY

DR. ANDREW WILSON, F.R.S.E., F.L.S., Etc.

LECTURER ON PHYSIOLOGY AND HEALTH TO
THE GEORGE COMBE TRUST; GILCHRIST TRUST
LECTURER; FORMERLY EXAMINER IN THE
FACULTY OF MEDICINE, UNIVERSITY OF GLASGOW

ASSISTED BY A STAFF OF EXPERT CONTRIBUTORS

PROFUSELY ILLUSTRATED BY COLOURED PLATES AND
MODELS, PHOTOGRAPHS, DIAGRAMS AND WOODCUTS

VOLUME II

CAXTON PUBLISHING COMPANY, LIMITED
CLUN HOUSE, SURREY STREET, LONDON, W.C.2.

Made and Printed in Great Britain by
Hazell, Watson & Viney, Ld., London and Aylesbury.
5450

PHOTO BY MAULL & FOX

MAJ.-GEN. SIR RICHARD HAVELOCK CHARLES, G.C.V.O., K.C.S.I., K.C.V.O., I.M.S., M.D.,Q.U.I., F.R.C.S.I., LL.D., F.R.S.L.

BORN 1858. KNIGHT OF GRACE OF THE ORDER OF ST. JOHN,
EDUCATED QUEEN'S COLLEGE, CORK; DUBLIN; LONDON; PARIS;
BERLIN; VIENNA, SERGEANT-SURGEON TO THE KING; FORMERLY
PHYSICIAN IN ORDINARY TO PRINCE OF WALES. PAST PRESIDENT
ROYAL SOCIETY OF TROPICAL MEDICINE AND HYGIENE; DEAN
LONDON SCHOOL OF TROPICAL MEDICINE; FORMERLY PROFESSOR
OF ANATOMY MEDICAL COLLEGES, LAHORE AND CALCUTTA.

CONTENTS

SECTION I

THE CHEMICAL COMPOSITION OF THE BODY

SECTION II

THE DIGESTIVE SYSTEM AND DIGESTION

SECTION III

DISEASES OF THE DIGESTIVE SYSTEM

Contents

SECTION IV

DISEASES OF THE SKIN

SECTION V

DISEASES OF THE KIDNEYS

SECTION VI

ANIMAL PARASITES AND THE DISEASES THEY CAUSE

Contents

SECTION VII

THE ANATOMY AND PHYSIOLOGY OF THE EYE

SECTION VIII

AMBULANCE OR "FIRST-AID" WORK

NOTE

A FULL GENERAL INDEX
WILL BE FOUND AT THE
END OF VOLUME V

LIST OF ILLUSTRATIONS

THE MODERN PHYSICIAN

SECTION I

THE CHEMICAL COMPOSITION OF THE BODY

In the previous volume of this work reference was made to the general build which the body of man exhibits. It was then shown that the bodies of all Vertebrated or "backboned" animals are constructed on one and the same plan. This plan practically exhibits a double tube arrangement. The upper tube, or that of the back (Fig. 1), contains the nervous system (*b*), and is represented by the skull and spine (*a*). The lower tube includes the rest of the body, being bounded below by the ribs and by the walls of the abdomen. This second tube contains, first, a portion of the nervous system, known as the "Sympathetic" (*f*); below it, and in the middle of the tube, lies the digestive system (*c*), whilst below this latter, in turn, and therefore nearest the ground when the animal walks, is the heart (*e*). This

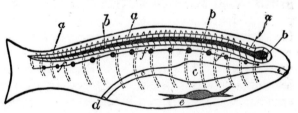

FIG. 1.—Plan of the Vertebrate Body, showing Spine (*a*), Nervous System (*b*), Digestive System (*c*), and Heart (*e*). The Sympathetic Nervous System is shown at *f*; *d*, anus.

disposition of organs and parts is universal throughout the backboned type of animals, and man agrees with all other Vertebrated animals on the general plan on which his body is constructed.

Organic and Inorganic Chemistry.—It is necessary, however, to dive a little more deeply into the constitution of the body in order to obtain an adequate idea of its construction. There are two phases of our bodily build which demand attention in order that our vital functions may be the more easily comprehended. The first of these aspects includes the examination of the *Chemical Composition* of the body, whilst the second aspect has reference to its *Microscopic Structure* or *Histology*, as this latter branch of science is termed.

Most readers are aware of the fact that *Chemistry* is the science which deals with the ultimate composition of matter, analysing out the different kinds and forms of matter into their ultimate elements. We may familiarly illustrate this statement by the example of the air we breathe or the food we consume. Chemistry in such a case supplies us with the definite knowledge of the composition of either substance. There is, however, a special department of chemistry which applies itself to the examination of the composition of living bodies; that is to say, to the nature of the tissues of animals and plants. This branch of the science is termed *Organic Chemistry*. It is so named in opposition to that branch of the science which deals with the composition of non-living substances, this latter aspect being known as that of *Inorganic Chemistry*.

It need hardly be said that the examination of living beings constitutes a much more complex matter than the analysis of non-living materials. Yet the science of the chemist has been more than adequate to the demonstration of certain very important facts regarding living bodies, such as lead us to a definite knowledge of the manner in which their functions are performed.

The Chemistry of the Body.—Dealing first of all with the composition of the human body at large, we find it to consist of a certain number of " elements," all of which, it should be noted, occur in the world around us. This last is an important and interesting fact, for it teaches us that, in so far as the chemical groundwork of our frames is concerned, there is no element found in our bodies which does not exist as part and parcel of the material universe around us. A parallel instance may be found in the case of astronomy, seeing that the astronomer, by the aid of the *spectroscope*, analysing the light of the sun and stars, shows us that a similarity of composition can be demonstrated to exist in our own planet and in " other worlds than ours." Regarded from a broad point of view, therefore, the chemical composition, not merely of our own bodies but of the world they inhabit and of the external universe as well, demonstrates an entire unity which is as remarkable as it is interesting to contemplate.

In a human body we find that about 30 per cent. consists of *solid matters* and 60 per cent. of *water*. This fact alone is of extreme importance, because, apart from the demonstration that our bodies are composed of water to the extent of two-thirds or thereby, it also teaches us the great importance of water as a food. It is because of this universal distribution of water in every tissue and cell of the body that it is imperatively and constantly demanded as an essential part of our food-supply. We also note in this fact the explanation of the greater pangs we suffer when deprived of water, as compared with those experienced from the lack of solid food Hunger, in other words, is a condition which tends, at first at least, to affect the stomach alone ; whereas in the case of the person deprived of water, every cell of his body may be said to be crying aloud for a supply of this necessary constituent of the food.

Our Solids.—The *solid matters* of our bodies may be divided into two classes. The first class includes substances which are also found in the outside world, and which may be called *Inorganic* in nature. The second class of substances found in the body includes materials peculiar to living beings. Hence these latter are termed *Organic* in nature. At the same time it must be noted that the "elements" which unite to compose both groups of materials are all found in the world around us. It is really the special mode in which certain "elements" are combined, that constitutes the difference between the *Organic* (or living) and *Inorganic* (or non-living) constituents of our frames.

Our "Elements."—An "element," chemically regarded, is any substance which cannot by analysis be split up or decomposed into two or more different substances. A "compound," on the other hand, is a substance built up, or composed of two or more elements. Thus *Hydrogen* is an element, as also is *Oxygen.* If the two be united in certain proportions we find water to be formed, the chemist denoting this compound in his own way by the symbol H_2O, thus implying that water is composed of two parts of *Hydrogen* and one of *Oxygen.* Similarly, common salt is a compound to which the chemical name of *Chloride of Sodium* is given, and if this substance be analysed it is found to consist of two elements, one known as *Chlorine* and the other as *Sodium.* The "elements" found in the human body consist of *Oxygen, Hydrogen, Nitrogen, Carbon, Sodium, Potassium, Magnesium, Ammonium, Lime (Calcium), Fluorine, Chlorine, Iron, Iodine, Silicon, Sulphur, Phosphorus,* with traces of *Manganese, Copper, Lead,* and in some cases even of *Arsenic.* These elements may be regarded as the chemical bricks of which the body is built up, but it should be noted that very few of them exist in the body as "elements." On the contrary, they are found to be represented mostly in the shape of "compounds," two or more of them uniting to form the latter bodies. We, however, find *Oxygen* existing in a free state, that is, by itself in the blood. *Nitrogen* is a gas which also occurs under like conditions. The compounds formed by the union of these elements, as we have seen, are classified into *Inorganic* and *Organic* substances. Examples of the inorganic compounds occurring in the outer world, as well as in our own bodies, are found in such substances as Water and the Chlorides of Sodium (common salt), Potassium, Magnesium, and Ammonium. *Phosphates* exist in the shape of these compounds of Lime, Sodium, Magnesium, and Potassium. *Carbonates* are represented by those of Lime and Sodium. In addition we find in the body Sulphates of Potassium and of Sodium ; whilst Fluoride of Lime is also to be reckoned with as a bodily constituent, although present in mere traces. In the gastric juice which the stomach throws out upon the food we also find a common acid known as " Hydrochloric Acid." It is known familiarly in ordinary life as "Spirits of Salt."

Inorganic Compounds.—The distribution of the compounds of "Inorganic" nature found in the body is of a very varied character. Thus phosphate of lime constitutes, as described in the section on the skeleton (vol. i.), the great bulk of our bones and of our teeth. The wide distribution of water in every tissue of the body has already been indicated. The compounds of potassium and sodium exist in the blood as part of its normal composition, and in this fluid also, we find iron giving the red colour to the blood. The practice of giving iron as a blood tonic is founded upon the knowledge of the fact that this element forms an essential part of the vital fluid. Common salt (chloride of sodium) is another example of a widely distributed inorganic compound in our bodies, seeing that it occurs in well-nigh every fluid of the body from the blood to the tears, and from the gastric juice of the stomach to the urine and perspiration.

Organic Compounds.—The *Organic compounds* of the body we have seen to be those which are peculiar to living beings. They represent, as it were, the special work of life as a chemical builder, but the materials used are the same as those which nature employs in forming her non-living compounds. It is the special mode of combination of the elements which imparts to the organic compounds their specific characters. Briefly detailed, the organic compounds found in our bodies are divided into those known as *Nitrogenous, Albuminous,* or *Proteid* substances, and not those termed *Non-Nitrogenous.* The "elements" entering into the composition of the nitrogenous compounds are *carbon, hydrogen, oxygen,* and *nitrogen,* with traces of *sulphur* and *phosphorus.* It may be said that such compounds represent the most vital or typically living parts of our frames. *Protoplasm,* or the "matter of life" itself, is a "nitrogenous" substance, as also are such bodies as egg-albumen (or white of egg), the nitrogenous part of muscle (*myosin*), the *serum-albumen* of blood, and also the *fibrin* of the blood, this latter compound being found when the blood clots or coagulates. Other examples of nitrogenous compounds are found in the *casein* or "curd" of milk, which bulks largely in the manufacture of cheese, in *gluten* found in flour and other vegetable products, and in the nitrogenous substance of peas, beans, lentils, known as *legumen*. It is this latter substance which renders these latter vegetables highly nutritious articles of food. In addition to these bodies, certain other nitrogenous compounds are found in the body, and are exemplified by *gelatin*, occurring in hoofs, horns, and bones, and by *chondrin* obtained from gristle or cartilage.

Fats, Starches, and Sugars.—The second class of "Organic compounds" found in the body is represented by *fats and oils*. These bodies represent the non-nitrogenous class, because, composed of carbon, hydrogen, and oxygen, they exhibit a want of nitrogen. Different kinds of fats are to be enumerated in our bodily composition. Thus, *stearin* found in tallow candles, *olein* obtained from olive oil, and *palmatin* are the chief ingredients in the fat of the body. Fat itself forms an important tissue. It is found in the body as a layer, which, being of non-conducting character, tends to preserve our bodily heat; whilst it may also be described as constituting a packing for various organs. The eyeball, for instance, rests on a cushion of this substance.

The second class of "non-nitrogenous" compounds is represented by *starches* and *sugars*, which are really very nearly allied in composition. Like the *fats*, they consist of carbon, nitrogen, and oxygen, but contain less carbon than fatty materials. In the starches and sugars the *hydrogen* and *oxygen* exist in the proportions represented in water. Whilst a large amount of starch and of sugar is consumed as food, very little of these substances is found stored in the body, but we find a form of starch called *glycogen* stored in the liver, whilst *grape sugar* occurs in the blood, *muscle sugar* (also called *inosite*) in muscle, and *sugar of milk* or *lactose* in that fluid.

A Summary.—Summing up the general features included in the consideration of the chemical constitution of the body, we may say that it consists primarily of two great classes of substances, of which water and mineral matters represent the inorganic constituents, whilst nitrogenous substances and the non-nitrogenous starches, sugars, and fats represent the organic matters, these last being found in living beings only. The percentages of the various substances going to build up a human body may be stated as follows: Water, 61.0 per cent.; minerals, 5.5; nitrogenous or proteid matters, 18.0; starches and sugars, 0.1; and fats, 15.4.

THE BODY'S MICROSCOPIC STRUCTURE

While the chemist has demonstrated for us in an interesting fashion the composition of our frames, viewed from a standpoint which teaches us the nature of the substances whereof our body is built up, the microscopist deals with the nature of our bodily composition from a different, but equally important aspect. Viewing the body as a living machine, it becomes necessary to understand the manner in which such a complex organism performs the many duties included in the discharge of vital actions.

Cells and Fibres.—The science of *Histology* is that which seeks to investigate the ultimate machinery of the body and the material composition of the tissues of which it consists. It is not sufficient for the purpose of the physiologist or medical man that the body should be regarded merely as a collection of organs, each devoted to the performance of a special work or duty. By aid of the microscope we have been enabled to peer into the inner working of animals and plants, and to gain a knowledge of the manner in which their organs are enabled to perform the often complicated duties which represent in their totality the act of living. Viewed thus by the microscopist, the body may be said to be built up of two sets of elements or structures. These are *cells* and *fibres*. As, however, the whole body originates out of a single " cell," and as in its earlier stages it consists of cells alone (fibres being ultimately formed from cells), we can realise the high importance of the " cell," so to speak, as the structural unit of the whole frame. We may assume that the element known as a " cell " represents the foundation not merely of man's body, but of the bodies of all other living things. The lowest animals and plants each consist of a single " cell," which is capable of feeding, moving, and reproducing its like as perfectly in its own way as do the higher animals and plants. Thus, as an *Amœba* and an allied *Animalcule* (Fig. 2), each represents a living " cell " which carries on within the limits of its own microscopic body all the duties of life. In the same way a *yeast plant* represents in itself one cell, giving rise through its vital actions, when placed in a solution of sugar, to the phenomena of fermentation.

The Bodily Country.—The most interesting, and at the same time the most satisfactory, fashion of dealing with the microscopic structure of the body is that of comparing it to a country, the inhabitants of which are grouped together in colonies. Each colony might be said to represent a group of individuals, the separate units of the colony being represented by its " cells." A colony of cells forming an organ of the frame, discharges its own special duties in the way of bodily work. A further view of the constitution of the body, regarded from the microscopical standpoint, would, however, teach us that, as in a country, all the individuals are not of equal rank and importance, so in our bodily territory the cells exhibit analogous differences and variations.

The Bodily Population.—Thus cells which form the upper layer of the skin (Fig. 3, 1 c) are, for example, of much less importance than the cells forming the under layer (b), and these latter in turn are of less value, so to speak, than, say, the cells found in the liver or those occupied in the manufacture of the gastric juice of the stomach. Again, as in a country, we have a govern-

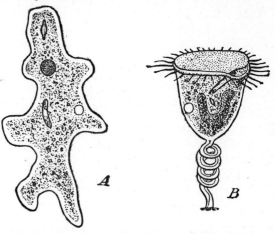

FIG. 2.—A, an *Amœba* (highly magnified), a low Animal composed of a minute mass of Protoplasm; B, an Infusorian Animalcule showing movement of coiling on its Stalk.

ing body, represented, say, by its Parliament, presumably composed of the best minds of the nation, so in our frames we find certain cells elevated to the position of controlling the interests of the whole economy. Such cells are termed *nerve cells*, these representing the highest development of our cell constitution. We may, however, go further, and if we assume that the Cabinet represents, in turn, the essence of the wisdom of the governing body, we may find in certain cells of our brain the highest type of the individual unit, representing the essence of our personality.

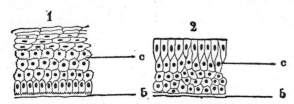

FIG. 3.—Epithelial Cells showing Arrangement of Cells in such a Layer as the Skin.

In 1 the cells form a basis (b) which gives origin to the upper layer of cells (c). These last are cast off and renewed from below. In 2 the cells are of different type—b is the basis, and c the upper cells.

The Importance of Cells.—From what has just been said, the conclusion may easily be drawn that the whole life and work of a human body is represented by the life and work of its cells. Every vital action is carried out through the agency of these microscopic units, which, it must be noted, are essentially living things. Like

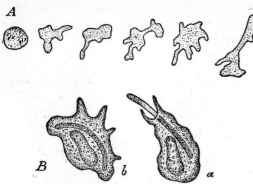

FIG. 4.—*A*, A White Corpuscle moving about through Changes in its Shape. *B*, Two White Corpuscles; one at *a* engaged in attacking a Disease Germ; at *b*, the same Corpuscle is seen having completely invested the Germ.

the ordinary population of a country, many of them die off to be replaced by others. The cells thus reflect, in their life-history, that of the body at large. Viewing them as the body's workmen, we thus discover that the cells of the liver, for example, are engaged in the manufacture of bile, and in the other duties which that organ discharges. The cells of the salivary glands are engaged in the work of manufacturing saliva, or the "water" of the mouth—the blood in each case forming the raw material out of which each group of cells is capable, in a very wonderful fashion, of elaborating the special products of the organ to which they belong. The cells of the glands of the stomach are similarly makers of gastric juice, just as those of the pancreas or "sweetbread" manufacture the particular secretion of that gland which is poured upon the food. Other cells existing in the blood (Fig. 4), as already described (vol. i. p. 92), discharge duties of an important nature comparable to the action of a sanitary police force, in that they are capable of attacking and destroying disease germs which may gain admittance to our bodies. Again, other cells, such as those of the skin and of muscle, assist in forming the tissues of the body. In the living bone (vol. i. p. 77) we find special cells which are not merely devoted to the work of bone-formation, but are also responsible for the repair of bone-

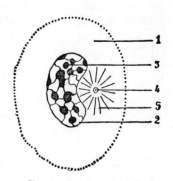

FIG. 5.—Diagram of a Cell.

1, The Protoplasm or Living Matter; 2, the Nucleus; 3, the Nucleolus; 4, the Centrosome; 5, Directing Sphere of Cell.

injuries. Finally, rising above these ordinary body cells in importance we find "nerve cells," representing, as we have seen, the controlling units of the organism, whilst included in this latter category are "brain cells," certain groups of which exercise the highest functions of mind.

Sizes of Cells.—This general view of cells will suffice to impart an adequate idea of the real constitution of our frames. With regard to the size of cells, it may be said that they are in all cases bodies of microscopic dimensions. Probably the largest cell connected with the frame is that which constitutes the *ovum* or *germ*, from which the body springs. The size of this cell is the $\frac{1}{120}$th part of an inch in diameter. Other cells vary in size from the $\frac{1}{300}$th part of an inch to the $\frac{1}{5000}$th part. Many of the cells of the nervous system exhibit the most minute sizes. It can therefore be understood that in dealing with the smallest cells the highest powers of our best microscopes are required for their examination.

FIG. 6.—Epithelial Cells from the Mouth.

1, Protoplasm; 2, Nucleus; 3, Borders of Neighbour-Cells.

What is a Cell?—The general idea of a "cell" is that of a microscopic body or structure varying in shape, but typically of a rounded form, and composed of *protoplasm* or living matter (Fig. 5, 1), in which is embedded a similar body, the *nucleus* (2). Attached to the nucleus we find a still similar particle, known as the *nucleolus* (3). In most living cells also is found a particle called the *centrosome* (4).

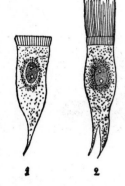

FIG. 7.

1, Cylindrical Epithelial Cells lining Digestive System; 2, Ciliated Cells from Windpipe and Lungs.

This latter body takes a prominent part in the process of division of the cell which results in the production of new cells.

Varieties of Cells.—As has been indicated, cells vary materially in their nature and structure, according to the position they occupy in the body, and according to the duties they are called upon to discharge. Simple cells are represented by those known as *epithelial cells*. They are represented by those of the skin (Fig. 3) and those of the lining membrane of the *mouth* (Fig. 6). More elaborate cells are those which discharge functions connected with the *breathing* or *digestive organs*. We thus find what are called *columnar epithelial cells* (Fig. 7, 1) lining the digestive system. In the windpipe and air passages of the lungs we find other cells called *ciliated cells* (Fig. 7, 2). Forming part of what is known as *connective tissue*, which is found under the *skin* in the covering of muscles, and constituting a general protective layer to the organs of the body, *cells* of another type (Fig. 8) are found, whilst fat itself consists of *adipose cells*, exhibiting a definite type of structure (Fig. 9). Fat cells vary in diameter from the $\frac{1}{400}$th part of an inch to the $\frac{1}{500}$th part.

The Work of Cells.—The cells of the body thus described, **it** may be again noted, are living things. Each cell, like the body to which it belongs, is capable of feeding and nourishing itself from the blood supplied to it, of reproducing other cells, and of discharging, as we have seen, the special work it is called upon to perform in the economy of the body. We have already noted that the essential constituent of every cell is *protoplasm*, or living matter. No doubt the qualities and characters of the living matter of such cells as brain cells are of an infinitely higher nature than those represented in, say, a cell of the liver, or in a cell of the skin; but the essential feature of the cell, as a bodily workman, is its living

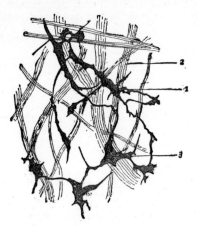

FIG. 8.—Cells of Connective Tissue.

1, Cells joined to others; 2, Connective Tissue Fibres; 3, Nuclei of the Cells.

character, and still more, its power in the case of the germ from which the body springs, of giving origin to all parts of the frame.

Cells and Disease.—The rôle played by cells in the production of disease is an important one. In most *tumours*, for example, we can detect in the substance of these growths cell elements showing that the tumour essentially represents an abnormal form of cell growth. This view of matters has already been discussed in connection with the subject of Cancer (vol. i. p. 111).

Fibres. — With regard to *Fibres*, representing the second class of structural elements found in the body, these are represented by such parts as the fibres of muscle, of nerve, of sinews (or *tendons*).

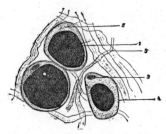

FIG. 9.—Fat or Adipose Cells from the Skin.

1, Cell Contents (Fat); 2, Protoplasm; 3, Nucleus; 4, Cell Wall; 5, Connective Tissue.

A familiar example of fibres is found in those of *yellow elastic tissue* (Fig. 10). Such fibres occur in the skin, in the ligaments that bind bones together, and also in the coats or coverings of blood-vessels. All the fibres of the body are formed primarily from cells. Some fibres illustrate merely the elongation of cells. This latter phase is represented in the case of the fibres of unstriped muscle (vol. i. p. 84), where the component parts of each fibre are seen to be represented by cells of spindle-shape. *Nerve-fibres* may also be mentioned as examples. These, as the telegraph-wires of the body, carry messages to and from the nerve cells which compose the *nerve centres.*

SECTION II

THE DIGESTIVE SYSTEM AND DIGESTION

Digestion is one of the most important functions which the animal and the plant are destined to execute. Upon the performance of the actions included in digestion depends not merely the due nourishment of the animal or plant, but also its growth in early life. Digestion may be defined as that series of actions through which food, or material derived from the outer world, is converted into such a form that it can be applied to the wants and demands of the body. It is a function which includes actions of very different kinds in respect of the effects produced upon the nutriment. It thus involves work of a purely mechanical character, represented for example by the division of the food by the teeth, and it includes chemical actions illustrated by the changes exerted on the food through the various secretions or fluids poured upon the food in the course of its digestive

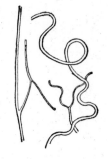

FIG. 10.—Elastic Fibres.

journey. This latter phase of action is represented by the conversion of the starches we consume, which are changed in the mouth into grape sugar, whilst it is also exemplified by the action of the gastric juice of the stomach on nitrogenous foods, and by the action of the bile on fats.

What is a Digestive System.—In order clearly to understand what is implied in the process of digestion, it is necessary, first of all, to refer to the nature of the *Digestive System.* This series of organs in any animal may be described as a tube (Fig. 1) running through the body, into which food is received, and along which it is propelled, being subjected at various stages of its course to the action of the different fluids poured upon it. Such a definition of a digestive system applies equally to the case of a worm and of a man. The difference between the digestive tubes of the lower and the higher animal depends upon, first, their length, and second, the amount of complexity seen in the tubes and in the organs connected therewith. It is easy to show that this tube idea of the digestive system conveys an adequate and correct notion of the organs in question. In the first place (Fig. 12), the *gullet* itself (3), leading from the mouth to the stomach, is a tube. The stomach is merely an expanded part of the tube (Figs. 11 and 12), widened in order that the food may undergo therein certain important changes. Succeeding the stomach, we find the *intestine*, or *bowel* (Fig. 12), which is again a tube of more or less complex character, straight in lower animals, but much convoluted and of longer extent in higher forms of life.

Digestive Glands.—A second idea of importance in connection with gaining a general idea of the digestive system, is that which directs attention to the fact, that attached to the side of the tube we find a series of organs known as *digestive glands*. Such glands are represented by the *salivary glands* of the mouth, by the *gastric glands* imbedded in the walls of the stomach, by the *liver*, by the *sweetbread* or *pancreas*, and by the *glands* which are found in the lining membrane of the *intestine* or *bowel*. Each *gland* opens into the digestive tube, so that it can pour upon the food the special secretion or fluid which the cells of the gland manufacture from the blood. It is the fluids supplied by the digestive glands which produce those changes and alterations in the food, resulting in its conversion into a form suitable for being added to the blood, which fluid it is destined to renew and repair. As the blood forms what we may call the general currency of the body, whence all organs and parts derive

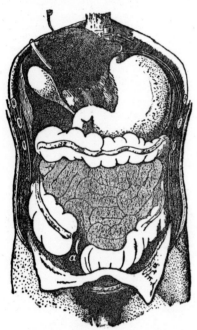

FIG. 11.—Abdomen opened to show the disposition of the digestive tube.

The stomach is seen above to the right, and the under surface of the liver and gallbladder to the left in the illustration. The small bowel and its folds occupy the middle of the body, and the large bowel is arched across; *a* is the *appendix*.

their nutriment, we readily note the high importance of digestion in preparing the way for the due renewal of the vital fluid.

The Digestive Tube.—Having thus gained a general idea of the nature of a digestive system, and of the functions it is intended to subserve, we may now proceed to discuss the various parts of the apparatus included under this head. The digestive tube has the *mouth* for its anterior opening, whilst the intestine or bowel ends at the *anus* (Fig. 12, 14), from which latter aperture are discharged effete matters, representing the waste of the digestive work. With regard to the general structure of the digestive tube, it may be regarded as composed essentially of three layers or coats. The *external* coat is one which, being of somewhat tough or fibrous material, gives shape and form to the tube. This layer is named the *serous coat*. The middle coat is composed of *muscular fibres* of the involuntary description. The *inner coat* is known as the *mucous layer*. Of the three the last is very important, seeing that it comes in contact with the food, and further, because it contains the glands, which, in the case of the gullet, stomach, and intestine, pour out secretions on the food. It may be added that in man the length of the digestive tube is about 28 feet. Of this length the gullet and the stomach each make up about 1 foot; the intestine or bowel comprising 26 feet. Of this latter extent, what is known as the small intestine forms 20 feet, the large intestine being 6 feet in length.

The Divisions of the Tube.—Various names have been given to the divisions of the digestive tube (Fig. 12). If we tabulate these in the order in which they occur, from the mouth onwards, the following table will represent the succession of parts:—

MOUTH.
PHARYNX.
ŒSOPHAGUS (Gullet).

STOMACH.

SMALL INTESTINE . . { Duodenum. Jejunum. Ileum.

LARGE INTESTINE . . { Cæcum. Colon. Rectum.

The Mouth.—The *mouth cavity* (which is bounded by the *lips* in front, by the *palate* above, by the *cheeks* at the sides, and by the *tongue* and a *muscular floor* below) contains not merely the *teeth*, but receives also the secretions of the *salivary glands*, already mentioned as supplying the "water" of the mouth. The roof of the mouth is known as the *hard palate*, formed by the *palatal bones*. At the back of the mouth the *soft palate* (Fig. 13, *d*) is found, this last being formed of muscles covered with *mucous membrane* (or the lining layer of the mouth), and appearing as a kind of fold or curtain arching over the upper part of the throat. In the centre of the soft palate we find a projection or fold, known as the *uvula* (*e*). Passing backwards between the soft palate and the tongue, we find an opening known as the *fauces*. This opening leads into the expanded upper part of the throat, or *pharynx* (*a*), otherwise known as the "food bag." This latter portion of the digestive tube forms, as it were, a connecting link between the mouth in front and the gullet (*j*) below. The pharynx is of high importance in connection with the act of swallowing. At each side of the pharynx we find a *tonsil*, whilst opening into the pharynx itself are the *hinder nostrils* (*c*), the *larynx*, or "organ of voice" (*h*) (representing the upper part of the windpipe), and the two *Eustachian tubes* (*k*), which place the pharynx

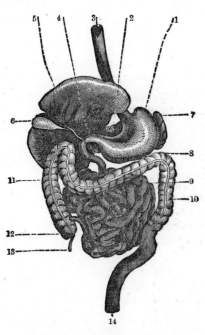

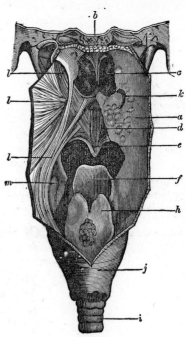

FIG. 12.—The Digestive Organs *in situ.*

1, Stomach; 2, Pancreas; 3, Gullet; 4, Pylorus; 5, Liver; 6, Gall Bladder; 7, Spleen; 8, Transverse Colon; 9, Small Intestine; 10, Descending Colon; 11, Ascending Colon; 12, Cæcum; 13, Appendix (note the small intestine ending in the large at a right angle opposite 12); 14, anus.

FIG. 13.—Dissection of Pharynx from behind.

a, Pharynx opened up; *b*, Base of Skull; *c*, Hinder Nostrils; *d*, Soft Palate; *e*, Uvula; *f*, Epiglottis; *h*, Cartilages of Larynx; *i*, Windpipe; *j*, Œsophagus; *k*, Eustachian Tube; *l*, Muscles of Palate; *m*, Tonsil.

in connection with the inner side of the drum of the ear (middle ear). The gullet itself, it will be understood, is the continuation of the pharynx downwards into the stomach.

The Mouth Glands.—The mucous membrane, covering both the hard and soft palate, is well supplied with nerves, which, along with those of the tongue, exercise the sense of taste; whilst in this membrane we also find numerous little mucous glands which throw out upon the surface of the membrane their secretion, known as *mucus*, devoted to keeping the parts moist, and lubricating them for the passage of the food.

Salivary Glands.—Opening into the mouth we find the *salivary glands* (Fig. 14). These number three pairs, and, as has already been noted, manufacture the *saliva* or "*water*" of the mouth. The largest of the three pairs is known as the *parotid glands* (*a*). Each of these glands lies in front of, and below the ear. The saliva it manufactures is carried into the mouth by a tube called *Stenson's*

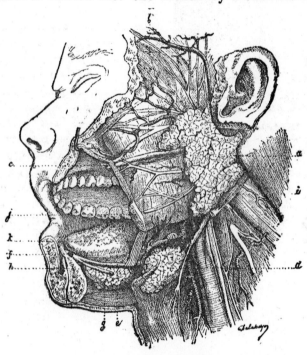

Fig. 14—Dissection of Face showing *a*, Parotid Gland ; *b*, Stenson's Duct ; *c*, its opening into the mouth ; *d*, Submaxillary Gland ; *e*, Wharton's Duct ; *f*, its opening ; *g*, Sublingual Gland ; *h*, Bartholini's Duct ; *i*, Masseter Muscle ; *j*, cut end of Muscle ; *k*, Tongue.

duct (*b*), which, passing through the cheek, enters the mouth opposite the *second* upper molar or grinding tooth. It is the parotid glands which become inflamed and swollen in the disease known as "Mumps" (vol. i.). The second pair of salivary glands are the *submaxillaries* (*d*). These glands lie, one on each side beneath the lower jaw, close to the angle of the bone. The saliva of these glands is poured into the mouth through a tube called *Wharton's duct*. This tube (*e*) on each side opens close to the structure called the *frenum*, which ties the tongue to the floor of the mouth. The third pair of salivary glands is known as the *sublinguals* (*g*). These are imbedded in the floor of the mouth. They open by numerous little *ducts* or *tubes* (*h*) near to "Wharton's duct" itself. In respect of their structure the salivary glands show us a branched and grape-like arrangement of their parts or *lobules* (Fig. 14), the cells which secrete the saliva being contained within the grape-like divisions (see Fig. 15). It may be added that variations in the quality and composition of saliva are noted in respect of the special glands by which it is manufactured. Most solids occur in the secretions of the *sublingual glands*, whilst that of the *parotid glands* contains the lowest percentage of such materials. It is probably the combination of the secretions of the three pairs of glands which represents the typical saliva of service in digestion.

FIG. 15.—The minute structure of a Salivary Gland.

The Tongue and its Papillæ.—The *tongue* (*k*), in addition to serving along with the palate as the organ of taste, also discharges important duties in connection with the preparation of the food for swallowing. It is attached behind to a special bone known as the *hyoid bone*, and consists of muscles covered with mucous membrane. Below it is attached to the lower jaw in front by the band already noticed, called the *frenum* or "bridle." On the upper surface of the tongue we find a number of projections known as *papillæ*. These are organs of taste, and also exercise the sense of touch. The papillæ are of various kinds. Thus at the back of the tongue, in a reversed "V"-shaped form, we find those papillæ known as *circumvallate*. These number from ten to twelve. At the point of the "V" a large papilla, known as the *foramen cæcum*, is found. These papillæ derive their name from the fact that each resembles in shape a Roman camp, having a central portion, with a groove or ditch around it. The other papillæ found on the tongue are known as *filiform papillæ*. They are very numerous, and are distinguished by the fact that their extremities are divided into brush-like *ends*. The third variety of papillæ is known as the *fungiform* kind. They are less numerous than the "filiform" variety, and are irregularly disposed over the surface of the tongue. It is these latter papillæ which, in the "strawberry tongue" of scarlet fever, appear as red points projecting from the coating of the organ. In all probability the "fungiform" papillæ assist in exercising the sense of *taste*. The "filiform" papillæ, on the other hand, are regarded as being more closely connected with the breaking down or trituration of the food. In certain lower animals, and notably in the lion and cat tribes, it is these *papillæ*, which, converted into horny projections, enable the animals to scrape flesh from the bones of their prey.

The Teeth.—The *teeth* form important objects in connection with the furnishing of the mouth. Each tooth is fixed in a socket, situated in the border of its jaw. Two sets of teeth are developed in man (Fig. 19), the first being known as the "milk" or "temporary" set, and the second series as the "permanent" set.

With regard to its structure, each tooth (Fig. 16) is composed of *dentine* or *ivory* (*b*). This substance, largely consisting of phosphate of lime, is not to be confused with bone, from which it differs materially in structure. Its examination under the microscope shows us that its substance is permeated by fine *tubes* running at right angles to the long axis of the tooth. These tubes, it may be added, contain fine projections of the *dental pulp* (*b*), which fills the *cavity* or inner hollow of the tooth. This "pulp" is a delicate substance, well supplied with nerves and blood-vessels. The pain of toothache arises from tooth-decay, exposing the pulp to the irritating influences of cold, or the secretions of the mouth.

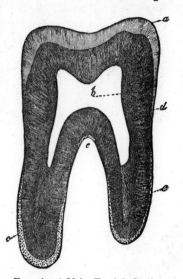

FIG. 16.—A Molar Tooth in Section.
a, Enamel; *b*, Ivory or Dentine; *c*, Cement; *d*, Body of Tooth (*b* is placed in the Pulp-cavity).

The *crowns* or tops of the teeth are formed of *enamel* (*a*), the hardest substance in the body, and one giving to the teeth their bright and shining appearance. At the root of each tooth we find a third substance, known as *cement*, or *crusta petrosa* (*c*). This latter substance, of all the structures found in a tooth, most nearly resembles *bone*.

The Nature of Teeth.—The development of the teeth clearly shows that they are to be regarded as *skin-structures*, and not in any sense as belonging to the skeleton proper. Each tooth is developed in a little *sac* or *bag*, which appears in the "gum" or lining membrane of the mouth. As this membrane merely represents the skin of the body folded inwards at the mouth, any structures formed by it must, therefore, be regarded as closely related to *nails*, *hairs*, and to the *feathers* of birds. Indeed, all these organs are formed in much the same fashion, the difference being chiefly seen in the material which is employed by nature in their formation. Limy material is thus found in the case of teeth, and horny matter in the case of nails, hairs, and feathers.

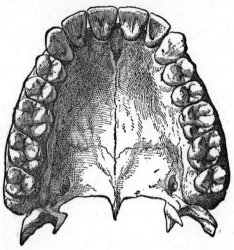

FIG. 17.—Teeth of the Upper Jaw in Position.

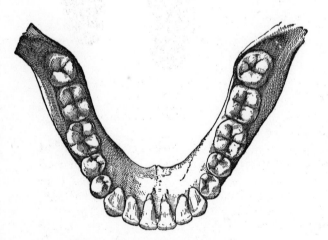

FIG. 18.—Teeth of Lower Jaw in Position.

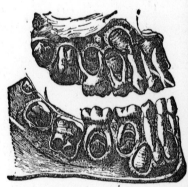

FIG. 19.—The First Set of teeth, showing also the developing teeth of the Second Set.

The Arrangement of the Teeth.—The arrangement of the teeth in the mouth presents similar details for the two *jaws* (Figs. 17 and 18). We find in each jaw four *incisors*, or *front* teeth. Behind these, on each side, lies one *canine* tooth, otherwise known as the "eye" tooth, or "dog" tooth. These teeth are long and pointed, and are specially developed in carnivorous animals. Behind the canine tooth, on each side, lie two teeth called *bicuspids*, on account of the fact that their crowns bear two little points or "cusps." These teeth are also known as *premolars*. Behind these latter teeth are found the three *molar* teeth, or "*grinders*," on each side. They possess two or three roots. The last or hindmost molar is termed the "wisdom tooth."

It will thus be seen that the teeth of man number sixteen in each jaw. This estimate, however, applies only to the second or permanent teeth. The first or "milk" set wants the six molars of each jaw, and they therefore number twenty only.

	PM	C	I	I	C	PM		
First Set of Teeth.	2	1	2	2	1	2	Upper Jaw.	
	2	1	2	2	1	2	Lower Jaw.	

	M	PM	C	I	I	C	PM	M	
Second Set of Teeth.	3	2	1	2	2	1	2	3	Upper Jaw.
	3	2	1	2	2	1	2	3	Lower Jaw.

The above table represents the arrangement of the teeth in the two jaws, the middle vertical line indicating the division between the teeth of the one side of the jaw and the other.

The Eruption of the Teeth.—With respect to the periods at which the teeth appear, the first of the milk teeth to be developed are the middle incisors of the lower jaw. As a rule, these are developed from the sixth to the seventh month of life. The first premolars appear at the twelfth month; then succeed the canines, or eye-teeth at the eighteenth month; the first set being completed by the appearance of the second molars at twenty-four months. As a rule, we find that the teeth of the lower jaw somewhat precede those of the upper jaw in their appearance. The teeth of the second set begin their development by way of replacing those of the first set (except the molars) at the age of six years, the molars appearing at this period. Then succeed the central incisors at the age of seven years, the side incisors being developed a year later. The premolars develop at the ninth and tenth years respectively. The eruption of the canines takes place at eleven years, the second molars appearing at about twelve years, whilst the third molars, or "wisdom teeth," vary in their period of eruption from seventeen to twenty-five years.

The "Wisdom" Teeth.—It is interesting to note in connection with the "wisdom" teeth of man, that in civilised races there exists a tendency towards their repression. The services of the dentist have frequently to be requisitioned for the purpose either of removing a "wisdom" tooth, for which there appears to be no room in the mouth, whilst in many individuals the "wisdom" teeth are developed in a rudimentary condition. In all probability this result is due to the shortening of the jaws represented in higher human races, a feature existing in marked contradistinction to the formation of the jaw and skull seen in lower races of men (vol. i. p. 44).

The Gullet.—The mouth, as we have seen, passes backwards into the cavity of the pharynx, or "food bag." From the pharynx the digestive tube is continued in the shape of the *œsophagus,* or *gullet* (Fig. 12). The average length of this portion of the tube is nine or ten inches. It begins about the level of the sixth vertebra of the neck, its termination in the stomach corresponding to the level of the tenth vertebra of the back. The gullet lies behind the windpipe in its upper part. Then passing downwards, it pierces the *diaphragm,* or great muscle, separating the chest from the abdomen, and ends in the upper part of the stomach. The gullet is in greater part a muscular tube, the food being propelled to the stomach by muscular action. The fibres of the gullet are of a voluntary nature in its upper part, and of involuntary character in its lower extent. Hence the action of swallowing is largely involuntary in its character, and we are, therefore, unable to return food from the stomach at will, this action being effected only by the act of vomiting. It is curious to note, however, that in certain individuals the power exists of emptying the stomach at will, this action being analogous to that whereby ruminant animals, or those that chew the "cud," such as oxen and sheep, return their food to the mouth for the purpose of being remasticated.

The Stomach.—Passing now to consider the *stomach,* we find this organ—which is essentially an expansion of the digestive tube— lying in the *upper* part of the abdomen, or lower cavity of the body. It occupies a somewhat oblique, or slanting position (Fig. 12, 1) in the body. In general form it may be described as pear-shaped, the large end of the pear or *fundus* being directed upwards. The smaller, or *pyloric end,* is directed downwards and to the right. It is continued to form the beginning of the *intestine* or *bowel.* To the right of the stomach, and sheltered under the lower ribs of that side, lies the *liver.* The *spleen* occupies a position to the left side of the stomach, whilst the *sweetbread,* or *pancreas,* lies below the stomach in front. The opening by which food enters the stomach is called the *cardia;* that by which food leaves it is called the *pylorus* (Fig. 12, 4). At this point the entrance to the bowel is guarded by a band of muscular fibres, called the *pyloric valve,* which remains closed until the proper time arrives for the food to be permitted to pass into the bowel from the stomach.

With respect to the *size* of the human stomach, that of an adult man is capable, when extended, of holding from five or six to eight pints of fluid.

Its Coats.—The outer or *serous coat* of the stomach is identical with that membrane called the *peritoneum,* which lines the whole cavity of the abdomen, or belly. The middle coat of the stomach is composed of *unstriped muscular fibres,* arranged, some of them, longitudinally, some in a circular fashion and some in an oblique manner. The *internal,* or *mucous coat* of the stomach is that with which the *food* comes in *contact,* and it is in this latter layer that we find situated the *gastric glands,* or those which supply the *gastric juice,* destined to act upon the food, in so far as the stomach's duties in digestion are concerned.

Its Glands.—The *gastric glands* may be compared essentially to minute pockets or tubes, imbedded in the lining membrane of the stomach. In this lining there can be seen, with a low magnifying power, shallow pits, having a diameter varying from the $\frac{1}{100}$th part of an inch to the $\frac{1}{200}$th part. Into these pits there open the mouths of the little glands just described, many thousands of these glands existing in the lining membrane of the organ. Two sets of gastric glands are described by anatomists. The first of these sets includes those known as *simple* or *mucous glands.* These resemble the glands found in the gullet and in other parts of the *digestive tube.* Their principal function is that of supplying a mucous secretion, probably adapted to lubricate the walls of the organ. The *true gastric glands* (otherwise known as *peptic glands*) are those which secrete the *gastric juice.* In *length* they average the $\frac{1}{25}$th part of an inch, their *breadth* being about the $\frac{1}{350}$th part of an inch. As has been noted, each gland is essentially a tube or pocket. It is lined by distinctive cells, which, however, vary in character as we pass from the upper part of the tube to its lower portion. The most characteristic cells, known as *peptic cells,* lie towards the lower part of the glands. Each cell averages about the $\frac{1}{1200}$th part of an inch in diameter, and appears of an oval or many-sided shape. It is these cells which, from the blood supplied to them by the blood-vessels of the stomach, secrete or manufacture the gastric juice that is poured out upon the food, and that exercises the stomach's digestive duties. Before the food enters the stomach its lining membrane is of a pale pink colour, and is thrown into folds, or *rugæ,* which run the long way of the stomach. After the entrance of food the lining membrane of the organ attains a deeper colour, owing to the increased flow of blood sent to it for digestive purposes (and chiefly for the secretion of the gastric juice), whilst the folds are flattened out by way of affording increased space for the food.

The Intestine.—The part of the digestive system which succeeds the stomach is known as the *intestine, bowel,* or *gut* (Fig. 12). As already indicated, it forms by far the greater portion of the

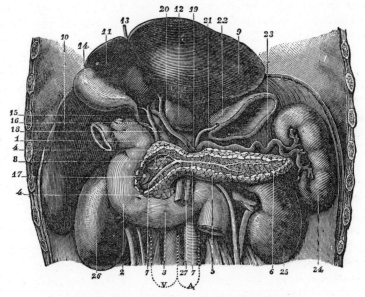

FIG. 20.—View from the front of the Digestive Organs.

1, First part of Duodenum ; 2, Its second portion ; 3, Third portion ; 4, Head of Pancreas ; 5, Middle portion ; 6, Its Tail ; 7, The Main Tube or Duct of the Pancreas ; 8, A Secondary Duct ; 9, Left, and 10, right Lobe of Liver ; 11, Front part of Liver ; 12, Spiegel's Lobe of Liver ; 13, Liver Ligament ; 14, Gall-Bladder ; 15, Hepatic Duct ; 16, Cystic Duct ; 17, Common Bile Duct ; 18, The Portal Vein with Hepatic Artery to the left ; 19, Cœliac Axis of Blood-vessels ; 20, Hepatic Artery ; 21, Stomach Artery ; 22, Cardiac part of Stomach ; 23, Splenic Artery ; 24, Spleen ; 25 and 26, Left and Right Kidneys ; 27, Superior Mesenteric Artery and Vein ; V, Inferior Vena Cava ; A, Descending Aorta.

digestive tube, extending as it does to the length of twenty-six feet. Of this length the *small intestine,* which immediately succeeds the stomach, comprises twenty feet, the *large intestine* making up the remaining length of six feet. It may be said that the greater part of the digestive work takes place in the intestine, where there are poured into the food the secretions of the liver, of the sweetbread, and of the glands, found in the intestine itself.

The *division* between the small and large intestine is a perfectly natural one, seeing that the calibre of the latter portion of the bowel is greater than that of the small intestine. The latter portion of the bowel exists in the *body* in the form of a very much convoluted tube, its folds being coiled up within the abdomen. This *portion* of the *intestine* is divided into three lengths, respectively known as the *duodenum, jejunum,* and *ileum.* The duodenum (Fig. 20, 1, 2 and 3) is that portion of the intestine which directly succeeds the stomach. Its name is derived from its length, which the older anatomists regarded as being equal to the breadth of twelve fingers. In length it varies from eight to ten inches ; it therefore forms by far the shortest portion of the small bowel. As regards its particular disposition, the duodenum curves (2) in a somewhat horse-shoe fashion from the pyloric end of the stomach to the level of the second lumbar vertebra, or that of the loins, at which latter point it becomes continuous with the jejunum. As it curves, the duodenum embraces the head of the pancreas or " sweetbread " in its fold (4).

This *portion* of the small intestine is especially important, from the fact that there open into it the *bile duct* from the liver conveying bile into the bowel, and the duct from the *sweetbread,* which similarly conveys *sweetbread juice* from that organ. We thus note that it is immediately after the food leaves the stomach that bile and sweetbread juice are poured upon it.

The Small Intestine.—The second portion of the small intestine is the *jejunum.* It forms about two-fifths of the length of this part of the bowel. The term "jejunum" is derived from the Latin word *jejunus,* signifying "empty," the name being applied to this part of the bowel on account of its usually being found empty after death. The walls of this part of the intestine are of a thickened character, and its lining membrane is typically developed into cross-folds known as *valvulæ conniventes.* These folds are intended to cause the food passing along the bowel to adopt a somewhat zig-zag course, thus giving an additional area over which the action of digestion may take place.

The *ileum* forms the third portion of the small intestine, making up the remaining three-fifths of its length. It is of thicker character than the jejunum, and joins the large intestine at the lower part of the abdomen or belly on the right side.

Structure of the Bowel.—The intestine resembles the stomach, in that it is composed of three chief coats or layers—a *serous* or outer coat, a *muscular* or middle coat (providing for the movements of the bowel), and a *mucous* or inner coat, with which the food comes in contact. The folds already alluded to in connection with the jejunum are also found in the ileum, but they disappear towards the end of this latter portion of the bowel, leaving its lining membrane for the lower third of its extent smooth.

Its Glands.—An important feature connected with the structure of the mucous membrane of the intestine (Fig. 21, 4, 5), is constituted by its *glands* and its *villi* (6, 7). Two sets of glands are found in the small intestine. Thus the *glands of Brünner* are found only in the duodenum, and present us with small structures of branching, or grape-shaped form. These glands open into the intestine, and supply a secretion adapted to exercise some function or other connected with the digestive work. The second series of *glands* is known as the *glands of Lieberkühn*. These latter occur practically throughout the whole length of the small intestines. Each gland is

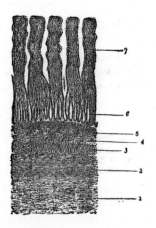

FIG. 21.—Section of the Intestine, showing the Outer Coat.

1, Muscular Fibres ; 2 and 3, The Mucous Layer ; 4 and 5, Tubular Glands ; 6 and 7, Villi.

FIG. 22.—A Gland (Peyer's Patch) of the Small Intestine or Bowel. Typhoid Fever specially attacks these Glands.

practically a tube, the length of which varies from the one-tenth to the one-thirtieth part of an inch. They open into the intestine, and being lined by special cells, may be regarded as also supplying a secretion destined to exercise a distinct purpose in the act of digestion. What are also known as the *solitary glands* of the intestine are, however, generally disposed throughout the length of the small bowel. Each of these glands has been compared in size to that of a millet seed. It is of globular shape. When the "solitary glands" become aggregated together in the intestine, they are termed *Peyer's glands* or *Peyer's patches* (Fig. 22). Each of these patches (forming structures *specially affected in typhoid fever*) varies in length from the one-fourth of an inch to three inches. They appear to be best developed towards the end of the ileum. None of them occur in the duodenum. It is also to be noted that in tuberculosis affecting the intestine "Peyer's glands" are specially attacked.

The Villi.—If the mucous coat or lining membrane of the small bowel be carefully examined, it is found to present the appearance of velvet, in that its surface is raised into a pile (Fig. 23). This appearance is due to the fact that we find rising from the membrane a large number of very fine projecting points. These are known as *villi* (1, 2). It is extremely important to note the occurrence of the "villi," because they constitute the structures through which such foods as are absorbed from the intestine find their way from the digestive system on their journey to the blood. Each "villus," consisting of a minute projection, exhibits a covering layer of *epithelial cells* (Fig. 24, *a*). Here and there among these *cells* may be seen other and different cells, called from their shape *goblet cells.* Inside each villus we find *blood-vessels*, consisting of *capillaries* (*bb*) (the finest blood-vessels of the body), which form a *network*, beginning in a small artery, bringing *blood* into the vessels and ending in a small vein (*c*) returning from the "villus." The length of each "villus" has been estimated at from a fourth part of a line to half a line. Inside the "villus" we also find a vessel or *tube*, known as a *lymphatic*, or otherwise as a *lacteal* (*d*). It is this latter vessel on which the duty of absorbing digested nutriment from the intestine devolves.

The Large Intestine.—The *large intestine* (Fig. 25) consists of three *portions*, named in the order of their occurrence in the body as the *cæcum, colon,* and *rectum.* It is of extreme importance to note the manner in which the small intestine joins the large. The *ileum,* or end portion of the small bowel, joins the large bowel at right angles (Fig. 12). Below the point of juncture lies the *cæcum,* or first portion of the large intestine. This last is practically a blind pouch or sac (Fig. 25, 6), measuring about $2\frac{1}{2}$ inches long.

The Appendix.—Below the cæcum there is found attached to it a curious little worm-like structure, known as the *vermiform appendix* (Fig. 25, 7). In length the "appendix" varies from three inches to five inches or more. In thickness it averages that of a goose-quill. A very fine canal occupies the centre of the appendix, which, however, like the cæcum, is a closed structure or pocket. Of late years much interest has attached to the "appendix," owing to the fact that when attacked by inflammation it gives rise to the disease known as *Appendicitis,* for the cure of which a surgical operation, having for its object the removal of the appendix, is frequently undertaken. The appendix may be regarded like many other structures in the human body as a rudimentary or vestigial organ—

in other words it represents a structure which, small in man, is found well developed in certain lower animals.   Indeed, we may regard the

FIG. 23.—The *Villi* of the lining membrane of the Small Bowel.

1 and 2, Villi ; 3, Opening of Glands ; 4 and 5, Closed Glands.

FIG. 24.—A Villus (highly magnified) showing *aa*, Epithelial cells covering it ; *bb*, its Arteries ; *c*, its Vein ; *d*, the Lacteal Vessel.

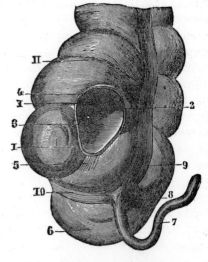

FIG. 25.—The Cæcum and Appendix.

1, Section of Large Intestine ; 2, Orifice of the Ileo-Cæcal Valve ; 3 and 4, the Valve itself ; 5, Muscular Fibres of the Ileum ; 6, Lower part of Cæcum ; 7, the Appendix ; 8, 9, and 10, Bands of the Intestine ; 11, A Constriction of the Intestine.

cæcum and the appendix together as representing a part of the large bowel, which in the case of man as well as in the higher apes has gradually decreased in size, owing probably to some process of evolution or other connected with their food habits. In certain lower animals, such as the horse and rabbit, the cæcum itself may attain a very large size.

Where the ileum joins the cæcum we find a valve developed, known as the *ileo-cæcal valve* (2, 3, and 4). This valve is formed by certain folds of the lining membrane of the bowel, its use being that of preventing matter which has passed from the small bowel into the large from escaping backwards into the ileum.

The Colon and Rectum.—The large bowel presents a sacculated appearance (Fig. 12, 11); that is to say, it exhibits a series of constrictions in its length. Succeeding the cæcum we find the *colon*, which, as it lies in the body, forms an *arch* lying to the front of the abdomen. Starting from the *lower part* of the belly, at the right side, the *ascending part* of the colon (Fig. 12, 11) passes in front of the kidney at that side, and reaches the *under surface* of the liver. It then passes across the body *beneath* the stomach to the spleen at the left side. Here it is known as the *transverse colon* (8). Turning *downwards*, in front of the left kidney to the lower side of the belly, on the *left* it completes the arch, and is known as the *descending colon* (10). Here it ends, and the last segment of the intestine begins. This is the *rectum*, which lies in the *pelvis* or *haunch cavity*, terminating in the *anus* (14).

With regard to the structure of the large intestine, it presents very much the same arrangement of coats or coverings as that seen in the small bowel. In the rectum particularly we find circular muscular fibres, or those surrounding the *bowel*, to be greatly increased in development. One special band of these fibres, situated within the *anus*, forms the *internal sphincter muscle;* another *band* existing outside the "anus" being termed the *external sphincter*. The *muscles* keep the *orifice* of the *bowel* closed, and relax only in the act of "defecation." In the large *bowel* there are no transverse folds, such as we have seen to be represented in the *small intestine*, and "villi" are also absent, seeing that little or no absorption of food occurs in this part of the digestive tube.

Digestive Glands—The Liver.—There remain for consideration, in connection with the digestive organs, the *liver*, *pancreas*, or *sweetbread*, and the *spleen*. This latter organ may be considered in connection with the digestive system, although properly speaking it exhibits only a faint relationship with the digestive work, and is to be regarded as a gland belonging to the *blood system*.

The *liver* (Fig. 26) is the largest organ in the body. In colour it is a reddish or chocolate-brown. It weighs between three and four pounds, and lies sheltered under the lower ribs to the right side of the stomach.

It is divided into several portions, named *lobes* (1, 2), each "lobe" being in turn divided into smaller portions known as *lobules*. Each lobule varies in size from the $\frac{1}{20}$th to the $\frac{3}{20}$th part of an inch. It may be said that a lobule of the liver in its way represents a complete liver on its own account, so that if we are able to determine the work performed by a single lobule of the liver, we should in this way gain an adequate idea of the functions discharged by the whole organ.

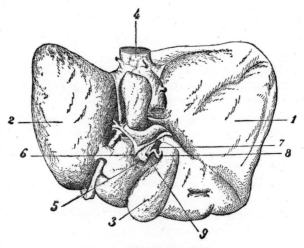

FIG. 26.—The Liver from below.

1 and 2, Right and Left Lobes; 3, Gall-Bladder; 4, Hepatic Vein; 5, Portal Vein; 6, Hepatic Artery; 7, Hepatic Duct; 8, Duct of Gall-Bladder; 9, Common Bile Duct.

The Liver Cells.—The *liver* presents us with an organ which illustrates very clearly the constitution of the body regarded from the point of view of its colonial nature, and of its consisting of groups of "cells," each group devoted to the performance of a particular work or function. The essential units of the liver consist of *hepatic cells*, or *liver cells* (Fig. 27). These *cells* are of irregular shape, and vary in diameter from the $\frac{1}{500}$th part of an inch to the $\frac{1}{1000}$th part. They contain "protoplasm," or living matter, and a *nucleus* (2), whilst within them are usually seen fat globules and yellow particles partly representing the colouring matter of the bile. Each globule of the liver, and therefore the liver at large, is composed of multitudes of such cells, constituting the veritable workmen, performing whatever duties the liver discharges.

We find that each *liver lobule* is thus composed of *cells* and *blood-*

vessels, bringing blood to the *cells* and carrying blood away from them, whilst also we find that between the cells of the lobule are minute passages (3) which, as they pass from the lobule, become larger, and are finally seen to join similar *ducts* from other *lobules,* ultimately ending in the *bile duct* which leaves the liver and conveys bile into the *intestine.* From this *view* of the liver we can, therefore, gain the idea that it is an organ into which blood is perpetually being conveyed, whilst from the liver another current of blood is perpetually carried away to join the general circulation. Also we know that, as one result at least of the action of the liver, there is formed within it the fluid known as *bile,* which is conveyed from the organ to the intestine, in order that it may act upon the food.

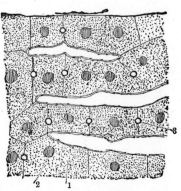

FIG. 27.—Cells of Liver showing, 1, a Cell; 2, its Nucleus ; and 3, one of the Canals (in Section) by which Bile from the Cells is conveyed from the Lobules.

The Liver's Vessels.—Into the liver a very large vein passes. This is known as the *portal vein* (Fig. 26). It returns blood from the digestive organs at large, its chief supply being derived from the intestine. This vein is, however, a great trunk, or main line (Fig. 28, *i*) into which run many other veins drawn from the sweetbread, stomach, and elsewhere. The nourishment of the liver cells is provided for by an artery called the *hepatic artery* (Fig. 26, 6), whilst passing out of the liver is a highly important vessel known as the *hepatic vein* (4), this last forming the channel through which all the blood of the liver is returned to the general circulation. This must be clearly kept in mind, seeing that whatever products the liver passes onward into the blood will escape from the organ by the vein last named.

The Gall-Bladder.—On the under-surface of the liver we find situated the *gall-bladder* (Fig. 26, 3, and Fig. 29). This organ is of pear-shape, a special tube or *duct,* known as the *cystic duct,* passing from it. This *duct* joins another known as the *hepatic duct,* which directly originates from the liver itself. The duct from the gallbladder (cc) and that from the liver (ch) unite together and form the *common bile duct* (c), which opens directly into the duodenum, or first portion of the *intestine.* The gall-bladder, it may be noted, has a capacity of from one to two ounces. It is a mere reservoir for the bowel. As the liver is more or less continually engaged in the work of bile-making, and as bile is not always required for digestive purposes, the gall-bladder presents us with a storehouse into which the bile passes, and from which a supply of this fluid can be easily obtained.

The Pancreas.—The *pancreas* or *sweetbread* (Fig. 20, 4, 5) is usually described in man as resembling a dog's tongue in shape. It lies across the body behind and below the stomach. Its average length is about six inches. The head (4), or broad portion, lies within the *curve* formed by the duodenum, whilst the tail, or slender end (6), is closely related to the spleen at the left side. The sweet-

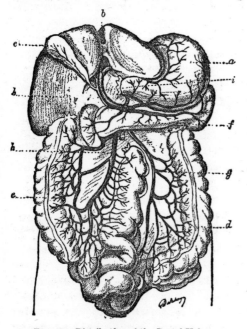

FIG. 28.—Distribution of the Portal Vein.

a, Stomach ; *b*, Liver ; *c*, Gall-Bladder ; *d e*, Large Bowel ; *f*, Sweetbread ; *g h*, Mesenteric Veins ; *i*, Portal Vein.

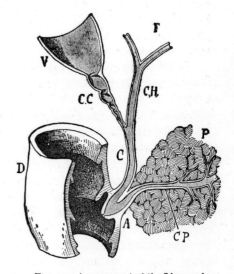

FIG. 29.—Arrangement of the Liver and Sweetbread Duct.

V, Gall-Bladder ; *CC*, Duct of Gall-Bladder ; *CH* Duct from Liver ; *C*, Common Bile Duct ; *F* marks site of Liver ; *P*, Pancreas ; *CP*, Pancreatic Duct ; *A*, Junction of Liver and Sweetbread Ducts in the Duodenum (*D*).

bread is an organ which, in respect of its structure, appears to present a certain resemblance to the salivary glands of the mouth. Throughout its course runs a tube or duct (7) known as the *duct of Wirsung*, this common tube receiving the secretion of the gland (or *pancreatic juice*), and ending either directly in the duodenum or uniting with the common bile duct (Fig. 29 *A*), so that bile and pancreatic juice are poured upon the food at one and the same point.

The Spleen (Fig. 20, 24) lies to the left side of the stomach, and attains an average weight of about six ounces. In length it measures about five inches, and in breadth from three inches to four inches. This organ is liable to vary in size, even in healthy individuals; and it also exhibits variations in bulk due to its physiological action. It is of soft, pulpy constituence, and of a dark purple colour.

The spleen is classified with certain other glands of the body under the name of *ductless glands*, for the reason that, unlike the liver and " sweetbread," no duct or tube exists by way of conveying any secretion from it. A very large artery (the *splenic artery*, Fig. 20, 23), enters the spleen, and a large vein (the *splenic vein*) leaves it. The substance of the spleen consists of a soft material, known as the spleen pulp. In this " pulp" the branches of the splenic vein commence. A kind of network forms the basis of the spleen pulp, and embedded in it we find certain minute bodies known as the *Malpighian corpuscles*. These latter bodies are intimately connected with the work which the *spleen* discharges as a blood gland, in which, in all probability, important changes are carried on in the matter of disposing of old corpuscles of the blood and in forming new ones. It is on this account that the spleen has been termed a " blood gland," since it is believed not merely to form white blood corpuscles, but also to produce red ones as well. In this organ it is also supposed the worn-out red corpuscles are broken down and disposed of. In many diseases the spleen undergoes enlargement, this fact being typically represented in *Ague;* whilst in a curious disease known as *Leucocythæmia*, in which a far larger amount of white blood corpuscles than is normal is discharged into the blood, the spleen is found to be enlarged. At the close of digestion the spleen appears to undergo a natural enlargement, and in this relationship it is believed to serve the purpose of a kind of blood reservoir, relieving pressure in the blood-vessels of the stomach and liver. It may be added that the spleen is capable of being removed from animals, and also from man, without serious result. The explanation of this circumstance is probably to be found in the fact that other glands known as *lymphatic glands* (to which reference will be hereafter made) are capable of taking upon themselves the duties of the missing spleen.

THE DUCTLESS GLANDS

Reference has just been made in dealing with the spleen to the fact that it has generally been termed a *ductless gland*. This expression was shown to imply that out of this gland there proceeds no " duct" or tube conveying from it any secretion or fluid manufactured therein. In this respect the spleen stands in contradistinction to the liver, the sweetbread, and the salivary glands, in all of which organs there is found a duct leading the respective fluids manufactured by the glands outwards so that these secretions may be poured upon the food. The spleen was further shown to be a *blood gland* in respect of the functions it discharges in connection with the corpuscles or solid bodies found in the blood. In this connection the spleen may be regarded indeed as forming part of that great system of glands concerned with the absorption of food products into the blood. To these latter organs the name of the *lymphatic* or *absorbent* system is given. Their functions will be described in connection with the process of digestion itself.

The Thymus Gland.—Certain other glands also fall to be considered under the head of ductless glands. The first of these is the *thymus gland*. This gland lies in the lower part of the neck to the front of the chest and behind the breastbone. It exhibits a division into two parts or *lobules*, and is of a greyish·red colour. Soon after birth the thymus gland exhibits its greatest development in size, but after the second year it begins to decrease in extent so that when adult life is attained it appears as a merely rudimentary structure. This gland is contained within a kind of fibrous envelope. From this envelope there pass into the interior of the gland certain processes which constitute the divisions between the lobules, and which support the blood-vessels supplying the gland. There are also *lymphatics* or *absorbent vessels* connected with it.

The curious fact that the thymus gland is largest in early life and practically disappears when the adult stage is attained, would seem to indicate that its functions are mostly connected with the infantile period of existence. It is a notable fact, however, that in animals which hibernate, or pass the winter in a state of sleep, this gland remains constant throughout life. When the period of winter sleep approaches in such animals, the thymus gland enlarges and develops a certain amount of fat. It would therefore appear to constitute one of the sources of the fatty material which supplies the hibernating animal with its store of winter food. The fat it contains is absorbed into the system and serves as a kind of bodily fuel. In man, however, such functions are not represented, and in all probability the thymus gland may therefore be regarded as an organ derived from lower states of existence, but whose functions, probably active enough in the infant, are not required in adult life. It may be presumed that in the infantile state this gland constitutes a source of fat supply for the body, fat forming, as we know, an extremely important constituent in the nutrition of the young child. Certain observers have also expressed the opinion that this gland, like the spleen, discharges the duty, in early life at least, of forming the colourless corpuscles found in the blood.

The Thyroid Gland.—The *thyroid* gland consists of two portions situated one on each side of the windpipe, and connected by a thin thread of tissue called the *isthmus*. It is situated in the neck close to the organ of voice. It appears to consist of certain sacs or cavities lined by cells. Inside these sacs a semi-fluid material is found, the gland itself being well supplied with blood-vessels, absorbent vessels, and also with nerves. It is notable that in these sacs of the thyroid gland blood corpuscles are found in a state of disintegration or breakdown. The thyroid gland, unlike the thymus gland, appears to be a body of great importance in adult life. It does not disappear like the latter gland, but remains in a state of activity throughout the existence of the individual.

Internal Secretions.—Of late years there has been much discussed in scientific circles what is known as the theory of *internal secretions*. By this term is implied the idea that it is the duty of certain organs to secrete fluids or products which, instead of being thrown out, say, upon the food, are poured into the blood, and in this way serve to maintain that fluid in a normal and natural condition. The sweetbread itself, in addition to its work in the digestive process, is believed to exert an influence in this latter direction, but the thyroid gland presents us with the most typical example of an organ the main function of which appears to be connected with maintaining a certain quality or property of the blood-supply.

The Gland in Disease.—We are led to these conclusions by the consideration of what occurs in the body when the thyroid gland is attacked by disease. In the first instance, if this gland be removed from the body, disease of a special kind speedily follows. When it is similarly diseased, or, as is sometimes the case, when it is undeveloped in children, a species of idiocy known as *cretinism* is found. In yet another instance, when the functions of the thyroid gland are interrupted the individual suffers from a disease known as *myxœdema*. In this ailment we find the whole constitution of the body altered. The mind becomes enfeebled, the skin appears to undergo a certain amount of overgrowth and to develop fat. The hair also falls off, the hands become thickened, and the general appearance of the body is that of a person affected with dropsy. It has, however, been discovered that if, to persons suffering from this disease, an extract of the thyroid glands of animals is administered, a cure is effected, this fact indicating clearly that myxœdema is really the result of the cessation of the proper duties of the gland in question. In all probability the secretion which the thyroid gland pours into the blood serves to regulate many of the bodily processes, and its absence therefore produces a complete disturbance of the whole constitution.

The Pituitary and Pineal Glands.—These structures are represented in the brain of man and other animals. The *pineal gland* itself has been discovered to be the stalk of a missing eye which occupies in some lizards and fishes its original position in the middle of the head. Man still retains in the shape of this gland the stem of such an eye, which was doubtless present in his prehuman and remote ancestors. The *pituitary body* is of reddish grey colour and is also situated in the brain. It consists of two parts or lobes with a canal running through the front of these lobes. Recent investigations render it extremely probable that this structure, like the thyroid gland, is connected with the production of some internal secretion or other which has to do particularly with the regulation of the work of the kidneys. Further investigations, however, are still required by way of placing this conclusion on a satisfactory basis.

The Suprarenal Glands.—This name is given to organs or bodies each of a somewhat triangular shape lying upon the upper ends of the kidneys. These glands appear to consist essentially of a centre part called the *medullary substance*, constituting a kind of network embedded in which are cells. Lying outside the central area is another portion called the *cortical part*. Blood-vessels are supplied to these glands, but it is undoubtedly the cells in the medullary or central portion which discharge whatever functions are performed by the organs under consideration.

The suprarenal bodies perform the duty of pouring some internal secretion into the blood. In 1855 Dr. Addison discovered that a certain disease (known as "Addison's Disease") was associated with alteration of these glands. One of the marked features of Addison's disease is a peculiar bronzing of the skin which takes place in man, but is not found in animals from which these glands have been removed. It would appear that the chief effects of the internal secretions of the suprarenal bodies is exerted on the muscles. If an extract made from these glands be injected into the blood, the muscular tone is markedly increased whilst a rise of blood pressure also takes place in the arteries. When the glands are diseased and their secretion is no longer available, the muscular symptoms produced are thus accounted for.

It may be repeated that the view taken of the ductless glands, namely, that they pour into the blood internal secretions each adapted to exert tonic or allied effects upon different parts of the body must exercise a very considerable influence not merely on our knowledge of the natural functions of the body and their preservation in health, but also, as will hereafter be shown, upon the cure of the diseases produced by any alterations in the glands in question.

THE PROCESS OF DIGESTION

The object of *digestion* is to convert the food into such a form that it can be readily added to the blood, which fluid it is destined to renew and repair. The common notion of digestion is that which states its aim as the conversion of food into blood. This is an entirely erroneous idea. The food, to begin with, exhibits a more or less distinct resemblance to the composition of the body itself. If the body, as we have seen in the previous section of this work, may be said to be built up of *water, mineral matters, fats, starches, sugars,* and *nitrogenous matters,* we can readily understand that such a list of substances exactly represents the composition of the food itself. Digestion, therefore, may be properly described as that series of actions whereby the principles contained in the food are made available for being added to the blood. The blood itself is an epitome of the frame; hence, as the blood represents the common currency of the body from which each organ and cell derives its own and special nutriment, we can see that digestion is merely a process through which the food principles are made available for incorporation with that fluid.

Digestion in the Mouth.—Digestion begins in the mouth. Here we find the food is duly mixed with the saliva or " water " of the mouth (*insalivation*). In the second place it is divided by the *teeth* or *masticated,* while in the third place it is swallowed, and is thus passed by the mouth into the stomach. This latter act is known as *deglutition.* These actions constitute the first of the three stages of digestion. The second stage is represented by the action of the *stomach* upon foods, whilst the third stage includes those processes which occur in the *intestine* or *bowel.* A fourth stage may be regarded as that of *absorption,* which may be defined as the process whereby the digested food is conveyed to the blood.

Saliva and its Uses.—Saliva, manufactured by the glands already described (Figs. 14 and 15), is a colourless fluid, which consists of about five parts of solids (the great bulk consisting of water) in one thousand parts. The solids consist of mineral matters and of materials derived from the mouth itself. The principal element in saliva is a substance known as *Ptyalin*. This last is a ferment, the action of which on certain foods will be presently noted.

The uses of saliva are threefold. In the first instance the food is moistened, and the sense of taste is thereby rendered capable of being properly exercised. Through the same action, that of moistening the food, swallowing is rendered capable of being easily effected, whilst it may be added that, in man, the function of speaking is more readily carried out through the moist condition of the mouth. The third duty of saliva is constituted by its peculiar digestive action. The "ptyalin" contained in the saliva discharges the function of converting starch contained in the food into grape sugar, in which form all starchy foods are intended to reach the stomach. It may here be added that all the starch we consume is only available for the purposes of the body when it has been converted into a sugar, this last being easily soluble in the blood, whereas starch is not.

The high importance of thoroughly masticating the food by the *teeth* can readily be understood when we take into account the fact that the saliva is aided in its action upon starchy foods by the effective division of our nutriment by the teeth; whilst also the importance of the work of the teeth can be readily understood when we reflect that the stomach itself is more likely to perform its duties efficiently when the food is presented to it in a finely-divided state.

A Hint to Mothers.—In connection with the digestion of food in the mouth, it should be noted that "ptyalin" is not found in the saliva of children until they attain the age of seven or eight months. Hence it is improper to give infants any food containing starch until they reach the age in question. Much illness in infants is caused by the administration to them of starchy foods at a period of their lives when the starch can only be passed on to the stomach as starch instead of being converted into sugar. Milk itself, nature's own food for the child, contains sugar ready made (milk sugar), but no starch. We thus note that the perfect work of the teeth, assisted by that of the saliva, forms a necessary preliminary to perfect digestion. Where defective digestion exists, and where the food is not properly divided, or masticated, the stomach's work is unduly increased. The beginnings of many cases of indigestion may be traced to defects in the teeth laying extra stress on the work of the stomach, both in respect of unchanged starch passing to the stomach and also because the stomach receives masses of food too large for easy digestion.

Swallowing.—The teeth having already been duly described, we may pass to consider the process of swallowing. This act is known as that of *deglutition*. It is somewhat complicated in its nature, but its main features may be readily enough understood.

The tongue, first of all, gathers together the particles of food in the mouth, and moulds them into a bolus or mass. Then, tilting this mass backwards, it forces it into the *pharynx* (Fig. 13, *a*), where it is grasped by the muscles of that part. Here we find the hinder nostrils are closed by the raising of the *soft palate* (*d*), so that the food has now presented to it a chance of passing either into the *gullet* (*j*), which is the road to the *stomach*, or into the *windpipe* (*i*), which represents the way to the lungs. In the latter case *choking*, of course, would result. This accident is prevented by the elevation of the larynx or voice-box, and by the action of the *epiglottis* (Fig. 13, *f*), or *lid of the windpipe*, which falls over, or is lowered, so as to cover the entrance to the lungs. The food, therefore, propelled by the muscles of the upper pharynx, has only one roadway to pursue, viz., into the gullet. Having passed into the upper part of this latter tube, it is seized by the muscles of the gullet, and is propelled downwards into the stomach

Digestion in the Stomach.—Having arrived in the *stomach*, that organ, as we have seen, receives an additional blood-supply for the purpose of affording its gastric glands the raw material from which the gastric juice can be secreted. The *gastric juice* is poured out upon the food from the stomach's glands in drops, but as thousands of these glands exist in the walls of the stomach, we can readily understand that, in the course of a single day, a large amount of this juice will be produced for digestive purposes. Gastric juice is a *fluid* of *acid character*, owing to its containing a small quantity of *hydrochloric acid*. Its other essential constituent is a ferment, called *pepsin*. It also contains a large amount of water and a variety of minerals. The pepsin and the acid constitute, however, the essential elements of this secretion. When food enters the stomach, the folds, or "rugæ," disappear, and the movements of the muscular walls of the organ circulate the food throughout its extent, so as thoroughly to mix the food with the gastric juice.

The Stomach's Work.—It is a common notion that the stomach is capable of digesting all kinds of foods, and that it discharges the chief part of the work represented in the assimilation of our nutriment. This is a serious mistake, because, as a matter of fact, the stomach has *little or no power of digesting fats, starches, or sugars*. Its duties are limited to its action on *nitrogenous foods*, of which white of egg, the juice of meat, the casein of milk, the gluten of flour, and like substances are examples. The action of the stomach on these substances is extremely interesting. It converts white of egg and other nitrogenous foods through the action of its pepsin and hydrochloric acid into substances called *peptones*. The chief feature of any substance of nitrogenous nature which has been converted into "peptone," is that it is capable of readily passing through the walls of the stomach and being absorbed by the blood-vessels. We shall note hereafter that this action of the stomach constitutes the chief means whereby the nitrogenous foods upon which it acts are capable of quickly leaving it, and of being placed at the service of the body.

The action of the stomach in digestion is thus seen to be of a comparatively limited nature, although it is to be regarded of vast importance from a physiological point of view. We may regard the stomach, in fact, as a kind of half-way house on the digestive journey, from which there are removed certain food products (viz. those of a nitrogenous kind) of great importance to the body, in respect of their functions of building and repairing its tissues. No doubt, from the stomach there are directly absorbed into the blood other food products, notably water, but the remainder of the food, consisting of starches, sugars, and fats, passes out of the stomach into the bowel practically unchanged. Their destination is the intestine, in which they undergo the changes necessary to fit them, in turn, for being absorbed into the blood.

The summing up of the story of digestion in the stomach may, therefore, be stated in the expression that it acts upon nitrogenous foods alone, that these are converted into peptones, which are absorbed by the blood-vessels of the stomach, and that the remainder of the foods, consisting of starches, sugars, and fats, are passed onwards, out of the stomach into the intestine, there to be dealt with and prepared for absorption.

Some other Points.—It may be said that a full meal does not leave the stomach under a period varying from two to three hours, much depending in this instance, of course, on the kind of food taken. At the close of digestion the materials in the stomach, consisting of fats, starches, and sugars, are known by the common name of *chyme*. With reference to the work of digestion, it may here be said that, as this action involves a considerable expenditure of nervous force and likewise demands an increased blood-supply being sent to the digestive organs, this last is a necessary condition for the secretion of the digestive juices. It is important for health's sake to secure rest after a meal. "After dinner sit awhile," is a proverb which is not merely founded on common sense, but also has the support of science at its back. By resting after meals we secure that the work of the stomach can be efficiently performed and a frequent source of indigestion avoided.

Digestion in the Intestine.—The food, in the shape of

"chyme," now passes into the first part of the *small intestine* or *duodenum*. Here it meets with *bile* from the liver and the *pancreatic juice* of the "sweetbread." Bile is an alkaline fluid of a yellowish-green colour. It is estimated that in the course of twenty-four hours 2½ pounds' weight of bile may be poured into the intestine. In addition to colouring matters and a substance known as *cholesterin* (found in gall-stones), the bile contains compounds of soda, and it is curious to note that when these soda compounds combine with the fats of the food they form a chemical soap. In this form the fat is fitted for being more easily absorbed into the blood.

The Liver and its Work.—The work of the liver, however, as we shall presently note, is of a much more important character than that which is included in its duty of producing bile, and of pouring this secretion upon the food. Bile, it may be mentioned, represents waste matters removed from the blood, so that the liver may be regarded as related to the lungs, skin, and kidneys, in that it is devoted, in part of its work at least, to getting rid of so much of the waste which is the outcome of bodily work. Bile, however, represents a waste product made useful, and there can be little doubt that the special action of the bile is that of acting upon the fatty matters of the food, and so altering them as to enable them to be more readily absorbed. In addition to its action on the fats of the food, bile exercises certain other functions worthy of notice. In the first place, when bile passes into the intestine it causes an increase of the muscular movements of the digestive tube. Bile is a kind of natural purgative, and in suppression of this fluid constipation is frequently represented. In the second place, bile exercises what may be called an "antiseptic" effect on the food, and prevents it from undergoing injurious changes in the way of decomposition.

The Pancreas.—With regard to the functions of the *pancreas* or "sweetbread," we find that the pancreatic juice, a clear fluid, contains, in addition to water and minerals, no less than four distinct "ferments," each of which exercises a special effect on the digestion of foods. There is first a ferment known as *trypsin*, which acts on *nitrogenous foods*, converting them into "peptones," so that if any of these foods have escaped the action of the stomach, they will be duly dealt with by the secretion of the "sweetbread." A second ferment in the pancreatic juice is known as *amylopsin*. This substance can convert starch into grape sugar, so that if any unchanged starch has passed from the mouth to the stomach, it will be dealt with by the pancreas. A third ferment is known as *steapsin*, which has an action on fats, and a fourth substance of this kind is known as *rennin*. The special action of this latter body is to curdle milk.

The functions of the sweetbread juice of late years have risen considerably in importance in the minds of physicians, seeing that its juice is the only digestive secretion which is capable of affecting *all kinds of food*. From these observations it becomes clear why, in cases of diabetes (vol. i.), the physician is accustomed to regard with much more serious consideration cases of this kind in which the pancreas is involved, than those in which the liver alone seems at fault.

Living without a Stomach.—A very interesting point in connection with the work of the sweetbread has reference to the fact that persons whose stomachs have been removed by surgeons for cancerous disease are capable digesting food. In such operations the end of the gullet is joined to the beginning of the intestine or "duodenum." The patients are found to be able to live on ordinary food. We note the explanation of this fact in the actions which the pancreas discharges. It can digest both nitrogenous and non-nitrogenous articles of diet, and in this way performs, more or less completely, the duties of the missing stomach.

The Liver's Duties.—The functions of the liver, however, are not limited to the manufacture of bile. It is an organ which discharges certain other duties of vast importance in the economy of the frame. In the first place, the liver deals with the "peptones," which we have already noted to be formed as the result of the action of the gastric juice of the stomach on nitrogenous foods. These peptones, absorbed by the veins of the stomach, are carried to the *portal vein* (Fig. 26, 5), which we have already noted to be the great main line of the blood-supply reaching the liver (Fig. 28). The cells of the liver (Fig. 27) receive the peptones and convert them into substances which can be allowed to enter the blood. If peptones, as such, were allowed to pass into the blood, they would undoubtedly give rise to symptoms of poisoning, and many cases of so-called "biliousness" are undoubtedly due to the work of the liver, in respect of its alteration of peptones being checked or modified. The liver in this respect may be compared to a filter, which stands between incompletely digested nitrogenous foods on the one hand and the blood on the other.

A second function of the liver is that which is concerned with its action in dealing with fats. There is little doubt that fat can be formed by the cells of the liver from substances which are not themselves of a fatty nature, such substances being chiefly represented by starches and sugars. We know that if animals are fed upon starchy matters and kept in close confinement, the liver develops an abnormal amount of fat, a fact illustrated in the case of the Strasburg geese, whose fatty livers are used to make the delicacy known as *pâté de foie gras.* These birds, cooped up in cages, are fed upon maize and other starchy foods. It is on this principle, as described in the section of this work dealing with " Obesity " (vol. i.), that an excess of starchy or sugar foods tends to produce extreme fatness in man.

Yet another function of the liver is that which concerns its dealings with the *sugar* brought to it by the "portal vein" as the result of digestion in the intestine. We have already seen that all the starch consumed in the body is converted into " grape sugar." This material, absorbed from the bowel, is carried up by the portal vein into the liver. Received by that organ, it is reconverted into a substance called *glycogen*, or *animal starch.* Claude Bernard, a famous French physiologist, noting this work of the liver, assumed that the liver stored this starchy material in its cells, and, reconverting it into sugar, paid it out to the blood by the hepatic vein (Fig. 26, 4). Conveyed by the blood to the lungs, he supposed that the sugar was chemically burnt therein, and constituted the source of bodily heat. We now know that the heat of the body is produced in the muscles, and not in the lungs, but the question for solution which remains is the ultimate destination of the sugar which the liver may be assumed to pay out to the body. Referring to the subject of *diabetes* (vol. i.), it will be remembered that an excess of sugar passed out from the liver into the blood constitutes the essential feature of the disease in question, the excess in such a case appearing in the urine, and being associated with symptoms indicating serious bodily disturbance. The general trend of opinion is that which regards the liver as a kind of banker, storing up starch which it can convert into sugar and pay out to the body as an important food demanded by the muscles and other organs. If this function exceeds its normal limits we get diabetes. Other authorities incline to believe that the liver in health does not part with any sugar whatever, the ultimate destination of the starch which it stores being held to be that of conversion into fat.

The Intestine's Work.—Retracing our steps to the stage in digestion when food left the stomach, we noted that there pass out into the bowel fats, starches, and sugars, which are acted upon by the bile and the pancreatic juice. It is difficult to say anything definite regarding the duties discharged by the glands of the intestine (Figs. 21 and 22), to which reference has already been made, but it is generally assumed by physiologists that these glands exercise a certain action upon the food, and that, in all probability, certain of them assist the passage of the foods along the bowel by their action in lubricating the interior of the intestine. When the food has been thoroughly mixed with bile and pancreatic juice, and is proceeding in its course along the small intestine, it ultimately appears before us as a milk-like fluid, to which the name of *chyle* is given. When "chyle" is analysed it is found to contain, as its chief constituent, a large amount of fat. If we have regard to the processes previously described we may note the following points. First, that the *nitrogenous elements* of the food have largely been dealt with by the stomach, and that the *peptones* representing such foods have been swept up into the liver, whence

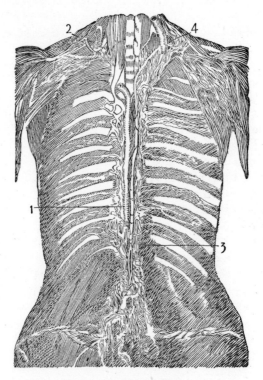

Fig. 30.—The Thoracic Duct.

1. The Thoracic Duct ; 2, Smaller Duct of right side ; 3, Cistern of the Duct or *receptaculum chyli* ; 4, Junction of the Duct with Vein at Root of Neck on the left side.

they have been passed onwards to the blood. In the second place, we have noted that from the bowel or intestine starches and sugars (the former converted into sugar) have been carried to the liver by the portal vein, and have been further dealt with by the liver itself. What remains in the " chyle " itself for absorption into the blood will therefore be largely represented by the fats of the food, along with a certain proportion of the other food-materials.

Absorption.—Referring back to the structure of the small intestine already described, we noted the presence therein of the numerous little processes known as *villi* (Fig. 23), within each of which the beginning of an absorbent vessel, or lacteal (Fig. 24), was found. As the "chyle" passes along the intestine, these "villi" are bathed in it, and the chyle passes through the cells of the "villi" into their absorbent vessels already mentioned. There is little doubt also that the blood-vessels of the villi (Fig. 24) are also concerned in the absorption of the digested food materials. The absorbent vessels of the intestine unite to form larger vessels (Fig. 31, 1), which finally end in a tube called the *thoracic duct* (Fig. 30, 21). This tube runs up the left side of the spine to the root of

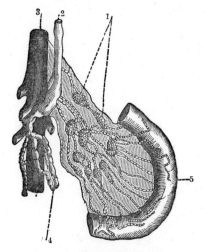

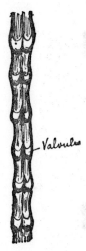

FIG. 31.—The Lacteal Vessels.

1, The Mesentery and its Lacteal Vessels and Glands; 2, Thoracic Duct; 3, Aorta; 4, Lymphatics coming from lower part of body; 5, Part of Intestine.

FIG. 32.—A Lymphatic Vessel opened to show its Valves.

the neck. There it ends at the junction of the internal jugular vein coming from the left side of the head with a vein from the left arm (Fig. 30, 4). This latter point, therefore, represents the junction of the food and the blood. It is here that what remains of the food to be absorbed directly from the intestine is poured into the blood current, with which it mingles, and which it is adapted to renew and repair.

In so far as the large intestine is concerned, it is not assumed that digestion continues in this part of the digestive tract. The large intestine practically contains what we may call excrementitious or effete matters, representing the waste of the food materials. They are ultimately excreted from the large bowel in the shape of the fæces.

The Absorbent System.—It is of importance here to add a

word regarding a system of organs of extreme importance in the body, known as the *lymphatic* or *absorbent system*. We have already seen that part of this system is devoted to the taking up of digested food materials from the intestine, and to the conveyance of these materials to the blood (Figs. 30 and 31). The special system of vessels engaged in this work are known as *lacteals* (Fig. 31, 1). These

vessels, however, form only a part of a larger system extending through all parts of the body (Fig. 33). They consist of delicate tubes provided with valves (Fig. 32) containing a clear fluid called *lymph*, hence the derivation of the name *lymphatics* also applies to the absorbent vessels. In order to extend the functions of this system, it is necessary to refer to the manner in which the body at large is nourished. When the blood passes into the finest blood-vessels (or capillaries) of the body, its fluid part, or *lymph*, escapes through the walls of these blood-vessels, and is received by the cells and tissues. There is, therefore, in the body (as described in the section on "Dropsy," vol. i.) a perpetual leakage or straining of lymph through these fine blood-vessels into the tissues. If the excess of lymph (not required for the body's nourishment) is not duly removed, we are face to face with the essential condition represented in *dropsy* itself, in which disease the tissues of the body may be described as "lymph-logged." In health, however, we find that the lymphatics, or absorbent vessels already described, exercise the function of taking up the lymph excess from all parts of the body and of conveying it back to the blood. These lym-

FIG. 33.—Lymphatics or Absorbents of Arm showing Glands in armpit.

phatic vessels thus carry unused lymph (which is practically blood) to the *thoracic duct* (Fig. 30), already noted in connection with the absorption of food materials. On the right side of the body there is another duct called the right lymphatic duct (Fig. 30, 2), receiving the lymph coming from the right side of the frame at large and carrying it to the blood. We thus see that the lymph representing the fluid part of the blood is a food product still available to the body, and is returned to the blood, being poured into the circulation respectively at the right and left sides of the neck.

In its course backwards to the blood the lymph passes through structures known as lymphatic glands (Fig. 34). These are found in the mesentery (Fig. 31, 1), or fold of the membrane, by means of which the bowel or intestine is attached to the wall of the body. They also occur in other regions of the body, represented by the armpit, the neck, and the groin (Fig. 33).

We note that these lymphatic glands are thus placed on the backward track of the lymph to the blood. The function of these glands, briefly detailed, is that of elaborating the lymph, and of rendering it in this way better fitted for being restored to the blood in order to renew and repair that fluid. Nature is here acting on the principle of an economical housewife, who utilises the remnants of one meal to form next day's dinner. The importance of thus "gathering up the fragments," in a bodily sense, may be realised when it is estimated that the total amount of lymph absorbed from the tissues and poured back into the blood, may equal in twenty-four hours the total amount of the blood in the body.

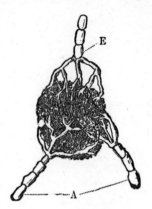

FIG. 34.—A Lymphatic Gland, showing Vessels.

A, A Vessel carrying Lymph to the Gland; and *E*, one leaving it.

THE SKIN: ITS STRUCTURE AND FUNCTIONS

The general idea of the skin entertained by people not conversant with anatomy or physiology, is that it simply serves as a covering to the general body surface. They are not aware that it discharges certain highly important duties or functions in connection with the general life and health of the body. We shall presently note that in addition to serving as a covering for the body, the skin may be said to perform duties analogous to those of the lungs and kidneys; so that if to start with, we attempted to make a catalogue of our bodily belongings, placing those organs or parts together which discharge similar functions, we should unite the *skin, lungs,* and *kidneys* in a kind of physiological trio. This fact would indicate that they perform essentially the same duties. In other words, they are *organs of excretion;* they are devoted, in part of their work at least, to the getting rid of the bodily waste which is the result of bodily work.

The Duties of the Skin.—It may be said in a brief statement of the functions the skin discharges, that it performs the following duties: First, it acts as a *general covering* to the body, protecting underlying parts from injury, and contributing by its elasticity to the necessary freedom of movement for the muscles lying beneath. In the second place the skin is *an organ of sense*, in that, through the presence of nerve ends therein, it discharges the work of common sensation, or in other the sense of touch. In this connection it may be noted that the hairs implanted in the skin through the sensitiveness which is imparted to them from their bulbs or roots, also aid in the discharge of the sense of touch. In the third place, as has already been remarked, the skin is *an organ of excretion*. It has been shown to discharge essentially the same work as that performed by the lungs and the kidneys. By means of certain glands, the *sweat glands*, it gives off so much waste matter which these glands remove from the blood. These waste matters are included under the general term of the *perspiration* or *sweat*.

The Skin and Heat Regulation.—In the fourth place, the skin may be regarded as an *important source of the heat regulation of the body*. Everywhere in the under tissue of the skin we find an immense network of capillary blood-vessels, these last being the finest vessels engaged in the work of the circulation, and through which the blood fluid is brought in contact with the microscopic cells and tissues of the body. So numerous are these capillaries that, as a popular observation may show, the prick of a needle, penetrating to the under surface of the skin, wounds them and suffices to draw blood. An immense mass of blood is thus circulating everywhere throughout the skin, and the minute blood-vessels being affected by changes of temperature, we can readily understand how, when the capillaries of the skin are contracted, the bodily heat will be increased, seeing that less blood is sent throughout the skin, and the skin itself being a bad conductor of heat the internal temperature is naturally raised. When this latter action takes place to an unwonted degree, as readily happens in the case of a chill, we see how, through the nervous relations of the skin, the effects of the chill may be propagated to distant organs resulting in various ailments, ranging from a simple cold in the head to inflammation of the lungs itself. On the other hand, when the capillary blood-vessels of the skin are expanded or dilated as by external heat, we see that so much blood must be withdrawn from the deeper parts of the body. Hence the body is then in the position of losing a large quantity of heat. This latter action is largely assisted by the excretion of the perspiration or "sweat." In turn, when this latter fluid evaporates from the surface of the body we find the balance of heat production to be regulated because of the cooling influence which is thereby exerted. It is when this process of cooling takes place too rapidly that again the consequence of chill may ultimately be found in the production of disease.

The Skin as a Lung.—Last of all the skin may be regarded as approaching the lung very nearly, in that it is also *a breathing organ*, for it can be proved that whilst it gives off *carbonic acid gas* as part of the waste products which it has excreted from the blood, it also absorbs *oxygen gas*. Such a function as that last described is much more typically seen in the case of certain lower animals than in ourselves. Thus in the frog the skin is a much more typical agent assisting in the breathing process than it is in man. A frog deprived of its lungs and kept in water will maintain life for a considerable period, through the skin acting in this way as a deputy breathing organ. We notice in this animal, as a condition enabling the skin to aid the lungs, a very large distribution of blood-vessels therein. On the other hand, in animals which either have a very thick covering of hair, or the outer surface of whose body is covered with scales, the skin must play a subordinate part in respect of its discharge of the duties of a subsidiary or assistant lung.

The Outer Skin.—In speaking of the skin at large we are apt to fall into an error in supposing that this tissue consists of a single layer. On the other hand, it may be regarded as consisting of no fewer than three distinct layers. The outermost layer of all is called the *epidermis*. This layer essentially consists of cells of that variety to which the name of *epithelial cells* (Figs. 6 and 38) is given. Such cells, as has already been described in the section of this work dealing with the microscopic structure of the body, are not merely found constituting the surface layer of the skin, but also occur in other forms and varieties in the digestive tube, in the breathing organs, and also assist in the formation of other parts of the body. If we make a section through the epidermis or outer layer of the skin, which by the way is completely destitute of nerves and blood-vessels, we notice that the cells of which it is composed form several layers. The upper layer consists of several strata of horny scales (Figs. 35 and 38), which practically represent dead cells produced from the under layer, and which have gradually made their way to the skin surface. It may be here noted that there is taking place a perpetual peeling off or *desquamation* of the superficial cells of the epidermis. This process may really be described as one of "moulting," so that whilst lower animals may part with their skin appendages once or twice a year, the human being may be described as in a position of constant moulting. These worn out microscopic scales are largely removed not merely by the friction of our clothes but also by the act of washing.

This upper layer of the skin is developed most distinctly on the palm of the hand, on the fingers, and on the sole of the foot. Below this layer comes a second, in which the cells are less scaly in nature, simply because they have not yet reached the upper layer of the skin. A third layer lying below that last described consists of true cells in a living state. These form what is known as the *Rete Mucosum* or *Rete Malpighii* (Fig. 36, 3, 4, and Fig. 37). The upper part of this latter layer consists of somewhat flattened scales, whilst the lower cells composing it are of a more active and vital character, the deeper of them forming a layer of somewhat elongated shape which rests on the under skin itself.

The Under Skin.—The under skin is also known as the *corium* or *dermis* (Fig. 36, 7). It essentially consists of a network of bundles of fibres known as those of connective tissue, whilst mixed up with this network we find elastic fibres. The upper surface of the under skin is projected into a large number of small cones, to which the name of *papillæ* is given. These papillæ are most numerous in places where the skin is thickened, as on the lower surface of the hand and foot, whilst they also occur typically in the scalp or skin of the head, on the lips and elsewhere. Inside the papillæ

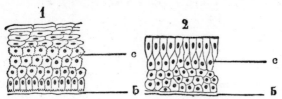

Fig. 35.—Plan of the Skin showing Arrangement of its Cells.

In 1 the Lower Cells (*c*) are seen to be well developed lying on the Basal Membrane (*b*), while above they become mere Scales which are shed off the Skin-Surface. In 2 other Epithelial Cells are shown of a different type.

we find the ends of the nerves (Fig. 37, E), which enable us to exercise the sense of touch. We thus note that in exercising this sense we touch or feel any object by aid of the nerve-ends of the under skin through the outer skin. Unlike the outer skin, which is destitute of nerves and blood-vessels, the under skin, as will be understood, is well supplied with both of these structures. A special layer in the *dermis*, lying somewhat low in its depth, is constituted by fat cells (Fig. 36, 8), forming what is known as the adipose or fatty layer.

The Glands of the Skin.—In the deep part of the true skin we find situated the sweat glands, otherwise known as *sudoriparous* glands (Fig. 37, H). Each of these glands may be compared to a coiled up tube, the diameter of the coil being about the sixtieth part of an inch on the average, and its uncoiled length about a quarter of an inch. In certain sweat glands, such as those of the armpit, the diameter of the coiled up portion of the sweat glands may exceed this extent by five or six times. The end of each sweat gland in the shape of tube or duct (the sweat duct) is continued upwards in a spiral or wavy fashion to the surface of the skin, and opens on the latter surface in what is popularly known as a "pore" (G). The sweat glands, it may be mentioned, are most numerous in the palm of the hand and the sole of the foot. They are probably least numerous in the skin of the back. The total number of sweat glands in the human skin has been estimated at over two millions. A popular computation of these glands has been given in the shape of the statement that if all the little sweat tubes in the human body were uncoiled and placed end to end to form a continuous string, they would average a length of over twenty miles.

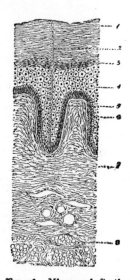

FIG. 36.—Microscopic Section of Skin.
r, Epidermis; 2, Duct of Sweat Gland; 3 and 4, Rete mucosum; 5, Lower Cells giving origin to the Epidermal Cells; 6, Basal membrane; 7, Dermis; 8, Fat Lobule of the Under Skin.

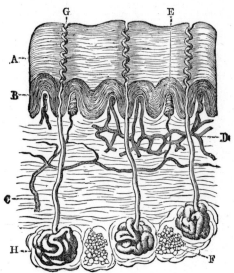

FIG. 37.—Section of the Skin (much magnified); A, Epidermis; B, Rete Mucosum; C, Dermis with Nerves; D, Duct of Sweat Gland; E, Touch-Corpuscle; F, Fat tissue under Skin; G, Pore; H, Sweat Gland.

The Hairs.—Hair forms the typical covering of the class of mammals or quadrupeds to which man belongs. Each (Fig. 39) hair has its root implanted in a bag or sac called a *follicle*. What is known as the shaft of the hair is the part that projects from the skin surface itself. Hair varies materially in its structure. It is most delicate in its nature in the surface of the eyelids, the middle of the arm and forearm. On the other hand those of the head, on the eyelids themselves, and the armpit, and of the whiskers and moustache, are of a much crisper character. The hair follicle descends into the tissue below the true skin; hence we find that the pulling out of a hair is an action which necessarily causes a certain amount of pain from the rupture of the nervous structures with which the hair sac is in relation. At the bottom of the hair sac we find a small projection or *papilla* (*p*). This last is composed of fibrous tissue, and also of cells, whilst it is also seen to contain a loop of blood-vessels. In the centre of the hair follicle we find the' root of the hair, which ends in an enlargement known as the hair bulb (*b*). This bulb practically encloses or embraces the papilla itself. It is composed of epithelial cells, and those cells which are placed immediately over the little papilla are undoubtedly the active cells in producing the growth of the hair. They become elongated, and ultimately when pushed out of the follicle form the cells of the substance of the hair. The hair substance itself is composed of cells which in reality may be said to correspond with the cells of the outer skin. The hair is solid, but its central cells are loosely packed, as compared with those forming the hair's exterior. On the surface of the hair we find a very fine covering or cuticle.

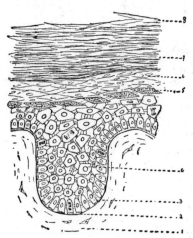

FIG. 38.—Plan of Cells in the Epidermis.

1, Dermis; 2, Basal Membrane; 3, Under Cells; 4, Malpighian Layer; 5, Granular Layer; 6, Stratum Lucidum; 7, Horny Layer; 8, Worn-out Upper Cells.

Hair Formation.—A hair may therefore be regarded as in one sense a living structure, in that in its production there is a constant development of the cells already described as existing in the hair sac, these cells being pushed upwards by the newer cells produced from below, in this way a continuous growth being illustrated. The hair itself is not supplied with blood-vessels or nerves, yet it exemplifies the result of a vital action in which both of these structures are concerned. The colour of the hair is constituted by small grains or granules of pigment or colouring matter interspersed in the fibres of the hair itself. It would seem that in white or fair hair little pigment is present. In red hair the pigment or colouring matter is of a very diffuse character. In grey hair, on the other hand, a certain amount of air is contained in the superficial layers of the substance of the hair, whilst in the latter variety of hair colouring matter is also wanting.

It is interesting to note that in certain animals special developments of hair take place in certain regions of the body. Thus in the dog, cat, and other animals we find special development of hairs in the neighbourhood of the mouth. These are known as *tactile hairs*, and undoubtedly exercise the sense of touch. They differ from ordinary hairs in respect of the fact that a large number of nerve fibres are connected with their root sheaths.

The Oil Glands of the Hair.—Opening into each hair follicle or sac we generally find one or more glands, known as *sebaceous glands* or *follicles* (Fig. 39 s). These appear as flask-shaped sacs or bags, which open by a short tube or duct into the hair sac near its surface. They contain large cells which secrete a kind of oily matter known as *sebum*. This latter secretion provides what we may call a natural oil or pomade for the hairs. As it is also poured out independently upon the surface of the skin, it may be considered to provide a natural skin oil, which has the effect of keeping the body surface moist and elastic. Each hair follicle, especially in the skin of the head, possesses certain bundles of muscular fibres of the unstriped or involuntary character. Each of these fibres constitutes a minute muscle known as the *Erector Pili* (Fig. 39 m). By the contraction of these muscles the hair follicle and the hair are together raised, so that we obtain in the skin when these muscles act the familiar appearance known as "goose-skin." When people talk about the hair "standing upon end" in consequence of fright or other emotion, this action is effected by means of the little muscular fibres just described. Another result of the action of these muscular fibres attached to the hair follicles is that of compressing the sebaceous glands (s), causing them to pour out an increased amount of their oily fluid upon the surface of the skin.

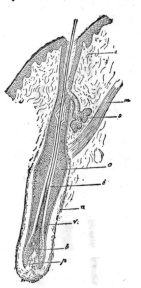

FIG. 39.—Structure of a Hair.

e, Neck of Hair Follicle; *s*, Sebaceous Gland; *m*, Hair-Muscle; *b*, Bulb of Hair; *p*, Papilla; *n*, Envelope or Sheath of Follicle; *v*, the Clear Membrane of the Hair.

Nails.—Included in the list of skin structures we find not merely the hairs, but also the *nails* and the *teeth*. As has already been described in the section of this work dealing with the teeth, these latter organs are developed from what is essentially a skin layer forming the lining membrane of the mouth. The nails (and it may also be added the feathers of birds) correspond essentially with hairs and teeth in the manner of their development. The nail is simply a horny structure like the hair, differing from it in that the cells of which it is composed are spread out and flattened, instead of forming what is essentially a hair fibre. The nail arises from what is called the *nail groove*, this in turn lying on another structure known as the " matrix," or bed of the nail. This latter layer practically corresponds with the under skin from which the cells are thrown off, as in the case of the hair, by way of continuing the growth of the nail itself.

The Skin and Touch.—It may be said that various modes of the termination of the fibres of nerves in the skin require to be noted in order to understand how the dermis exercises the sense of touch. Such organs are named *end organs*. Of these there are various kinds. The first are known as *Pacinian corpuscles* (Fig. 40), which are oval bodies, and found especially in the nerve ends of the hands and feet. They also occur in other parts of the body. Each of these capsules averages about the one-twelfth of an inch in length. It is attached by a narrow stalk to the nerve from which it springs, and is formed by several layers of membrane and of connective tissue fibres. From the stalk of each capsule a single nerve fibre passes, which ultimately enters the central core of the corpuscle, where it branches out. What are known as *end bulbs* form a second variety of nerve endings. They are chiefly found in the *conjunctiva* of the eye, and also occur in the skin and lips. Each of these end bulbs averages in diameter $\frac{1}{500}$th of an inch, and is oval in shape. In the centre we find the curved end of the nerve fibre. The third variety of nerve endings in the skin is that including bodies known as *touch corpuscles*. These are chiefly found in the papillæ of the fingers and toes. They are of oblong shape, and average about the $\frac{1}{300}$th part of an inch in diameter. In these corpuscles we find the nerve fibre winds round the corpuscle before it enters and ends in it.

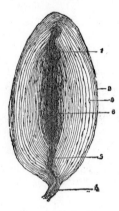

FIG. 40.—A Pacinian Body.

I, Termination of Nerve Fibre ; 2, the Capsule ; 3, Lining Membrane ; 4, Nerve Supplying the Body ; 5, Nerve Stalk ; 6, Central Mass of the Body.

Skin Sensibility.—With regard to the sensibility of different parts of the skin, an interesting series of experiments was made by E. H. Weber, who, employing a pair of compasses, estimated the sensitiveness of different areas of the skin by noting the power of distinguishing the two points of the compasses when separated largely or the reverse. Thus the tip of the tongue could distinguish the two points of the compasses when separated only to the extent of the one twenty-fourth part of an inch. The surface of the eyelid exercised this faculty when the compass points were separated to the one-sixth of an inch. The tip of the nose distinguished the two points separated to the extent of one-fourth of an inch, the palm of the hand five-twelfths of an inch, the centre of the hard palate half-an-inch, the back of the hand an inch and one-sixth, the back of the foot, near the toes, an inch and a half, the back of the neck, near the head, two inches, the middle part of the forearm two and a half, middle of the thigh two and a half, and the middle of the back two and a half inches.

The Perspiration.—We have seen that the skin being abundantly supplied with sweat glands acts as *an organ of excretion*. An analysis of sweat shows us that it consists of over 98 per cent. of water. Solids amount to about 2 per cent., composed of minerals (chief among which is common salt), 0.8 of this amount representing organic matter derived from the *débris* of the skin cells. A certain amount of fat is contained in the sweat, and also traces of *urea*, a substance largely given off by the kidneys, and representing the ultimate breakdown in the body of the nitrogenous foods we consume. Sweat is acid in its nature, and contains a small amount of carbonic acid gas.

Different animals exhibit great variation in the amount of activity which their skin exhibits. It would seem that rats, cats, and rabbits do not perspire at all by the skin. Pigs are said to sweat by the snout. In the case of dogs and cats, perspiration is given off by the pads of the feet, whilst the ox is also said to exhibit a much less amount of excretion by the skin than does the horse or the sheep.

The Secretion of Sweat.—It must be noted that the skin is always acting in ordinary life, and in the absence of exercise the amount of perspiration which is given off from the skin is entitled *insensible perspiration*. The increased amount which is excreted through exercise is known as *sensible perspiration*. The average amount of sweat given off by an adult man in twenty-four hours is estimated at two pounds. There can be little doubt that the secretion of perspiration as well as its amount are actions duly regulated by the nerves which supply the minute blood-vessels of the skin. The essential process of the excretion of sweat may be readily understood. We have seen that the skin is amply provided with capillary blood-vessels, which have been noted to be the finest vessels in the body. These surround and encompass the sweat glands on all sides. The blood circulating in these blood-vessels is therefore separated from the cavity of the sweat tube only by the thin wall of the blood-vessels and the thin wall of the sweat gland itself. Through the operation of a natural law the waste matters represented by the sweat strain through from the walls of the minute blood-vessels into the sweat glands, and are ultimately excreted at the surface of the skin by means of the *pores* in which these glands open.

Relations of Lungs, Skin, and Kidneys.—It is of importance finally to note in so far as the relations of lungs, skin, and kidneys are concerned, that their physiological connection is of a very close character. Seeing that all three organs discharge much the same duties, a knowledge of this relationship is of extreme value to the physician in his treatment of many diseases. Thus in many affections of the lungs it is of importance to cause increased skin-action through the administration of certain medicines which promote this latter end. Similarly, in ailments of the kidneys, the skin is encouraged to perform extra work, so that the kidneys may be relieved. Nature herself teaches us this principle of stimulating one organ by way of relieving another, when it is discovered that in certain cases of kidney disease more urea is given off by the skin than takes place in health. Where, on the other hand, urine is given off from the kidneys in large quantities, or where we find the digestive system parting with watery matters, the skin will generally be found to be dry. On the other hand, where the urine is of scant character through some interference with the work of the kidneys, the skin, taking upon itself part of the kidneys' work, will be found to be moist, and to have the amount of its perspiration much increased. So also we find in summer when the skin acts freely, less urine is passed than in winter when the skin action is lessened.

THE KIDNEYS AND THE URINARY APPARATUS

The *urine* constitutes part of the waste matters of the body which result from the performance of bodily functions and duties, these last including what is known as the *metabolism* or the changes which food undergoes in the course of its being made available for the wants of the frame. The apparatus which is devoted to excreting the urine consists of the *kidneys* (Figs. 41 and 42), from each of which passes a tube called the *ureter* (UU) to the *bladder* (V), or receptacle in which the urine accumulates. This last communicates in its turn with the exterior of the body by a passage known as the urethra (Fig. 41, *u'*). In connection with the skin, we have already noted that along with the kidneys and lungs it forms a physiological trio engaged in the work of excretion—that is, the getting rid of bodily waste. Whilst all three organs practically perform the same work, differences are to be noted in respect of the amounts of the respective waste materials which they excrete from the blood.

The Kidneys.—The kidneys (Fig. 41) number two, and are situated in the *lumbar region*, or that of the *loins*. They correspond in their position to the lowest dorsal vertebra, or that of the back, and of the two upper lumbar vertebræ, or those of the loins. The right kidney is situated somewhat lower down in the body than the left, this result being due to the position of the liver above. In length each kidney averages between 4 and 5 inches. It is about $2\frac{1}{2}$ inches in breadth, and exceeds 1 inch in thickness. The weight of each kidney in the male is about $4\frac{1}{2}$ ounces, that of woman being somewhat less. From each kidney, and from that part of it termed the *hilus*, the *ureter* (Fig. 42, C) takes its origin, this being the tube conveying the urine to the bladder. The upper end of each ureter is expanded, and is known as the *pelvis*. The phrase "kidney-shaped" indicates accurately enough the shape of these organs (Fig. 41). Each is convex on its outer side, and somewhat indented on its inner side. This indentation forms the *hilus* already mentioned, and at this portion of the kidney the blood-vessels, consisting of the renal artery entering the kidney, and the renal vein leaving it, are found (Fig. 42, A, B). The ureter lies behind these vessels. Around the kidney we find a layer of fat, which is very well developed in the sheep and the ox. The organ itself is covered by a thin capsule, which is easily stripped of its surface.

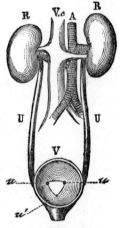

FIG. 41.—The Kidneys and Bladder.

RR, Kidneys ; *uu*, Openings of Ureters in Bladder; V, Bladder; *u'*, the beginning of the Urethra; Vc, Vena Cava Inferior, large Main Vein; A, Aorta, Main Artery of Body ; UU, Ureters.

The Structure of the Kidney.—In a section of the kidney (Fig. 43) made in its long direction, we see that it may be divided into two portions. The outer *cortical portion* (*a*) is of a bright-red colour, and passes into the interior of the organ, leaving the middle or *medullary portion* projecting into the pelvis as a number (varying from eight or ten to fifteen) of conical masses. These masses are called the *pyramids* (*c*) of the kidney. The base of the pyramids lies towards the cortical portion, whilst their tips, or *papillæ*, project into the pelvis formed by the expanded part of the ureter. These projections lie in recesses or hollows of the pelvis known as *calices*. When the summit of each papillæ is examined, we find a number of openings which represent the ends of small tubes known as *uriniferous tubules* (Fig. 44). In respect of their direction, if we trace them from the papillæ, we find them running in straight lines backwards to the edge of the pyramids. At this portion they become twisted or convoluted. Then they turn back into the pyramids in straight lines, and penetrate into the medulla or central portion. Their later course exhibits a return into the cortical part of the organ, where convolutions or twistings are again seen before the tubules end in bodies known as the *Malpighian capsules* (Fig. 45). Described in the reverse direction, we find that the *uriniferous tubule* (each of which on an average measures the $\frac{1}{600}$th part of an inch in diameter) leaves the Malpighian body (6 and 7), and then exhibits its first convolutions or foldings. It then assumes a straight course, and passes into the medulla as a descending

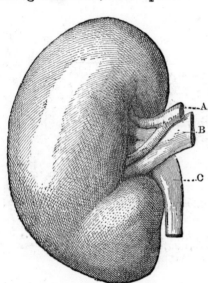

FIG. 42.—The Right Kidney seen from the Front.

A, Renal Artery; B, Renal Vein; C, Ureter.

tubule. Next, turning round, it forms a loop, and passes up to the cortical or outer portion of the kidneys, assuming a larger diameter, and again becoming convoluted or twisted. Finally, narrowing again, it forms a straight course through the medulla, where, along with other tubules, it opens on the surface of the pyramid. The *renal artery*, which has been already mentioned as entering the kidney, is a relatively large vessel which carries pure blood into the organ. The *renal vein* is also proportionately large, and carries blood away from the organ. As the renal artery enters the kidney it divides into branches, which are ultimately found forming loops or tufts within the Malpighian bodies already mentioned (Fig. 45). Each ball of capillaries is called a *glomerulus*. The artery which enters the Malpighian body is known as the *afferent* vessel, that which issues from the capsule in the shape of the vein being known as the *efferent* vessel. These capillaries resulting from the division of the artery are continued to form a much smaller vessel in the shape of a vein which leaves each Malpighian body. These smallest veins, ultimately uniting together, at last constitute the renal vein leaving the kidney, and by way of it blood is conveyed out of the organ.

The Kidney's Work.—With reference to the particular structure of the Malpighian bodies of the kidney and of the *uriniferous tubes,* which, like rivers coming from lakes, originate from them, we find that each *tubule* consists of an extremely delicate membrane

lined by special cells. Very important differences are noticed in
the *cells* of the tubules (Fig. 45). Some of them are much
larger than others, and no doubt represent those which are engaged
in the more active work of the kidney. In other parts of the
tubes they are smaller, and evidently of less functional importance.
Inside the Malpighian body itself we also find a lining of cells (4).
The importance of noting the cell arrangements of the kidney
will be apparent when we reflect that the duties of the organ do
not merely consist in separating from the blood waste matters,
but likewise include a certain amount of
secreting or manufacturing action. It
is in connection with this latter duty
that the importance of the cells becomes
apparent. If we consider that each
kidney may be held to represent an
apparatus which filters waste matters
from the blood, we may assume that
the work of pure filtration or separation
occurs in the Malpighian bodies, and
especially takes place from the tufts of
blood-vessels already described as being
contained within them. The fluid which
is excreted from the blood into the
Malpighian body may be described as
largely consisting of water, with a few
mineral constituents in addition.

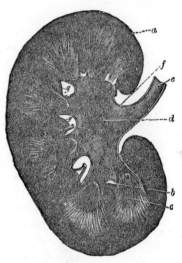

FIG. 43.—Kidney in Sections.
a, Cortical Part; *b,* Calyx; *c,* Pyramids;
d, Pelvis; *e,* Ureter; *f,* Hilum; *g g,*
Pyramids and Vessels.

Here it is of great importance to
recall to mind the fact that the vein
or vessel which leaves the Malpighian
body is *much smaller* than that which
enters it. We thus see that the blood enters each Malpighian
body under great pressure, and that as it cannot easily escape
by the smaller vessel leaving it, such pressure is calculated to
produce the desired result, namely, that of forcing fluid from the
blood in the vessels into the Malpighian body itself. In other words,
on account of the greater pressure of the incoming blood the filtering
action of the kidney is in this way exercised. It is here a case of a
supply-pipe being of greater calibre than the overflow or escape pipe,
with the result that on account of the pressure exerted on the walls
of the blood-vessels the filtering action is expedited.

It must here be noted that the vessel passing out of the Malpighian
body in its course passes over the convoluted or twisted portions of
the uriniferous tubules. These last have been already noted to be

lined by special cells. It is here that the work of *secretion* as distinguished from that of mere separation of fluid taking place in the Malpighian body comes into play, for there can be little doubt that the cells of the tubules separate certain substances from the blood, which ultimately appear in the urine or excretion of the kidney itself. To sum up, two distinct functions are thus discharged by the kidney. The first of these is the mere act of filtration taking place in the Malpighian bodies, whilst the second is a work of secretion effected from the blood by the cells of the tubules.

The Urine.—Urine is passed by an adult man to the extent of about fifty or sixty ounces per day. In this amount about one and a half ounces of solid materials will be contained. The secretion of urine depends very largely on the general condition of the body, and also upon the nature and quantity of the food. If a large quantity of fluids be taken, we find an increase in the amount of the urine present. On a somewhat dry diet the quantity of urine is lessened. In the same way, where cold checks the action of the skin, an increase in the action of the kidneys takes place. Similarly, where the external temperature is high and the skin acting freely, the activity of the kidney decreases. In so far as the composition of urine is concerned, we find that it consists in a thousand parts of about 958 parts of water, and 42 parts of solids. Of the solids *urea* forms the chief element, being present to the extent of 23.3 parts. In addition, we find in the urine various minerals represented by common salt, phosphoric acid, and phosphates of lime and magnesia. *Uric acid* is also present to the extent of about 0.5 of the solids, whilst other substances in the shape of sulphuric acid, ammonia, &c., are also natural constituents of this fluid. The gases of the urine are found to be carbonic acid, oxygen, and nitrogen. They are present, however, in small quantity only. The specific gravity of ordinary urine varies from 1015 to 1025. If it sinks low, the physician may suspect the existence of albumen in the urine, a condition associated with Bright's disease. On the other hand, if it rises high, say over 1030, the presence of sugar may be suspected. Indeed, in some cases of diabetes, the specific gravity of the urine may rise as high as 1050.

Urea and Uric Acid—The most important constituents given forth by the kidney are therefore *urea* and *uric acid*. These substances represent practically the breakdown in the body of the

FIG. 44.—Plan of Kidney. 1, Interlobular artery; 2, a Kidney Lobe; 3, Cortical Part; 4, Uriniferous Tube; 5, Interlobular Artery; 6, Medullary Part with Pyramid; 7, Secondary Pyramid.

nitrogenous foods we consume, represented by the white of egg, juice of meat, and the like. Urea itself consists of carbon, hydrogen, oxygen, and nitrogen, the nitrogen bulking very largely in its composition. Hence, we may consider that, whilst the lungs and skin are devoted largely to getting rid of non-nitrogenous waste, represented by carbonic acid, water, and heat, the kidneys, in addition to excreting water and heat, are more especially devoted to the separation from the blood of the nitrogenous waste of the frame. In so far as the relations between urea and uric acid are concerned, physiologists are generally inclined to believe, that as urea represents the last stage of the breakdown of nitrogenous matters in the body, so uric acid represents a previous stage in this work. In the

section (Vol. I.) devoted to the description of *gout*, it was shown that that disease probably arises from an accumulation of uric acid or its derivatives, its further conversion into urea being from one cause or another obstructed. The great importance of the examination of the urine as not merely indicative of kidney diseases, but also of other abnormal states of body, will be apparent. This topic will be specially treated in another part of this work.

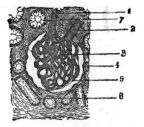

FIG. 45.—A Malpighian Capsule Magnified.

1, Afferent Vessel; 2, Efferent Vessel; 3, Capillary Network; 4, Lining Membrane of Cells; 5, Endothelial Cells of Capsule; 6 and 7, Uriniferous Tubes in Section.

With regard to the original source of urea, it is held by many physiologists that this substance is really formed in the liver, the kidneys, however, playing the part of filters, specially devoted to ridding the blood of this substance. Of uric acid, in all probability, the same remark holds good. It is not formed, as far as we know, by the kidneys, because when these organs are removed, the acid continues to be produced, and is found specially in the liver and in the spleen. Here also we may assume that it is the duty of the secreting cells of the kidneys to deal with uric acid, and to remove it from the blood in a similar fashion to that in which we have seen them act in the removal of urea. The cells of the kidney tubules, it may be noted, also exercise yet another function. Whilst it is part of their duty to remove from the blood the waste products just mentioned, it must be equally their duty to prevent the useful constituents of the blood from passing away from that fluid. In this fashion we may consider that they exert what has been called a "selective" action, irrespective of the matters with which they are called upon to deal in the shape of the blood constituents. The blood which passes away from the kidney by the renal vein is amongst the purest blood in the body, seeing that it has just had removed from it the waste materials just described. This blood, however, soon joins the general stream of blood in the great vein (Fig. 41, Vc), leading upwards to the right side of the heart. This vein contains a stream of impure blood, containing waste matters gathered from all parts of the body and returned to the heart, whence it is sent to the lungs for the purpose of purification.

The Ureter.—The *ureter* we have seen to be the tube or duct of the kidney, which ends in a widened extension in the pelvis of the organ (Fig. 41, U U). It passes into the cavity of the bony pelvis or haunch so as to reach the inside of the bladder. In length each ureter is about eighteen inches, its diameter being described as that of a goose quill. It consists of three coverings, the outer of which is composed of fibrous tissue. The middle consists of longitudinal and circular muscular fibres of the unstriped variety, whilst the inner covering is composed of mucous membrane. In cases where the mineral constituents of the urine form concretions in the kidney and constitute the disease known as *renal calculi* or "stone" in the kidney, such matters tend to pass downwards from the kidney into the ureter, and thence into the bladder. In cases where such concretions are of fairly large size, their passage through the ureter may give rise to excruciating pain.

The Bladder.—The bladder (Fig. 41, V) is contained within the pelvis or haunch cavity. It is a somewhat oval bag or sac when full of urine, but of a triangular shape when empty. It lies behind the pubes or front of the pelvis upon the *rectum*, or lowest portion of the large bowel. The middle part of the bladder is named the *body*, its lower part is called the *base*, while the upper part is known as its *fundus*. The narrow portion which ends in the urethra or tube leading from the bladder to the external surface of the body is termed its *neck*. The neck of the bladder itself is encircled by a gland, known as the *prostate gland*, which exercises certain functions connected with the organs of generation.

The bladder itself consists of an outer or *serous coat* and of a middle or *muscular coat* composed of involuntary fibres forming several very distinct masses, whose function it is to contract the bladder in the expulsion of urine. Round the neck of the bladder, we find a special development of these fibres known as the *sphincter muscle* whereby the bladder is kept closed. Beneath the muscular coat we find another layer called the *submucous coat*, whilst the inner layer of the bladder appears as a thick and smooth *mucous membrane* which is covered by epithelial cells. In the floor of the bladder is a smooth space known as the *trigone* (Fig. 41), where the lining membrane is somewhat finer than in the other parts of the organ. At the hinder part of this space the ureters enter the bladder, its front angle being directed towards the neck of the organ.

The bladder, as we have seen, is a storehouse for the urine, which, coming through into the ureters from the kidneys, passes into it in drops. The emptying of the bladder is accomplished through a nervous action known as a *reflex act*—that is to say, when the proper period arrives for the bladder to part with its contents, a nervous message, so to speak, is sent to a nerve centre, situated in the spinal cord. From this centre a reflex or return message acts on the sphincter muscle, causing it to relax, whilst at the same time the muscular walls of the bladder are made to contract, and so to expel the urine through the urethra.

SECTION III

DISEASES OF THE DIGESTIVE SYSTEM

REFERRING to the sections dealing with the digestive organs and with the process of digestion, it has already been noted that the digestive system is in reality a tube along which the food is made to pass so that it may undergo the changes necessary to fit it for being added to the blood by way of renovating that fluid. The stomach has been shown to be merely an expanded part of this tube, the greater length of which is represented by the bowel or intestine, measuring in extent twenty-six feet. Another important item in connection with the digestive system is the fact that attached to the sides of the tube we find certain organs known as *digestive glands*, amongst which the liver, the sweetbread, the salivary glands, and the gastric glands of the stomach, stand conspicuous. The object of these glands was shown to be that of providing certain fluids or " secretions " which are poured on the food in its journey along the digestive tube. It is through the agency of these secretions that the food is chemically and otherwise altered so as to fit it for absorption by the blood.

Dealing with diseases of the digestive system we can readily understand how such ailments present themselves to us in a great variety of forms. In the first instance such diseases may be due to *deficient secretion of the digestive fluids* or to some alteration in their natural and normal composition. An example of this class of digestive disorder is afforded us when for example we find a deficiency of pepsin in the gastric juice of the stomach. Another example of like kind is found in the case of what is known as *acidity*, a common symptom of that hydra-headed trouble known as *indigestion* or *dyspepsia*. If the secretion of the *liver* (bile) be deficient in quantity or quality, disturbance of the digestive functions is apt to ensue, and very serious disorder may be associated with a want of power on the part of the *sweetbread* to discharge its special duties.

Organic Disease.—The foregoing examples illustrate what may be called "functional" diseases of the digestive system. They depend, in other words, upon the upsetting of the normal work of one or more of the organs concerned with the assimilation of food. There may be no actual disease of the organs themselves. Their action is for the most part of irregular character, and the ailments are susceptible of cure when the functions of the organs are duly and naturally resumed. The case is of a very different nature when we have to take into account diseases of the digestive organs depending on what may be called *organic causes*. By this phrase is meant that the ailments depend upon some definite alteration in the structure and substance of the organs concerned (see vol. i. p. 24). If for example *ulceration of the stomach* is present, the function of digestion is seriously inter-fered with owing to the inflammation of the stomach producing serious disturbance of its duties. In *cancer of the stomach* another illustra-tion is found of organic disease. Where any *stricture* or narrowing of the digestive tube occurs, we come face to face also with an organic ailment. This latter condition depending on the presence of a tumour or the folding of one portion of the bowel within itself, naturally offers a serious impediment to the natural performance of the digestive work. Similarly, a tumour of the liver or sweetbread would represent an organic digestive ailment. It need hardly be said that all organic troubles present themselves to view as ailments of a more serious character than those in which some mere irregularity of function exists. No doubt this latter condition is also represented in organic disease, but reconstruction of health is a much more simple matter and also more rapidly accomplished where a mere irregularity of the working of an organ has to be cured than when an alteration of its structure has to be combated.

General Symptoms.—It may be said in a general way that the symptoms of digestive diseases are easily noted, in the sense that discomfort and pain in the performance of digestive work speedily ensue. In the first volume of this work reference was made to the appearance of the tongue as a guide to the presence of disease. The reader may further be referred to the section in question by way of noting the nature of the information to be obtained from an inspection of this organ. The special characters of the tongue shown in digestive diseases will be again alluded to in connection with the present subject. Valuable information is also afforded in digestive troubles from the character of vomited matters, whilst an examination of the fæces (or matters discharged from the bowel) may afford an important indication of the presence of certain ailments directly affecting the digestive apparatus.

Ailments of the Mouth and Tongue.—Diseases of the mouth and tongue are, for the most part, of simple nature. The most serious disease which can affect these parts is undoubtedly *cancer*, this affection being definitely marked by increasing pain and hardness of the tongue, the disease extending to the glands of the mouth and to those of the neck. It is needless to say that in a serious case like this, the only treatment is represented by removal of the cancerous growth. The operation of removal of the whole or part of the tongue is a relatively simple one, and it may interest readers to know that in the absence of the tongue speech can be almost perfectly performed.

Ulceration of the Tongue.—This is by no means an uncommon affection. It frequently arises from the contact of the organ with the broken edges of teeth. The services of the dentist in this event must be called in in order to remove the irritating cause. Sometimes sores on the tongue form as the result of stomach derangement. The cure here will naturally depend upon the relief of the stomach complaint itself. The tongue may also be the seat of ulcers of syphilitic nature, usually found on its sides and also on the insides of the lips. In the mouth also, syphilis may produce what are called *mucous patches*. These appear of whitish character but do not ulcerate. Wherever syphilitic disease is present, remedies must be adopted for the cure of that condition, the tongue symptoms being mere manifestations of the ailment. Ulceration may also be a sign of commencing cancer. (*See* SYPHILIS.)

Where the mouth is affected through stomachic derangement, in addition to attending to the latter ailment, a saline purge should be given. In the treatment of such simple mouth affections no drug is of greater service than chlorate of potash. A mixture composed of two drachms of chlorate of potash, one ounce of glycerine, and eight ounces of camphor water may be used. The dose of this is a tablespoonful every four hours. In addition, a chlorate of potash lozenge or tabloid may occasionally be allowed slowly to dissolve in the mouth. The condition of the teeth should be rigidly attended to, and regular brushing morning and night with carbolic tooth powder practised. A useful mouth wash is that made by adding a few crystals of permanganate of potash to half a tumbler of tepid water.

Another mouth wash consists of a few drops of tincture of myrrh added to tepid water, whilst the mixture of myrrh, honey, and borax, sold by all chemists, also forms an extremely useful preparation in irritated states of the mouth.

Toothache and the care of the Teeth.—The structure of the teeth was duly described in the section of this work dealing with the digestive organs. Of the high importance of attending to the welfare of the teeth nothing requires to be said, seeing that defective teeth, causing imperfect division of the food, forms a frequent source of indigestion. *Tooth decay* is a process depending upon the attack on the teeth of germs or microbes which, collecting in the mouth, appear to produce in conjunction with the food-*débris* processes of fermentation. These processes develop acid substances which have the effect of attacking the enamel and ivory of the teeth, and in this way of causing their decay. The rule should be followed of brushing the teeth at least once a day. To brush them *at night* is perhaps the most typical procedure, seeing that the night brushing gets rid of the particles of food which have accumulated in the mouth during the day. There is no reason of course why the teeth should not again be brushed in the morning. A tooth-powder should be used and the teeth brushed, not merely across, but in the up and down direction, in order that the bristles of the brush may dislodge any particles lying in the interstices of the teeth. Many dentists also recommend that occasionally a thread should be drawn through the spaces between the teeth by way of further ridding them of *débris*. Where *tartar* accumulates on the teeth, it should be scaled off by the dentist.

Treatment of Toothache.—Where a tooth has undergone the process of decay to a slight extent only, the services of the dentist should be requisitioned. Indeed, on the first appearance of any tooth defect, the dentist ought to be at once consulted. Many defective teeth can thus be saved and be made to continue as useful parts of our dental apparatus, whereas, through neglect, the process of decay quickly renders them utterly useless. Toothache must be distinguished from neuralgia affecting the gums. The latter is confined to no one tooth but affects the gums at large. It arises from cold or a low state of the system, and will be duly dealt with in the section dealing with nervous diseases as a branch of the larger subject of *neuralgia* in general. The common cause of toothache is of course decay exposing the tooth-pulp and its nerves to the influence of irritation. Where toothache affects an apparently sound tooth, for example, examination will often reveal the presence of a small cavity indicating the commencement of decay. In the case of ordinary toothache a remedy which, carefully used, is capable of abolishing the pain, is found in carbolic acid. Care must be used in dealing with this acid. It must not be allowed to touch any part of the gums, a small piece of cotton wool soaked in the acid being placed in the decayed tooth. If allowed to remain for some time it eases the pain, and a further application may result in the destruction of the nervous pulp. A dentist's rule in the treatment of toothache is that a decayed tooth should practically be left open, whilst on the other hand a tooth in which decay is just commencing should be stopped. In some cases, powdered antipyrin or exalgin placed in the hollow of a tooth will assuage the pain. A mixture which has been highly recommended by an authority for application to an inflamed and exposed tooth-pulp is composed of three drachms of collodion, three drachms of crystallised carbolic acid, and ten grains of cocaine. The cavity of the tooth must first be well dried out with cotton wool and a little of this mixture carefully placed in the hollow.

It may be added that where inflammation of the gums occurs, and especially at the part where the gums and teeth join, it is likely that a special form of inflammation of the tooth-sockets has occurred. In such a case a dentist should be at once consulted, and for the relief of the pain the remedies already indicated in connection with inflammation of the mouth in the shape of mouth washes, might here be found useful. In addition it is important that a saline purge should be used as often as necessary by way of reducing the feverish state.

Diseases of the Palate.—These diseases are by no means common in adults, but they are frequently seen in children. They will be duly treated in the section treating with children's diseases. Thus *thrush* is a well-known condition occurring in infants, and probably depending on some error in feeding. More serious is that disease known as *cancrum oris*, where we find ulceration destroying the cheek, and even spreading to the jaw.

Diseases of the Tonsils.—Under the name of throat troubles, ailments of the *tonsils* fall to be considered. Other throat ailments will be duly treated of under the head of affections of the breathing organs, seeing that the condition known as *sore throat* mostly applies to ailments affecting not the throat itself, but the organ of voice and upper part of the windpipe at large. The tonsils, however, in virtue of their situation at the back of the throat, fall to be considered as organs which, properly speaking, may be said to form part of the digestive tract. The tonsils belong to that series of organs already noted under the name of *ductless glands* (see p. 31). They are placed at the back of the throat, and are probably organs devoted to the manufacture of white globules of the blood, such as have been shown (vol. i. p. 92) to perform important duties connected with the destruction of microbes gaining admittance to the system. These organs may also, like the *thyroid gland*, pour some secretion of their own into the blood.

Tonsils which are enlarged or *hypertrophied* are very apt to become infected by germs, thereby causing tonsillitis or quinsy. These tonsils are a menace to health, as these germs are the commonest cause of rheumatic fever and pericarditis. Hypertrophied tonsils should always be removed by the operation of enucleation.

Tonsillitis is an acute inflammation of the tonsil. On inspecting the back of the throat the tonsil will be seen to be red and inflamed, and in some cases several little points of pus or matter will be seen on the surface.

Treatment.—A saline purge, such as Epsom salts, may be given at first. Aspirin in ten-grain doses or a mixture of salicylate of soda ten grains, bicarbonate of soda fifteen grains, and water one ounce with some flavouring agent, taken three times a day will reduce temperature. The tonsils should be sprayed or painted with peroxide of hydrogen, and afterwards gargled with Glycerin-thymol Compound one part to four of warm water.

Quinsy may start with the condition described above in tonsillitis. In some cases instead of yielding quickly to treatment, one tonsil, and in other cases both, continue to swell; the uvula also becomes swollen and gelatinous looking. Pain is intense and swallowing almost impossible. The temperature rises, the breath is very offensive, and the side of throat affected will show swelling in the neck, and pain shoots from the neck to the ear.

Treatment.—Here it is extremely advisable to administer a saline purge by way of commencing the treatment. In order to reduce the fever the tincture of aconite, described in the section (vol. i.) dealing with inflammation, should be used in the case of an adult. The mixture consists of fifteen minims of tincture of aconite, and two ounces of water. The dose for an adult is a teaspoonful taken every fifteen minutes for the first hour, and then once an hour for the succeeding six or eight hours. If this treatment is begun early in quinsy, the inflammation may be prevented from proceeding onwards to the stage of suppuration. Another remedy of use in tonsillitis is guaiacum. It may be prescribed for an adult in tonsillitis as follows: Ammoniated tincture of guaiacum, three drachms; tincture of aconite twenty minims; gum mucilage one ounce; and camphor water up to six ounces. The dose is two tablespoonfuls twice daily. As aconite is contained in this mixture, that containing aconite alone should not be used at the same time. To relieve the more immediate symptoms and pain of tonsillitis steam may be inhaled from an ordinary inhaler. Some physicians recommend linseed meal poultices applied to the neck by way of hastening the formation of matter, and thus bringing the case to an early termination. Certain throat affections may also be noted to depend upon *a rheumatic condition of body.* Where this condition exists, remedies for rheumatism should be given. Thus salicin in a dose of twenty or thirty grains given thrice daily, or salicylate of soda in a dose of ten grains given thrice daily will probably afford relief. Surgical treatment in the shape of puncturing the tonsil at the softest spot or freely incising with a bistoury will let out the pus and give the most immediate relief. This should be done as soon as suppuration is suspected.

Diseases of the Œsophagus or Gullet.—This portion of the digestive system is not specially subject to the attack of disease. It is liable occasionally to develop *cancer*, although this must be esteemed a relatively rare form of the disease. *Inflammation of the gullet* marked chiefly by difficulty in swallowing may arise from the extension of mouth inflammation downwards. Vomiting may be a symptom of this latter ailment, the pain being referred not to the stomach itself but between the throat and the latter organ. In the case of cancer of the gullet great pain exists with difficulty of swallowing, whilst the voice will also be of a husky character and cough will be present. The glands of the side of the neck in such a case will also be found to be enlarged. The only adequate treatment for cancer here, as elsewhere, is that to be had at the hands of the surgeon.

Stricture of the Gullet.—Stricture of this portion of the digestive tube is usually found as the result of swallowing some corrosive or burning poison, the inflammation set up having a tendency to narrow the width of the tube. The treatment for this condition, which is sometimes an extremely serious one from its interfering with the swallowing of food, is of a surgical nature, and consists in the dilatation of the œsophagus by the surgeon by the aid of a bougie. This instrument is passed downwards, and after repeated applications has the effect of widening the canal.

Spasmodic Stricture of the Gullet is a different affection, and is one chiefly seen in hysterical persons, and most often in young women. Difficulty of swallowing is complained of with a sense of choking, although, when the patient's attention is diverted from her ailment, swallowing as a rule can be easily enough performed. We may be somewhat suspicious of the existence of this condition when we have regard to the age and sex of the patient, and also to the fact that the signs of any more serious disease are wanting. The treatment here is that which is followed out in cases of hysteria at large, an affection to be more fully dealt with under the heading of nervous ailments. It may however be said that the main lines on which a cure should be attempted are represented by change of air and scene, firm but resolute moral treatment, and by the use of tonics of which iron and quinine are examples. The tonsils should always be examined for local irritation.

DISEASES OF THE STOMACH

The ailments which affect the stomach, as has been explained in the introduction to this section of the work, may be classified into those of *organic kind* and those of *functional nature*. Dealing first with the organic troubles, manifested by some alteration in the structure of the stomach, we may select for discussion inflammation of the organ.

Inflammation of the Stomach.—This ailment is medically known as *Gastritis*. It appears in two forms, the first of which, *acute inflammation*, is comparatively rare, whereas the *chronic* variety is of much more common occurrence. Some authorities, indeed, consider that acute inflammation of the stomach may be practically considered to be represented as a consequence of dyspepsia or indigestion of a certain type; in other words, the functions of the stomach are not merely upset, but certain changes also occur in respect of its structure. The acute form of the disease is marked by the sudden onset of pain not of a very severe character. The patient vomits frequently, and after bringing up whatever food has been undigested, the matters expelled ultimately appear in the form of a fluid of a glairy character representing the mucous secretion of the lining membrane of the stomach. In this disease headache is present whilst constipation also exists. The cause of this ailment, which is generally found in middle life, and occurs more frequently in women than in men, is to be referred to some error in diet. Thus the taking of cold water when heated may induce an attack, but unquestionably gastritis of the acute kind is most common as the result of over-indulgence in alcoholic liquor, and it is frequently associated with that liver trouble known as *cirrhosis*, a typical ailment of drunkards.

In the case of children another form of stomach inflammation is liable to occur. The patient complains of pain after food and on the stomach being pressed. The vomiting here is generally more or less continuous, and is brought up with considerable difficulty. Diarrhœa may also be present. It should be noted as a point worthy of remembrance, that if vomiting be due to any disease of the brain it is of an easy character, whereas when produced by stomach affection, retching is frequent and vomiting painful.

Treatment.—Reserving the consideration of chronic gastritis for the section dealing with indigestion, we may sum up the procedure to be adopted in the acute form in the expression that the stomach must be made to rest from all its duties for at least a period of twenty-four hours. No measure is more valuable in cases of irritable stomach than *rest*. Ice may be sucked in order to relieve thirst. If the patient is extremely weak, nutritive injections may be administered by the bowel. It is needless to remark that if there has been over-indulgence in alcohol, all stimulants must be at once cut off, and it is recommended that five grains of calomel be placed on the tongue and swallowed with a spoonful of iced water. A seidlitz powder or dose of sulphate of magnesia may be given eight hours after the calomel has been taken. Such a treatment, one authority remarks, may often cut short an attack. In cases where any irritating food has been swallowed, the stomach should be emptied by giving the patient large quantities of hot water so as to produce vomiting. If pain is especially severe in the region of the stomach, a warm poultice applied over the organ will relieve it. If the vomiting is extremely persistent, iced champagne in sips should be given. A dessert-spoonful of the liquor of bismuth diluted with a little water, or thirty grains of carbonate of bismuth, may suffice to soothe the stomach. These drugs are to be given when the stomach is empty. When ordinary food is resumed, the diet should consist at first of easily digested substances such as soups, chicken, milk puddings, and the like. It is necessary in all such cases to avoid heavy meals, and to take the food frequently and in small quantities.

Gastralgia.—This term is applied to *pain in the stomach*, a symptom undoubtedly characteristic of many ailments affecting the organ. It is also known by the name of *gastrodynia*. Many physicians regard this ailment as a mere symptom rather than as constituting a disorder in itself. Pain limited to one spot, and often extending to the back, is a symptom of *ulcer of the stomach*. Pain less distinctly limited is also characteristic of severe indigestion. Some authorities are, however, inclined to believe in the existence of a separate ailment known as *gastralgia,* this ailment being regarded by them as a form of *neuralgia of the stomach.* The pain in this disorder is not specially connected with periods of food-taking nor is it associated with vomiting ; also, in its periods of invasion, it is somewhat erratic in its coming and going. A typical subject of stomach pain is generally a spare thin person of a neurotic or nervous temperament.

Treatment.—It is advised that from one-sixth to one-half a grain of cocaine be given in such cases just before meals, or ten minims of nepenthe, or of the liquor of opium in water, may be administered in the place of the cocaine. The general health should also be supervised, and constipation if present specially corrected. Ten grains of antipyrin may be taken as a remedy in this ailment or fifteen drops of the tincture of belladonna in water twice daily before meals. Where ordinary remedies fail, the physician will recommend rest in bed for two or three weeks, whilst careful attention is paid to the diet of the patient, which should be extremely light.

Ulcer of the Stomach.—*Ulceration* is a process the nature of which will be found duly detailed in the section on " Inflammation" (vol. i.). This is one of the results of the inflammatory process. It is liable to occur in connection with the stomach in two forms. In the first instance there is the *acute* form of ulceration, and secondly the *chronic* form. It is the acute variety which constitutes the more important phase of the trouble, seeing that under certain circumstances it may threaten life itself. This ailment, it may be noted, may appear in the course of other diseases, and is known to occur in the course of erysipelas and typhoid fever. In such instances, however, the typical symptoms of ordinary gastric ulcer are wanting, and the severe pain which marks the independent affection is absent.

Symptoms.—A typical subject of ulcer of the stomach is an anæmic woman. A marked feature of the disease is the occurrence of pain in the stomach referred to one particular spot as a rule, *and commencing within ten minutes or quarter of an hour after a meal has been taken.* We can readily understand the meaning of this prominent symptom, seeing that the pain is due to the movements of the stomach affecting the diseased portion. Vomiting occurs, and relief is experienced when the stomach is emptied. *The vomited matters may contain traces of blood.* The patient generally presents an emaciated appearance, and constipation is as a rule present. What happens in this disease is that a limited portion of the lining membrane of the stomach develops inflammatory symptoms. The inflammation proceeds to the stage of ulceration of the inner coat of the stomach, producing what may be practically called a small raw area in the interior of the organ. The great danger represented in this ailment is the breaking through by the ulcer of the coat of the stomach, thus producing the condition known to physicians as *perforation.* In such an event the contents of the stomach are of course liable to escape into the general cavity of the abdomen and by their presence to set up *peritonitis* or general inflammation of the lining membrane of that cavity. This last, it need hardly be stated, constitutes in itself a most dangerous condition.

An ulcer of the stomach is of circular shape and presents a punched out appearance. It may vary very much in size from that of a small pea, to the occupation of a large area of the stomach's lining membrane. Ulcers of this description most frequently occur on the hinder wall of the stomach. The ulcer is more dangerous if it develops on the front wall. Another result of ulceration proceeding to an extreme degree is that adhesions may be set up between the stomach and other organs, thus limiting the digestive movements and inducing further disturbances of the digestive functions.

Causes.—The causes of this disease are somewhat obscure, but most physicians incline to attribute it to some altered condition of the gastric juice. Thus, if this latter secretion is of too acid a character, or if the natural protective powers of the stomach are lessened, or if both causes operate, the lining membrane is liable to undergo the inflammatory changes resulting in ulceration. Behind these causes there probably lies another represented by some condition affecting the blood-supply of the stomach and altering the circulation through the organ. This ailment appears to be in many cases susceptible of a natural cure. Thus, if the ulcer heals of itself, a cure may be accomplished. In many cases, however, the patient dies of exhaustion from the pain and also from inability to affect the due nourishment of the body. We have already alluded to the fact that death may occur from the ulcer perforating or breaking through the wall of the stomach.

Treatment.—All physicians agree in placing *rest* of the stomach as the foundation of treatment. We can see the reason for this declaration when we reflect that so long as the movements of the stomach are liable to continue in the act of digestion, so long will the prospects of the ulcer's healing be delayed. The patient is placed in bed, no food being given by the mouth. For a varying period, all nourishment must be supplied through *injections* or *enemata* of nutritive material, that is, food must be given by the bowel. Wash out the bowel first with a simple warm water enema. An author speaking of this mode of feeding says : " It is hardly necessary to point out that in order to be well retained, an enema must be small in bulk, the temperature lukewarm, and that it must pass gently and slowly into the bowel. A heaped teaspoonful of prepared malted food with a little milk and enough hot water to sufficiently raise the temperature and to make the whole quantity up to one and a half ounces, or two teaspoonfuls of beef peptonoids in two or three tablespoonfuls of warm water are typical examples." All injections must consist of easily digested foods such as will be duly described in the sections dealing with "Nursing" and "Invalid Cookery."

The stomach being allowed to rest in this way for a time, milk may then be given by the mouth in small amounts. Mouth-feeding must be at once stopped if symptoms of bleeding from the stomach reappear. With the milk it is a good plan to mix a little potash or soda water. Peptonised milk is a valuable food in this ailment. Later on corn flour or arrowroot in fine powder may be given in the milk in a cooked form, whilst Invalid Bovril, meat juice, soft boiled eggs, and milk puddings may gradually, as time passes, be added to the diet. Each case must be judged on its own merits regarding the return of the food to the ordinary character, but a golden rule here is that of noting that it is safer always to err on the side of prolonging care in the feeding than of being in any haste to return to the usual dietary.

Medical Treatment.—With regard to medicinal treatment for any bleeding which may occur, small pieces of ice may be swallowed and an ice-bag placed over the stomach. Hazeline in a teaspoonful dose may also prove beneficial. Vomiting may be also treated by the giving of ice, or a small dose of morphia. A capsule containing one minim of creosote may be tried if the vomiting is persistent. Some physicians regard bismuth as a necessary part of the treatment. This may be given either in the form of a dessert-spoonful of the liquor of bismuth or in a dose from five to ten grains of the subnitrate of bismuth, this amount being given thrice daily. The latter drug is often given in much larger doses.

In the case of collapse, indicating that perforation of the wall of the stomach has taken place, the services of the surgeon must be at once requisitioned. An operation can be performed for the relief of the condition and the saving of life.

Dilatation of the Stomach.—This term is applied to a condition, the main feature of which is the enlarged capacity of the organ. Ordinary dilatation is a condition apt to be represented both in "chronic gastritis" itself and in dyspepsia. That which seems to occur in this ailment is an expansion of the stomach, due probably to some want of contracting power in its muscular coat, so that instead of the organ when empty contracting in a natural fashion it remains more or less expanded. In all probability this condition is a common result of indigestion, or it may be of some error in diet, bringing about as a result a loss of tone in the coats or membranes of the organ. The ordinary causes of dilatation of the stomach, however, are those which depend upon some obstruction to the free egress of the food into the intestine, that is to say where the *pylorus* (or opening of the stomach into the bowel) is unduly narrowed or blocked through the presence of a tumour or of cancer itself. Occasionally also, some degree of stricture of the pyloric opening, due to inflammation, may be responsible for the dilatation. Other causes are found in adhesions taking place between the stomach and other organs, the effect being to distend it; and yet another cause is found in some injury to the nerves of the stomach, bringing about paralysis of its muscular layer.

Symptoms.—The onset of this disease and its progress are usually slow. We first find symptoms of indigestion accompanied by acidity. Vomiting is also a notable symptom in such cases, and the vomited matters are found to be peculiar in respect that they are of dark colour, extremely acid in character, and containing sundry microscopic fungi of the nature of yeasts (*Sarcinæ*). Constipation is present in this disorder, whilst the urine as a rule is scanty and shows deposits. The abdomen itself is distended, and there is a greater fulness towards the left side. A splashing sound is heard when the lower part of the abdomen is manipulated or pushed upwards.

Treatment.—Great care in the selection of food is here necessary. It will be better to avoid as far as possible all foods containing starch and sugar. Little fluid must be taken with meals, seeing a condition which very largely favours the occurrence of dilatation of the stomach is that of consuming large amounts of fluids with the food. It is better in this case that nutriment should be taken at short intervals and in small amounts than that a heavy meal should be consumed at once. The more digestible the food, the better for the patient. At first liquid foods may be alone ordered. Strong soups, beef jellies and the like may be given, whilst later, sweetbread, tripe, white boiled fish and chicken may be added to the diet. If pain be present after solid food is taken, it will be wise to limit the diet to articles of a fluid nature.

Drugs.—Drugs are mostly given in this ailment by way of relieving urgent symptoms. To correct the acidity bismuth may be given, as already prescribed in other stomach troubles. A favourite remedy is salicylate of bismuth, of which ten to twenty grains may be taken after food twice or thrice daily. Between meals it is recommended that a draught containing five grains of sulphocarbolate of soda combined with twenty minims of spirits of chloroform, and half an ounce of compound infusion of gentian, should be taken. The object of these remedies is to prevent the occurrence of acid fermentations, a result also attained by the limitation of starches and sugars in the diet.

Lavage.—Dilatation of the stomach, however, is mostly treated by " lavage," a term implying the washing out of the stomach by aid of the stomach-pump or similar appliance. A patient by the aid of what is known as a stomach-siphon can perform this operation upon himself. A rubber tube is passed into the stomach, and is provided at its upper extremity with a funnel. When the tube is passed into the stomach, the funnel is filled with fluid. Just before the fluid passes from the funnel the latter is rapidly lowered, when the contents of the stomach are siphoned out into any convenient receptacle. The fluid used to wash out the stomach is tepid water to which a little bicarbonate of soda has been added in the proportion of about two grains to the ounce. In other cases a saturated solution of boric acid is used. A few pints of fluid represent the amount to be used at each washing, the operation being performed first once or twice daily and afterwards less frequently as progress is made. The object of lavage is to remove irritating matters from the stomach and to stimulate its muscular layer to increased action.

Cancer of the Stomach.—Cancer is unfortunately a frequent disease of this organ. It appears to be slightly more common in males than in females, and may be considered to be a disease of later life. The most frequent seat of cancer is the pyloric or hinder orifice of the stomach. The symptoms consist of digestive disturbance, acidity and flatulence, followed by vomiting and pain after food is taken. This pain in the majority of cases appears when digestion has proceeded for some time. When the disease has become established the vomited matters will be found to contain blood, giving them an appearance known as "coffee ground vomit." The pain is not conspicuously relieved by vomiting as in gastric ulcer, whilst we find the patient growing rapidly thin, and on examination a tumour or swelling can generally be detected towards the right extremity of the stomach. We have seen that in gastric ulcer the subject is generally a female and the disease common in the young, whilst pain in this disease comes on very soon after a meal has been taken.

Treatment.—It can be understood that all treatment here can only be directed to relieving the symptoms, the only cure, if cure be possible, being represented by a surgical operation. The food must be given in small quantities only, and should consist chiefly of liquid nutriment. Many physicians recommend that the stomach should be washed out as described in the case of dilatation of the organ. If constipation is present, it must be relieved by an enema. Creosote to the extent of one minim enclosed in a capsule may be given after food. Where much collapse and weakness are present, small quantities of champagne form a most suitable stimulant.

Dyspepsia or Indigestion.—" Indigestion " forms one of the most difficult ailments the physician can be called upon to treat. In the first place its causes are very numerous, whilst its symptoms vary extremely in different patients. In the second place the treatment which is adapted for one case is found to be unsuitable for another, hence each case has to be treated on its own merits. We have already seen that *gastritis* is a condition associated with a certain amount of change in the structure of the stomach. On the other hand in a pure case of dyspepsia (as indigestion is also termed), we have to consider simply a case of defective action of the organ, not typically associated with any alteration in its structure. The leading symptom of all cases of indigestion may be taken to be represented by pain or discomfort associated with the taking of food and with digestion, in so far as the stomach is concerned. Along with this discomfort we may find other symptoms represented by *flatulence, acidity, constipation,* and the like. These various symptoms are not developed in any single case of indigestion in an equal fashion. As a rule we find one symptom much more prominent than another, although in all cases the discomfort during the process of digestion is more or less distinctly marked. In an extreme case of dyspepsia, indeed, the patient may be reduced to such a state that "whilst hungry he fears to eat." Chronic gastritis was mentioned as a condition represented in certain cases of indigestion, and no doubt dyspepsia itself is a symptom of this ailment, but it must be clearly understood on the other hand that ordinary dyspepsia may exist without the presence of gastritis, so that the distinction between these two conditions may be briefly alluded to by way of assisting the recognition of the one disease and the other. In the case of *gastritis* there is usually a history of abuse of alcohol or of some long-standing ailment of system. Vomiting is frequent, especially in the morning, and the pain is not relieved when the stomach is emptied. Again the pain in the stomach may be severe, especially when the organ is pressed upon. Turning to ordinary *dyspepsia* on the other hand, we find that there may be no distinct or single cause to be found by way of accounting for the ailment, but rather a multiplicity of causes mostly representing in themselves errors in diet. Vomiting again is not frequent, but when it does occur the patient feels relieved. There is no marked thirst such as we see in chronic gastritis. In a word, in the latter disease the symptoms point to one or two distinct causes, whereas in indigestion where the symptoms may be less severe we may find a multiplicity of causes.

Symptoms.—A prominent symptom of dyspepsia is found first of all in the *loss of appetite.* Occasionally, however, the patient may exhibit an appetite of more than usual activity, in which case if he indulges it he is likely to pay dearly for his neglect of the precautions he should have observed. Possibly a lack of appetite for food represents an attempt of nature to limit the amount of diet which the individual should take. A good appetite must usually be regarded as a sign of health, and its absence in the present instance must therefore be considered as due to a distinct cause represented by the inability of the stomach to deal properly with what it is offered.

Flatulence.—This symptom is generally spoken of by dyspeptics under the name of "wind on the stomach." It is a common result of what may be regarded as a deficiency of chemical action on the part of the stomach induced by the fermentation of food producing certain gases. Occasionally the gases brought up from the stomach may possess a highly disagreeable odour. With regard to *pain* we have noted that in indigestion it is not present in a marked degree. There may be occasional cramps or passing pains felt in the stomach, whilst another symptom is of a more pronounced character, and is popularly known as *heartburn* and by physicians as *cardialgia*. Heartburn is no doubt produced by the *excessive acidity* of the gastric juice, its cure from a popular point of view being accomplished through the taking of such substances as are of alkaline nature, the most common of these being bicarbonate of soda. Another symptom of dyspepsia is that known as *pyrosis* or *waterbrash*. This symptom is marked by the bringing up from the stomach of a watery fluid. It frequently accompanies heartburn itself, and there is no doubt that it arises from the imperfect digestion of certain elements of the food, certain of those microscopic fungi already alluded to in connection with stomach dilatation probably taking part in its production. Vomiting forms yet another symptom of dyspepsia, but as has already been noted it may be absent in many cases of this ailment. In all probability it is most likely to occur when certain indigestible foods are taken.

Cases of ordinary indigestion as distinguished from those included under the head of chronic gastritis, are styled those of *atonic dyspepsia*, this latter phrase indicating that the general cause of the ailment may be regarded as a want of tone represented in the whole operations of the stomach.

Causes.—We have already noted the causes of indigestion to be extremely numerous. It is necessary, however, to enumerate them in detail, inasmuch as the first step toward the betterment of the patient must consist in his own intelligent supervision of every detail of his life and habits, not limiting this investigation to the matter of food alone. In the first place, *deficient teeth*, causing a person to bolt his food in place of masticating it thoroughly, may be set down as a frequent cause of the beginnings of indigestion at least. *General weakness* or debility of body, arising from organs other than those devoted to digestion, may induce this ailment. After fevers and the like an immediate return to ordinary diet would undoubtedly be followed by dyspepsia. In the third place, from one cause or another, we may find *some deficiency or alteration* to be represented in one or more of the *various secretions* of the digestive system. If the gastric juice of the stomach, for example, exhibits an abnormal condition, if the bile be deficient in quantity or quality, and if the sweetbread juice be not properly elaborated, we can understand how assimilation of the food cannot be perfectly effected. In the same way the bolting of the food, which we have seen to be a cause of indigestion, interferes with the proper action of the saliva of the mouth on the starchy matters contained in the food. We find here another adequate reason for the thorough chewing of all our articles of diet.

Habits.—There can be little doubt that many cases of indigestion are directly caused by erroneous habits and an unwholesome mode of life. Thus indigestion is extremely apt to follow upon intemperance in eating and drinking. Intemperance is not confined alone to the abuse of alcoholic liquors. It may be very typically represented, indeed, in the man who eats far beyond the needs and requirements of his body. There is a story told of the famous Dr. Abercromby in which, after listening to the account given by a patient suffering from indigestion of the amount of food consumed, he told the patient that the source of his complaint lay in the fact that whilst he had only one stomach he ate enough for five. Moderation in eating and drinking constitutes one of the primary rules for the preservation of health, and there can be little doubt that dyspepsia occurring in men about middle age is frequently due to their consuming as much food at say forty or fifty years of age as they did when they were twenty years younger. With regard to the excessive use of alcohol, this is a frequent cause of digestive trouble of the kind we are considering. We have noted how intemperance is a natural cause of gastritis. The use especially of raw or ardent spirits tends to inflame the lining membrane of the stomach, and thus to bring about irregularity in its action. Equally to the point is it that excess in tea and coffee is liable to produce indigestion; this latter cause operates very frequently in the case of women, and especially in the case of poorly fed girls, who imagine that tea and coffee are foods, and who, therefore, under this erroneous idea use these fluids in excess.

The taking of an excessive quantity of a fluid during meals is another cause of dyspepsia. Part of the result thus produced is extreme dilution of the gastric juice, which is thus rendered incapable of perfectly acting upon the food. A vast deal of the dyspepsia from which Americans suffer can be traced to the habit of drinking large quantities of iced water with food. Another frequent source of indigestion is that of neglecting the old saying, " After dinner rest a while." Digestion we have seen to be a work involving a considerable expenditure of nervous force, hence all exertion, whether mental or physical, after a meal should be avoided. The typical state after a full meal is that of resting for a time. Whether or not the " after dinner nap" is a healthy procedure or the reverse, has been made the subject of much discussion, but the balance of opinion founded upon physiological considerations would seem to point in the direction of the statement that for the young or middle-aged healthy person sleep after dinner is not a natural phase of daily life. It may be different in the case of old persons whose bodily powers require to be conserved. It is perfectly probable that in a state of sleep the digestive functions are somewhat modified in their action. If it be unadvisable to go to bed immediately after eating a heavy supper, it must be equally injudicious to go to sleep after dinner.

Treatment.—The treatment of indigestion is naturally as varied as are its causes. In the first place it may be noted as a useful rule that where an acute attack of indigestion comes on within a limited time after a meal, no pain being represented, but where the food, as the phrase goes, lies " like lead in the stomach," the proper course is that of emptying the organ. This may be done by the swallowing of tepid water in which a little salt has been dissolved, or by giving thirty grains of powdered ipecacuanha, to be followed by several tumblerfuls of warm water. In this way the stomach is at once relieved of the food which is temporarily obstructing its action ; and mothers should remember that causing a child to vomit is often the quickest way of cutting short an attack, the result of taking improper food. An ordinary acute attack of indigestion requires little more than abstinence from food for some time, and the taking of some liquid nourishment in the shape of milk with or without soda-water. Rest, here, as in other cases, gives the stomach the best possible chance of recovering its tone. If any drug or medicine be required, the liquor of bismuth in a dessert-spoonful dose may be taken on an empty stomach. Occasionally for the relief of acute dyspepsia, a powder of the following nature has been prescribed : Carbonate of bismuth, three drachms ; carbonate of magnesia, three drachms ; hydrochlorate of morphia, one grain. These ingredients are to be mixed and divided into eighteen powders. One powder may be taken thrice daily about one hour after meals.

Where much pain exists a mixture composed of two drachms of bicarbonate of soda, twenty-four minims of dilute hydrocyanic acid, and eight ounces of infusion of gentian, may be tried. The dose of this mixture is two tablespoonfuls taken thrice daily between meals. For the relief of flatulence a charcoal biscuit may be taken after food, whilst another favourite remedy is a mixture composed of dilute hydrocyanic acid, forty minims; aromatic spirits of ammonia, two drachms; compound tincture of cardamoms, four drachms; tincture of ginger, three drachms; spirits of chloroform, two drachms; and carraway-water to make up six ounces. The dose is a tablespoonful, which may be taken four or five times a day when the flatulence is troublesome. For acidity an old-fashioned cure is that of eating an apple, whilst a mixture composed of light carbonate of magnesia, half a drachm; bicarbonate of soda, twenty grains; tincture of orange-peel, half a drachm; and peppermint-water up to one ounce forms a draught which may be taken when acidity is troublesome. Five or ten grains of bicarbonate of soda dissolved in water make a simple draught which relieves the acidity. Sucking a bicarbonate of soda lozenge or a bismuth lozenge will also tend to relieve this symptom. A tabloid of carbonate of soda and mint allowed to dissolve in the mouth has also an excellent effect. Where "water-brash" presents itself as a troublesome symptom, it may be treated by giving the patient buttermilk to drink. A dose of thirty grains of carbonate of bismuth may be taken to relieve this condition half-an-hour before meals in a little water thrice daily. If the fluid passing into the mouth is of an acid character, it would be proper in such a case to give a mixture containing dilute hydrochloric acid, two drachms; dilute hydrocyanic acid, twenty-four minims; and compound infusion of gentian to make up eight ounces. Two table-spoonfuls of this mixture may be given thrice daily half-an-hour before meals.

Pepsin.—In cases where the disease may be presumed to arise from some deficiency in the secretion of the gastric juice, physicians are accustomed to administer *pepsin*. This substance, being itself represented in the secretion of the stomach, its administration presumably increases the digestive power of the organ. It may be administered in a powder consisting of four grains of powdered rhubarb, and three grains of pepsin. This powder should be taken after each meal. A tabloid consisting of pepsin, bismuth, and charcoal also forms a useful mode of administering this substance; one to three of these tabloids may be taken after meals. Another substance has also been used in the shape of *papain*. This is a vegetable ferment. Two or three papain tabloids may be swallowed twice or thrice daily just after food. *Pancreatin* is another digestive agent obtained from the sweetbread. It is best given in the form of what is called a peptonic tabloid. One to three of these may be taken after meals twice a day.

The Diet in Dyspepsia.—Having thus noted the chief points connected with the treatment of indigestion by means of drugs, we may finally pass to consider an equally, if not more important topic, that of the foods which it is proper for the dyspeptic respectively to take and to avoid. It may here be said that a very large part, if not the chief part, of the cure of this trouble is to be found in the proper regulation of the diet. If one cause of this ailment is the taking of improper articles of food, it is clear that their avoidance and the substitution of proper nutriment must tend to counteract the ailment. It may be said that no definite laws save very general ones can be laid down for the feeding of dyspeptics. As a rule, indeed, medical authorities agree in expressing the opinion that it is most unwise to judge one dyspeptic by all in the matter of diet. Therefore occasionally a patient's tastes or appetites may constitute safer guides to the kind of food likely to agree with him than those prescribed by hard and fast dietetic rules. If any general treatment can be formulated for guidance in this matter, it might take the shape of the general advice that the food of the dyspeptic should, on the whole, be of light character. He should avoid all indigestible substances, of which cheese, pickled and salted foods, pickles themselves, pastry, and the like are examples. The most easily-digested foods are first of all, meat soups, milk puddings, white boiled fish, tripe, and chicken. Mutton and beef require a longer time for digestion in the stomach, mutton being the more digestible of the two. An authority on diet gives a very important hint when he remarks that certain fats tend to produce acid and cause dyspepsia, especially fat contained in meats which have been baked. Tripe is an excellent food, seeing that it is most easily digested. Amongst other articles which are placed under the ban of the physician in so far as the dyspeptic patient is concerned, are pork, veal, baked meats, and also boiled and stewed meats; rabbit, eggs, and shell-fish are better left alone, whilst as regards vegetables, nuts, young potatoes, carrots, cucumbers, and parsnips are to be regarded with grave suspicion. The bread eaten should be stale, and taken for the most part toasted. With regard to meat, it has been remarked that a tender beefsteak of small size properly cooked upon the gridiron, slowly eaten and well masticated, suits dyspeptics admirably. With regard to vegetables, a very little cabbage or the heart of a cauliflower is permissible. Vegetable marrow, stewed lettuce, and celery are also allowed.

Beverages.—A dyspeptic may find that a cup of cocoa will suit him much better than tea, and he must certainly avoid coffee, for the reason that it exerts a slowing or retarding effect on the digestive process. To milk, diluted with soda-water, there can be no objection. Many dyspeptics find relief by taking one or two tumblerfuls of hot water between meals, and also at bedtime and on rising in the morning. The water, however, must be really hot, and not merely tepid. In the latter case it is apt to produce nausea. With regard to *alcohol* it is difficult to lay down any hard and fast rule. Much will depend on the ordinary habits of the patient in this respect. Any excess of alcohol is to be of course prohibited, and with regard to beer and stout, and also acid wines, sherry, port, and the like, it will be wise that they should be avoided. Physicians are generally agreed that the safest form of alcohol for dyspeptics where alcohol is taken at all is a little old Scotch whisky, diluted either with plain water or an alkaline mineral water such as Apollinaris or Johannis. Finally, it is well to bear in mind the caution that it is better always for the patient to rise from table feeling that he could have eaten more, than to end his meal feeling a sense of repletion. With regard to tobacco it may be added that there can be no objection to its moderate use on the part of those who have been accustomed to enjoy their pipe or cigar. The smoking of innumerable cigarettes, it should be noted, especially on the part of the young, is a practice which, in addition to lowering the standard of their general health, tends to give rise to the symptoms of dyspepsia.

DISEASES OF THE INTESTINES

In dealing with diseases of the intestine or bowel we may remind ourselves that this tube (26 feet long) is divided into two portions— the *small intestine*, which is a continuation of the stomach, measuring 20 feet, and the *large intestine* or hinder part of the canal, measuring 6 feet in length. It is in the small intestine that the greater share of the work of digestion takes place. Certain diseases are directly associated with this part of the digestive tract. Thus typhoid fever and dysentery (vol. i.) are ailments closely connected in respect of their seat with the small and large intestine respectively. But the intestine itself may also be the seat of special ailments which fall to be considered in the present instance.

DUODENAL ULCER

The first part of the small intestine, just after leaving the stomach, is called the *duodenum,* and an ulcer in this situation is the cause of one of the most obstinate forms of indigestion. Formerly this was looked upon as a rare condition and vaguely connected with burns. Later it was recognised as a much more common disease, not always associated with hæmorrhage, perforation, and peritonitis. It was then almost invariably treated by the operation of joining the stomach to a further point of the intestine, the ulcer thus being given rest and time to heal. The question then arose, cannot this be done by medical treatment ?

Symptoms.—The symptoms are those of an acute indigestion; the pain, as a rule, being above and to the right of the navel, with some tenderness. Pain comes on generally some two hours after food, and is somewhat relieved by eating. In dangerous cases there is blood in the stools, black in character, and this, associated with a condition of collapse, will call for immediate operation.

Treatment.—The medical treatment consists of rest in bed and strict dieting. Milk and milky foods may be given in small quantities every two hours, while for medicine Dr. Hurst advises half an ounce of olive oil before each feed in the day, and a powder of prepared chalk 10 grains and bismuth oxycarbonate thirty grains after feeds taken in the night. Belladonna has also been recommended to reduce the secretion of gastric juice.

DIARRHŒA

The diarrhœa so common in summer is almost invariably caused by taking some food or milk which contains harmful bacteria.

Symptoms.—The symptoms, as a rule, are a sudden call to empty the bowels and violent abdominal pain, sometimes accompanied by vomiting. The motions are repeated at frequent intervals until they are of a thin character, almost like rice water, and the patient becomes cold and collapsed.

Treatment.—The abdomen should be carefully examined to see that there are no signs of any acute specific trouble such as appendicitis. As the exciting cause is an irritant in the stomach or intestine, our effort must be to get rid of this efficaciously, and with the least amount of further irritation of the intestine. An immediate dose of one ounce of castor oil, with ten minims of chlorodyne or tincture of opium if the pain is very acute, or a little brandy if the patient is faint, will check almost any attack. If, however, this is deferred, further treatment by drugs may be necessary to allay the inflamed condition of the lining of the intestine.

Examples of such mixtures are found in one containing tincture of catechu, three drachms; tincture of opium, one drachm; compound cinnamon powder, one and a half drachms; and chalk mixture up to six ounces. The dose is a tablespoonful after each motion of the bowels. Another mixture useful in ordinary diarrhœa is that composed of two drachms of dilute sulphuric acid, one drachm of opium, one and a half drachms of spirits of chlorform, and eight ounces of water. The dose of this latter mixture is two tablespoonfuls given every four hours. Another mixture adapted for general use in diarrhœa, arising from whatever cause, is that composed of tincture of catechu, four drachms; tincture of kino, four drachms; tincture of opium, two drachms; spirits of camphor, three drachms; and chalk mixture up to six ounces. The dose here amounts to two teaspoonfuls taken every four hours.

If much pain exists, hot fomentations should be applied to the abdomen, or warmth may be afforded by the use of linseed meal poultices. Hot bottles may be applied to the feet and the body kept warm generally if symptoms of collapse appear.

It may be noted that at the two extremes of life diarrhœa may prove to be a somewhat dangerous ailment. The *summer diarrhœa*, or *infant cholera*, so prevalent in our large centres of population and attacking children under one year in the hot months of summer, is responsible for an enormous mortality. This ailment will be duly treated in the section of this work devoted to the consideration of the *Diseases of Children*. In old persons also, a smart attack of diarrhœa is apt to produce weakening effects of a very decided character. In such cases the diarrhœa may be easily set up through chill or some error in food, and its cure may be an extremely difficult matter. In such a case the prescription already detailed containing catechu, kino, and opium may be used. Another point of importance in the diarrhœa of the aged is that of watching carefully the signs of any collapse, in which latter case stimulants may be freely given.

Chronic Diarrhœa.—Diarrhœa in its chronic form is an extremely troublesome and curious complaint. The subject of this complaint is more or less continuously affected with what, in popular language, is known as "looseness of the bowels." He exists in an exactly opposite condition to the person who suffers from constipation, and although such an ailment may persist for months or years without apparently affecting the health in a material degree, the condition may nevertheless be described as one of a decidedly wearing-out character. Hence it is of importance that attention should be paid to the means to be adopted for the relief of this annoying condition. Another form of diarrhœa is recognised by physicians in the shape of a form of the ailment common in nervous people. This trouble is characterised by the symptoms appearing soon after food has been taken, the commencement of the digestive process evidently causing some physiological action which has the effect of inducing the intestine to part with its contents. In a case of this kind the best remedy is that which consists of two minims of Fowler's solution of arsenic with five minims of laudanum in water, just before meals. It is necessary here to attend rigidly to the general health.

Treatment.—In the case of a person affected with chronic diarrhœa, the food and the general habits of the individual should be closely scrutinised. An intelligent examination of the diet-list should afford some indication regarding the foods more liable to cause diarrhœa than others. With respect to the examination of the general health, note should be taken if the ailment is more prevalent at one period than another. In the case of this disease it is known that removal from one locality to another will sometimes effect a cure. In the same way a change of habitat may give origin to the disease. These facts are probably to be explained by a reference to the water-supply, or it may be in some cases even to the soil and general surroundings of the patient.

Diet.—The subject of chronic diarrhœa should as a rule begin his cure by avoiding green vegetables and potatoes. The bread he eats should be of stale character. Fruits should also be avoided, and the diet as far as possible should be confined for a time to milk, raw meat, peptonised foods (*see* INVALID COOKERY), and powdered meat. An authority on this subject maintains that if the patient will subsist for a time on a diet consisting solely of milk, he is certain of cure. The milk diet is succeeded by a diet of raw or powdered meat, whilst peptonised foods are also given in conjunction with raw meat or at a later stage. Another authority speaks very highly of *Koumiss*. This last is fermented mare's milk; but in this country it can be made from cow's milk, and can be had at any of the large dairy establishments.

Drugs.—A large quantity of drugs have been prescribed in the treatment of chronic diarrhœa. Amongst them probably the most useful remedy is represented by twenty minims of aromatic sulphuric acid given three times a day in water. Fowler's solution of arsenic two minims in water after food, or ipecacuanha two grains in a pill twice a day after food may be tried if other remedies fail. A podophyllin pill containing one grain of that substance is likely to be useful if taken at night when the motions passed are of a pale colour, indicating that the functions of the liver are not duly performed. A three-grain dose of calomel taken at night may also act usefully under like conditions. A tablespoonful of the tincture of rhubarb taken twice a day in water is also a simple but excellent remedy. It should be administered between meals.

Constipation.—If one were asked to indicate an ailment which might be described as the most prevalent of the troubles represented in modern life he might well select *constipation* as the typical example. Whether the conditions of civilised existence promote this ailment, or whether the fact that modern cookery is responsible for its occurrence are matters which need not here be discussed. Suffice it to say that whilst ineffective action of the bowels is a symptom of many diseases it may nevertheless be regarded as exemplifying, like diarrhœa, a condition worthy of being regarded as a distinct ailment. As in the case of dyspepsia, we find the causes of constipation to be very varied. It may be well in the first instance to devote attention to the *common causes* which suffice to induce the ailment under consideration. We are here speaking of what may be termed habitual constipation, in which there exists an opposite state of matters to that found in chronic diarrhœa. There the bowels too rapidly part with their contents; here the bowels show little or no disposition to excrete waste matters. One important point connected with constipation at large is that found in the observation that it represents a condition extremely liable to develop into a chronic state. Most of the bodily actions connected with our daily life are ruled by *habit*. Sleep, for example, may be considered to be a habit of our frame. Sleeplessness is another kind of habit which replaces that which is natural. In the same way the duty of getting rid of the waste matter resulting from the digestive processes comes to be a habit of the digestive system. When from one cause or another this natural duty falls into abeyance, it is replaced similarly by the constipated habit, and as time passes increased difficulty exists of inducing the intestine to resume its normal work.

Causes.—The causes of constipation may be enumerated as consisting, first, *in errors of diet*. If a person takes a superabundance of foods not easily digested and tending to cause slowness or difficulty of bowel-movement, the beginning of constipation may be thus accounted for. In the second place, *particular modes of life* may induce constipation. A person who is accustomed to a sedentary life will be more apt to suffer than one who leads an active and out of doors existence. An author remarks that where a sedentary person introduces into his life the habit of taking a brisk walk morning, noon, and night, a cure of the constipated condition may sometimes in this simple way be effected. In the third place *sex* exercises an appreciable effect as regards the origin of constipation. It is a notable fact that women are much less attentive to the state and action of the bowels than are men, and in a large proportion of cases in which females suffer from such ailments as headache, a bad colour of the skin, and other symptoms, constipation will be found to constitute the root of their troubles. Finally other causes of this ailment are to be found in the matter of *locality and surroundings*. Persons who visit the seaside are liable to suffer from constipation during the earlier days of their stay, just as in the case of a sea voyage constipation may be represented. The water-supply of a district may through its hardness induce constipation, just as under other circumstances a particular drinking water causes diarrhœa.

Symptoms.—This ailment induces a general upset of the entire bodily functions. Headache is commonly complained of, the appetite is impaired, the tongue is often coated, indigestion may be present, the skin is liable to exhibit a sallow and unhealthy character, and the nervous system is affected in the way of depression. Results of constipation are seen very frequently in the production of *piles*, produced by the pressure of the loaded bowel on the veins which return blood upwards in the body. Coldness of the feet is also complained of, this condition probably arising as a result of pressure on the nerves. On the whole, then, constipation is a condition in which the human body may be compared to a house with a more or less imperfect drainage system. Matters which ought to be carried out of its bounds are retained, and an unhealthy condition of affairs appears as the natural result.

Treatment.—A wise writer in the matter of treatment has first of all insisted upon the necessity for the patient cultivating the " habit " of soliciting nature by sitting in the closet at a regular hour each day. This habit practised at a fixed hour should be persisted in ; even if no success follows for some days, it should nevertheless be subjected to a prolonged trial. The cure of constipation, it may be said, is one which must be undertaken *by diet and not by drugs*. This statement does not minimise or lessen the value of drugs in the treatment of this ailment ; it only emphasises the fact that diet forms the real sheet-anchor of the patient, whilst drugs appear only as subsidiary aids. The value of this advice can readily be demonstrated. If a patient relies upon purgative medicines alone, it will be found that in a short time these lose their effect. The dose has therefore to be increased and further augmented as time passes, so that at the end of a certain period, a person may be found swallowing, without effect, quantities of pills and potions sufficient to render an ordinary healthy person extremely ill. One of the curses of modern life may, indeed, be described as the habit of continually swallowing purgative medicines in the hope of curing constipation.

Diet.—Dealing first with the question of diet the patient should avoid all such foods as cheese, salt meats, pickles, and the like. Rich food, regarded generally, should be avoided. The diet of the constipated person should contain a fair proportion of vegetable matters and fruits, salads (especially those made with oil) are excellent, as also are green vegetables at large. Potatoes had better be taken in limited quantity from the fact that they tend to encourage the development of flatulence. Fruits are excellent, and the eating of an orange or apple at breakfast and after dinner is a practice to be encouraged, whilst an orange taken the last thing at night often aids the cure. Stewed prunes and stewed figs are also excellent. No better vegetable can be taken by a constipated person than a stewed onion. Many varieties of bread are now made adapted for the use of constipated persons. These may be summed up generally in the name of "wholemeal breads." They act by producing a certain amount of irritation in the intestine, thus stimulating the tube to activity. A writer recommends the taking of a tablespoonful of olive oil each morning after breakfast. If the patient cares to substitute cod liver oil therefor, he may find the latter to act in the same fashion. A Spanish onion, well boiled and taken for supper, is also recommended by physicians as an excellent aid to cure. The summing up of dietetic hints in this disease further consists in the advice to limit meat foods and to increase the amount of vegetable matters contained in the dietary. The drinking of a tumblerful of cold water or of warm water immediately on rising is also calculated to be of service. It is notable that tobacco has a decided action in stimulating bowel movement, and the pipe or cigar after breakfast on the part of men may be said to exercise a distinct effect in preventing constipation. *Massage* of the muscles of the abdomen has also been recommended by way of cure. This process undoubtedly has an effect in stimulating bowel movement. It is worth while pointing out that in the case of women the habit of tight lacing, in that it not merely compresses the lower part of the chest injuriously, but also exercises pressure on the bowels, may be regarded as a frequent cause of constipation. The remedy here is of course obvious.

Drugs.—A very large number of drugs are used in the treatment of constipation, the list of purgatives and aperients being a very large one. The caution already given must be borne in mind that the use of any drug is merely an aid to the diet-cure, and must not be regarded in any sense as supplanting the latter. Glycerine has been used with success in the cure of constipation, assisted that is by diet. If injected into the bowel by aid of a special syringe in teaspoonful doses, it frequently produces the desired effect. An enema of cold water amounting to about a tumblerful in extent may also produce a like result. A medicine much used in late years in the treatment of constipation is that known as *cascara*. The advantage of this drug is that it has no cumulative effects. It may be given thrice daily after meals in a dose of ten minims of the liquid extract. This treatment may be persisted with for some weeks, and must be stopped if at the end of that period no improvement is effected. Occasionally cascara is combined with other remedies. A favourite formula is that of combining two ounces of the liquid extract of cascara; three drachms of tincture of nux vomica; three drachms of tincture of belladonna; and glycerine to make up four ounces. The dose is a small teaspoonful taken at night in water. Aloes is also a favourite remedy in the case of habitual constipation. This drug may be taken in the form of a pill composed of half a grain of extract of aloes, half a grain of extract of nux vomica, half a grain of powdered ipecacuanha, and one grain of powdered capsicum. One of these pills may be taken every day before food. Another useful "dinner pill" is that composed of one grain each of compound rhubarb pill, and colocynth pill, together with extract of hyoscyamus half a grain. This pill may be taken once a day after meals. A very valuable pill is that composed of half a grain of extract of nux vomica, one and a half grains of aloin, one and a half grains of dried sulphate of iron, extract of belladonna one-third of a grain, and extract of cascara one grain. This pill may be also taken once a day after food.

The Liver and Constipation.—There can be little doubt that in many cases of constipation the *liver* may be at fault, inasmuch as a deficient supply of bile, which is a natural purgative, may be associated with sluggish motion of the intestines. Such being the case it may be found that in certain persons the stimulation of the liver by appropriate drugs, associated with some purgative medicine, may represent all that is necessary in the way of drug treatment. Thus a pill composed of half a grain of euonymin, half a grain of leptandrin, half a grain of podophyllin, and two grains of extract of hyoscyamus, is recommended to be taken at bedtime. The action of such a pill will be aided if a dose of aperient water be taken in the morning. One of the best waters of this class is known as Apenta water. The old-fashioned black draught taken at night, aiedd by a seidlitz powder in the morning, acts on a like principle, and may be recommended where headache is a prominent feature of constipation.

The two warnings which may be given in quitting this subject are that no drug whatever may be taken continuously. If, with the aid of diet, one form of medicine is not sufficient to cure the case, another must be substituted for it. It must also be remembered that in all cases drugs are merely to be used by way of starting the action which diet, exercise, and attention to the ordinary details of healthy living may render permanent. The second caution is that which teaches us, that whatever medicines be used for the cure of constipation, all drugs of the nature of " salts," such as sulphate of magnesia, Epsom salts, sulphate of soda, and the like, should be strictly avoided. These medicines, useful enough in certain cases for producing increased bowel action (as in many cases of fever and the like), are utterly unsuitable for the cure of constipation.

Peritonitis.—The term peritonitis is generally translated in a popular sense to mean *inflammation of the bowels*. Strictly speaking " peritonitis " is inflammation of the *peritoneum*, or *lining membrane of the abdomen*, a membrane which also passes into the pelvis or haunch cavity, and is reflected over the stomach, bowels, and other organs. Inflammation of the peritoneum undoubtedly may affect the bowels as well, and the inflammatory process extending to the intestines may glue them together and thus to a certain extent interfere with their natural movements.

Peritonitis, it may be noted, is a secondary process arising from germ infection, or from such an accident as is represented by perforation of the stomach or intestine. If the contents of either escape into the general cavity of the body inflammation is set up in all probability through germ action, with the result that the peritoneum and the organs with which it is in contact become the subjects of an acute attack of this disease.

Symptoms.—Taking first *acute peritonitis* as that form of the ailment which is most frequently represented, we find this disease to be more common in females than in man. A common cause is exposure to cold and chill, whilst, as we have seen, it may follow perforation of the intestine, and may occur as the result of wounds and of operations performed on the abdominal organs, or on those of the pelvis. The symptoms of an attack of peritonitis consist in the presence of great tenderness and pain over the belly. It is tense and drum-like in its characteristic. The pulse is quick and of what is termed " wiry " character, capable of being distinctly felt under the fingers. Constipation is present, and vomiting occurs. The tongue is dry and coated. Hiccough may be present, and the temperature rises to 104 or 105 degrees. The slightest touch, or even the movements of breathing, may cause great pain in the belly. The patient in consequence generally takes a characteristic attitude, by lying on the back, the legs being drawn up and the knees bent. The face exhibits an anxious expression, which has been sometimes described under the name of *Facies Hippocratica.* An author has described this appearance as entailing "a sharp nose, hollow eyes, collapsed temples ; the ears cold, contracted, and their lobes turned out ; the skin about the forehead being rough, distended, and parched ; the colour of the whole face being brown, black, livid, or lead colour." As a rule the patient does not become unconscious.

If perforation takes place of any organ the pain becomes intensified, and the patient describes his feeling as if something had burst or given way. Where an effusion of fluid takes place, the result of this form of inflammation shows a distinct tendency to develop into *pus* or "matter," thus differing from inflammation of the pleura (*pleurisy*) or lining membrane of the chest, in which there is exhibited an unlikelihood of such a result being represented. In all probability the fact that the abdomen contains the digestive organs, and exhibits therefore much more likely conditions in respect of infection, we may be able to account for the difference between the two inflammations. In a favourable case the turn for the better is noted in the lowering of the temperature and of the pulse rate. Vomiting ceases, and the pain in the abdomen markedly lessens. Natural movement of the bowels may take place, and the patient passes from a dangerous condition into one of comparative ease.

Treatment.—If *rest* is a condition obviously essential for the cure of "gastric ulcer," it is also equally important in the treatment of *peritonitis.* The patient should be allowed to rest in bed in the position in which he finds himself most comfortable. If the weight of the bedclothes oppress him, they must be raised by an ordinary nursing cradle. The principle of rest-treatment here extends to the bowels. In his practice opium is the mainstay of the physician. From one to two grains of opium may be given every four hours until all pain and bowel-movement is suppressed. Another mode of treatment is that of commencing with one grain of opium and of repeating the dose after an interval of an hour. At the end of the second hour two grains of opium are given, this dose being repeated in another two hours if the effects of the drug in producing a slight degree of stupor are not represented. Grain doses of opium may thereafter be given at intervals, the patient being carefully watched for a period varying from ten to fourteen days ; then, when in a favourable case the inflammation has decreased, an injection may be given by way of promoting bowel action. In some cases a dose of castor-oil may be substituted for an enema. A golden rule in connection with the treatment of peritonitis is that in this disease *no purgatives whatever must be given*, but the lower bowel may be acted upon if necessary by an injection of hot water. Such injections tend to lessen the tense and distended state of the abdomen.

Further Hints.—It is a general rule in medicine that where peritonitis, instead of affecting the whole surface of the abdomen, is limited to one spot or area, leeches may be applied. Some cases of this latter character are treated by the constant application of ice-bags, whilst hot fomentations may be employed where great pain exists and where the abdomen is much distended. Flannels wrung out of hot water, sprinkled with turpentine, and then covered with bath-towels to retain the heat will be found a measure of soothing character. In respect to the diet, milk thoroughly cooled by means of ice may be given in small quantities, with occasional spoonfuls of beef-tea or similar nutriment. It may here be mentioned that where perforation takes place, or rather where a case of peritonitis is due to some such accident having occurred, allowing the contents of the intestine to escape into the cavity of the abdomen, a surgical operation must be instantly performed. Many lives, formerly sacrificed, are now saved through such a procedure.

Chronic peritonitis is a condition arising from tuberculosis, from tumours, or from chronic inflammation of the intestine or of such organs as the womb and its appendages. In such cases dropsy may be present. In the peritonitis due to tuberculosis, a disease more frequently found in males than in females, the body becomes rapidly thin and diarrhœa is present. In such cases it is noted the belly becomes swollen and its veins extremely prominent. In the case of peritonitis arising from cancer, any treatment if available at all must be of an operative character. In that variety arising from infection from tuberculosis, the patient must be treated for the disease which has given rise to the inflammation. In some cases of peritonitis of this latter type, an operation by way of removing the affected glands may be successfully undertaken.

Appendicitis.—This disease consists of an inflammation of that part or rudiment of the large bowel known as the appendix (Fig. 12, 13). This structure and its nature has already been fully described in the section dealing with the digestive organs (p. 25). Along with the cæcum (Fig. 12, 12), or first part of the large intestine, the appendix is liable to undergo inflammatory processes. What is known as *typhilitis* implies inflammation of the cæcum itself; the name *perityphilitis* denotes inflammation of the tissues outside the cæcum, and joining it to the muscles lying beneath. For the purposes of this work, the disease known as *appendicitis* may be practically held to include the other two forms.

Causes.—Appendicitis, as a rule, occurs in the young. It is caused by various circumstances and conditions. Constipation, cold and chill are represented amongst its causes, whilst probably inflammation of a low type affecting the cæcum itself, and spreading to the appendix, may be regarded as a frequent origin of the disease. Indigestible food may be also ranked amongst its causes, and the swallowing of the seeds of fruits or other foreign bodies, such as the hairs of tooth-brushes, pins, pieces of bone, and the like has also been known to set up this disease. The danger here is that of perforation taking place and of fatal peritonitis being thus set up.

Symptoms.—The symptoms consist of fever, a quick pulse, and constipation. These symptoms are accompanied by vomiting; pain is present and may be general over the belly-surface or may be referred to the region of the cæcum and appendix, namely to the lower part of the belly on the right side. What is known as "McBurney's point" is recognised as a spot situated about one and a half to two inches from the crest of the haunch bone, in a line running from this point to the navel. Pressure on this point causes extreme pain. The course of this disease exhibits the ordinary sequence of internal inflammation In some cases the inflammation appears to be of what is called a *subacute character*, the pain and symptoms not being markedly developed. Such cases if treated without operation are extremely liable to recur, hence in most cases of appendicitis the question for the physician is that of deciding when an operation for the removal of the appendix should be undertaken.

Treatment.—From what has just been said, it will be understood that *the removal of the appendix* represents practically the only satisfactory treatment of any case in which the symptoms are of a severe character. It will be for the doctor to decide whether such an operation should be at once undertaken, or whether it may be delayed until the patient recovers and presents therefore a better subject for such treatment. For the rest the treatment already described as that for peritonitis applies in the present case. It is recommended, however, that the bowels should be emptied by the use of an enema of soap and water once a day. Sometimes leeches are applied over the painful part, whilst warm fomentations may also be resorted to for the relief of pain. It need hardly be remarked that complete rest in bed for such a case is necessary, and that care must be taken that the patient after recovery does not indulge in any exercise at too early a period. In cases in which the symptoms are of a subacute character and where no immediate danger of perforation is apprehended, the application of ice in bags continually over the affected part serves to check the inflammation. A rule has been generally followed of late days in acute appendicitis to the effect that if the active symptoms do not change for the better in from twenty to thirty hours a necessity for operation becomes apparent.

Obstruction of the Bowels.—Obstruction of the bowels arises from various causes. In the first instance there may be some narrowing of the tube from within. In the second place the bowel may be twisted as the result frequently of some unusual exercise. Thirdly, a portion of the bowel may slip within itself after the fashion of the finger of a glove pushed inwards upon itself. Fourthly, the bowel may be blocked by hard concretions represented by indigestible foods, gallstones and the like ; whilst, fifthly, tumours of various kinds and adhesions, the results of inflammation, may produce obstruction.

Symptoms.—The first symptom which attracts notice is constipation owing to the blockage of the bowel, then succeeds vomiting, whilst the pulse is rapid, the skin cold, and the appearance of the face that described under the head of peritonitis. Pain exists, and the patient, if unrelieved, passes sooner or later into a state of collapse. Vomiting of bowel contents may also exist as a symptom.

Treatment.—In such a case *the administration of any purgatives is to be strictly avoided*, all attempts to cause bowel action when one or other part of the tube is twisted or otherwise occluded, can only result in rendering the case much more serious. The administration of opium as already described under the head of peritonitis, forms the proper treatment in so far as a temporary measure is concerned, but it can be readily understood that nothing short of a surgical operation can possibly remedy a state in which the bowel has become twisted or otherwise had its canal blocked and interrupted.

There has been described a mode of treatment for simple bowel obstruction which may be practised early in such cases with some hope of relief. This consists in introducing into the bowel the tube of a stomach-pump. Through this warm water is slowly forced so that the bowels become distended. Pressure and movement is made on the belly by the hand so as to endeavour to separate the one fold of the intestine from the other and so to overcome the obstruction. This proceeding, it need hardly be said, is of such a nature that it can only be safely practised by a medical man.

PILES, OR HÆMORRHOIDS

This affection essentially consists in enlargement of the veins which return blood from the lower portion of the *rectum*, this last being the terminal portion of the intestine or bowel. From one cause or another, some obstruction existing to prevent the upward return of the blood, the veins swell, and as a consequence tend to become permanently distended, appearing in the form of enlargements of varying size, some situated at the anus or orifice of the bowel and others within the rectum itself. Amongst the common causes of piles, *constipation* must be reckoned as that which is most paramount in producing them. Congestion or other ailments affecting the liver and hindering the upward flow of blood must also be regarded as a frequent cause of this ailment.

In a simple case of piles we meet with venous enlargements which are subject to exhibit pain at intervals, and more especially during the act of defecation. Any irritation or friction of the clothes is also apt to cause irritation, whilst in depressed states of the body at large, inflammation of the piles is liable to occur. Occasionally, however, piles, and especially those situated within the bowel, may discharge blood, in which case they are known as *bleeding piles*. The quantity of blood thus lost may occasionally be very considerable, and may tend to produce great weakness in the patient, including anæmia itself. It may be added that piles frequently occur in women who are pregnant, this result being due to the pressure of the uterus or womb upon the vessels. The affection is more common amongst cultured and well-to-do people than amongst the working-classes, and there can be little doubt that sedentary habits of life and over-luxurious feeding are features which tend markedly to contribute towards their development.

Treatment.—For the radical cure of piles the surgeon's aid must be obtained. They may be excised by the knife or be tied by means of ligatures, or be otherwise removed. In grave cases probably this is the only satisfactory means of dealing with the case, more especially where attacks of hæmorrhage or bleeding forms a common feature of any case. In so far as care of the body is concerned, the patient must be warned against sitting in any cold place, and especially on any damp seat. There can be little doubt also that cold and chill, acquired by using closets in exposed situations, must exercise a distinct effect in the production of this ailment. With respect to the treatment of an ordinary case of piles, it is necessary that the patient should be duly impressed with the necessity of securing free and easy movement of his bowels. The regularity of defecation is another point which should be rigidly attended to. The avoidance of constipation, which causes unnecessary straining, is of course necessary, and the remedies already recommended under that heading for the cure and relief of the condition in question should therefore be followed out. With reference to questions of personal habits, it should be noted that in using paper after defecation it should be of a fine quality and destitute of all hard or gritty particles. Much injury is often caused by the use of printed papers in the closet. The person who is afflicted with piles should keep by him a special sponge, which should be used to wipe the anus after he has been at stool.

Remedies.—A vast number of remedies have been used for the cure and relief of piles. A favourite ointment is the ointment of gall and opium. A more useful ointment perhaps is that known as the ointment of conium, with ten grains or so of sulphate of iron added to the ounce of ointment. This may be freely used to the piles, and may be introduced by the finger into the bowel in the case of internal piles. Where piles pass into a stage of inflammation leeches may be applied around the anus, whilst fomentations of hot water may also be tried by way of relieving the pain. Frequent attacks of inflammation, however, should necessitate a consultation with a surgeon.

Occasionally piles are apt to protrude from the anus, in which case they are said to exhibit a state of *prolapse*. They should be returned into the bowel, and the bathing of the piles with a small quantity of cold water and the application of the conium and iron ointment already mentioned will generally suffice to give relief. A substance which has attained a very high reputation in respect of the treatment of piles is the tincture of hamamelis. For bleeding piles a teaspoonful or so of this tincture added to eight ounces of water may be used internally, the dose being two or three teaspoonfuls of the mixture every three hours. For local application to ordinary piles this tincture is also admirably adapted. Two teaspoonfuls may be added to half a pint of water, and applied on lint which is covered with oiled silk. The application may be renewed as often as necessary. A little of this lotion may also be injected into the bowel in the case of internal piles. The ointment of hamamelis is also sold by most chemists or can be prepared by them, and forms a handy mode of application. One mode of treating piles is to use a small plug of wool soaked in hamamelis tincture, this being pushed up into the bowel. Over this a larger plug soaked should be applied to the anus, a small portion of this second pad being pushed within the opening. In this way a kind of pad is formed, which acts as a support to the bowel and is extremely successful in arresting bleeding. Hazeline is another but weaker preparation of hamemelis. It might be used pure as an application to piles, or a little may be injected into the bowel in the case of internal piles. *Suppositories* are also used in the shape of bullet-like preparations, which, containing certain drugs, can be slipped easily into the bowel, where, through their melting, the drugs they contain come into contact with the piles. A suppository which can thus be introduced into the bowel for the cure of internal piles is composed of chrysarobin one grain, iodoform one quarter of a grain, extract of belladonna an eighth of a grain, oil of cocoa thirty grains, and glycerine a sufficient quantity. These amounts are made into one suppository, which is introduced into the bowel. It should be noted that in all cases in which treatment of this kind is applied to piles, the patient should see that the bowel is empty, and it is better to wash the parts and cleanse them thoroughly before applying any remedies.

Diet and Habits.—With reference to the diet and general mode of life of a person who suffers from piles, it may be added that the food should be of plain and non-stimulating character. All rich foods should be avoided, and also any excess of meat. Pickles, salt foods, pastry, and cheese are all improper articles of diet in this disease. With respect to alcohol also, great care should be observed, strict temperance being a condition absolutely necessary for the relief and cure of piles. In some cases a vegetarian diet has been found to act in an extremely satisfactory fashion, and this latter hint may therefore be found worthy of consideration in connection with the cure of the ailment we have been considering.

DISEASES OF THE LIVER

The structure and functions of the liver having been duly described (see section dealing with the Digestive Organs and Digestion), it remains to note the more prominent affections to which this organ is subject.

Congestion of the Liver.—Congestion of the liver is much more common in tropical countries than in Britain. The symptoms here are tenderness on pressure over the organ, with pain extending to the right shoulder. This pain appears to be increased when the patient reposes on the right side, and it may also be more acute after eating. The tongue is coated, a want of appetite is complained of, and the bowel discharges are generally of a loose character containing biliary matter, whilst the urine is high coloured.

Treatment.—Apply hot fomentations, and give a purge. Calomel is one of the most useful drugs for the treatment of this condition. Five grains of calomel may be taken, followed in the morning by a dose of Apenta water. Care in the taking of food, with a diminution of the amount of flesh meat consumed, is part of the treatment. A mixture of use in such cases to be taken when the acute symptoms have disappeared, is composed of two drachms of dilute nitro-muriatic acid, three and a half drachms of compound tincture of gentian, and liquid extract of dandelion up to six ounces ; a dessert-spoonful may be taken thrice daily. If much pain exists, hot fomentations may be applied over the surface of the liver.

In the case of liver disturbance allied to congestion and marked by pain, heartburn, flatulence, and headache, it may be well to give at night a pill composed of four grains of euonymin, whilst the old fashion of taking a black draught in the morning will be found to relieve the symptoms in ordinary cases. The mixture just described may also be employed with advantage in such cases, and the use of certain mineral waters, such as Friedrichshall water or Püllna water, may also be recommended, as tending to act not merely on the liver itself, but to produce what is of great importance in all such cases, free action of the bowels.

Jaundice.—This term may be regarded as denoting a series of symptoms rather than a disease in itself. The name is derived from the French word *jaune*, meaning yellow, a prominent feature of this disease being the yellow colour which the skin assumes, a result due to the fact that bile is absorbed by the blood, and is excreted into the skin. This yellowness even extends to the painting of the white of the eye a yellow tint. In addition we find digestive disturbance, sickness, and flatulence. Constipation may exist, but is often succeeded by diarrhœa. The matters passed from the bowel are of a pale character, and the pulse in this ailment has been noted to beat extremely slowly. A certain amount of irritation of the skin may also be present.

Causes.—As jaundice arises from some obstruction to the free flow of bile from the liver into the intestine, we may note that such a result may be produced by a large variety of causes. Thus the bile ducts may themselves be narrowed or otherwise blocked. A gall stone may represent a foreign body in the bile duct, preventing the bile from escaping from the liver. A tumour pressing on the gall duct may also be a cause of jaundice. Enlargement, or disease of the liver itself, may be attended with jaundice as a symptom, this being seen not merely in enlargement of the liver, but also in cases where the liver is subject to what is known as atrophy or decrease in its normal size.

Catarrhal Jaundice.—In respect to jaundice, whilst the remark already made that this condition is to be regarded more typically as a symptom of disease than as an ailment in itself, we must note, however, that a distinctive affection, termed by physicians *catarrhal jaundice*, has been definitely described. By some authorities this affection is regarded as representing the true and ordinary form of this affection, depending, it will be understood, not on any obstruction to the passage of the bile from the liver into the intestine, but upon conditions specially affecting the liver itself. The common explanation of this disease is that a form of inflammation has passed upwards from the first portion of the small bowel (or duodenum) to the common bile duct, the inflammation from this tube spreading to the gall bladder itself. The ailment would appear to be one of early life, and to be frequently the result of some irritation proceeding from the stomach and bowel itself, due usually to indigestion and the taking of unsuitable food, whilst it appears to be capable of being directly caused by cold and chill.

Symptoms.—In this ailment the jaundice *is preceded by signs of digestive disorder*, pain in the back, and towards the right side, being noticeable. The jaundiced condition of the skin appears in from three to four days. Matters discharged from the intestine are clay coloured, whilst bile may be discharged from the kidneys. The liver as a rule is tender, and may show some degree of enlargement. Constipation is common in this disease, but diarrhœa may also form one of its symptoms. Vomiting is present, and headache may be of a very persistent character. In such cases the pulse, as has already been noticed, exhibits a tendency to develop an uncommon degree of slowness. It is of importance in considering jaundice to note whether or not the symptoms appear suddenly. If jaundice is rapidly developed, the person having previously been in a good or fair state of health, we may assume that the condition is most likely to be produced by some actual obstruction of the bile duct. More especially is this likely to be the case if the pain is of a severe character, coming and going, this latter symptom in all probability indicating the presence of gall stones, which, becoming temporarily fixed in the bile duct, prevent the exit of the bile. Where, on the other hand, the jaundice is developed, as we have seen in the case under consideration, after or during an attack of indigestion, with a history probably of chill and cold, we may assume that the affection is probably due to the extension of inflammation upwards into the bile duct and gall bladder, thus temporarily affecting the discharge of bile.

Treatment.—The treatment of jaundice constitutes a somewhat difficult subject in view of what has already been said regarding the various causes which may give origin to this condition. Treating the subject on general lines, where constipation exists a dose of calomel may be given, followed, as already indicated in the section dealing with congestion of the liver, by a black draught or a dose of Apenta water in the morning. The practice of giving one drachm of Carlsbad salts dissolved in a tumblerful of warm water to be sipped on rising, is also a measure calculated to relieve the constipation. For the treatment of the diarrhœa, ten grains of salicylate of bismuth have been recommended, whilst salol, ten grains between meals, is another remedy which has been prescribed to this end. A remedy given with great success in simple jaundice of the catarrhal kind, not depending upon any mechanical obstruction of the liver ducts by gall stones or otherwise, is that composed of an ounce and a half of bicarbonate of soda, two drachms powdered rhubarb, four drachms of powdered ginger, six drachms of powdered calumba, and one drachm of compound of ipecacuanha powder. These ingredients are to be mixed, and a small teaspoonful taken in a small tumblerful of aerated water every four or six hours. It is of great importance here that the diet should be of an extremely simple character. All alcohol should be avoided, and the amount of sugar and fat limited. The food should consist mostly of rice or tapioca puddings and other farinaceous matters. For the pain, warm poultices may be applied over the liver. The yellow condition of the skin should be treated by hot baths, and an occasional Turkish bath will also be found to be of service in this latter respect. The mineral waters which have enjoyed a high reputation in the cure of conditions of this kind are those of Carlsbad and Homburg.

Gall Stones.—The name "gall stones" is applied to concretions which result from some chemical change or other affecting the bile and producing a solidification of its contents. These concretions are chiefly found in the gall bladder, and may vary very much in size from that of a small pea onwards to that of a walnut or even larger. Gall stones may be of round or oval shape. In many cases, however, their angles being rubbed down they present us with the appearance of flat or faceted surfaces. In colour they are usually of a yellowish-brown tint, and are somewhat soft in nature. The number of these concretions may vary from a very few to even hundreds. The chief substance found in their composition is that known as *cholesterin*, along with the colouring matters of the bile and certain other minerals, chiefly the carbonate of lime.

Causes.—It is difficult to account definitely for the conditions under which these concretions are formed. In all probability, how-ever, an inflammatory or catarrhal condition affecting the bile ducts and gall bladder may be regarded as that most frequently tending towards their production. A recent theory inclines to the belief that certain microbes or germs present in catarrhal conditions in some way or other may induce or at least favour their formation. Women suffer from gall stones more frequently than men, young people as a rule not being affected. This affection is essentially a disease of middle life. Certain physicians are inclined to assume that the occurrence of gall stones may be regarded as a matter of heredity. So also luxurious and indolent habits accompanied by excess of food have been credited with assisting their formation. An extremely interesting theory has also been propounded in the shape of the fact, that if people allow long intervals to elapse between meals, so that the bile is not evacuated from the gall bladder and used for digestive purposes, gall stones are apt to be formed.

Symptoms.—The symptoms of gall stones are naturally pro-duced by these objects leaving the gall bladder and passing down its duct. If they do not escape in this natural fashion by the bowel, and if any obstruction to their free passage exists, the first marked symptom of seizure is then produced in the shape of a sharp pain arising from the liver and passing upwards towards the shoulder-blade on the right side. The pain is not constant but recurs at intervals, and is therefore of the kind which physicians term *paroxysmal pain.* It is usually of an excruciating nature, due naturally to the fact of the attempted forced passage of these concretions down a narrow tube. Vomiting occurs, the matters passed upwards from the stomach ulti-mately becoming of a bilious nature. Later on, if the obstruction still persists, jaundice appears, whilst the urine becomes of a dark colour from the excretion of bile by the kidneys, and the matters passed from the bowels are of a pale tint owing to the absence of the colouring matters of the bile. Relief is obtained sometimes naturally when the gall stones succeed in forcing their way downwards into the bowel, but when they remain long in the gall bladder they may tend to set up inflammation and ulceration of adjacent parts and thus escape into other parts of the body. Even when they have been passed into the bowel they have been known to obstruct that canal itself.

Treatment.—The first aim of the physician in treating gall stones is naturally directed towards the relief of the intense pain. The doctor is usually accustomed to administer morphia by an injection under the skin, but two grains of opium, or twenty grains of chloral, may be tried. One grain of exalgin dissolved in a teaspoonful of hot water and given every half hour until three or four doses have been taken, frequently succeeds in giving ease. A hot water bath is also an admirable means of affording relief, the patient being kept in the bath for some time at a temperature of from 104 to 108 degrees. Hot fomentations or hot poultices applied over the liver may also be tried. Some physicians rely on giving large draughts of hot water in each of which twenty grains of bicarbonate of soda have been dissolved. These draughts may be given repeatedly until relief is obtained. For vomiting, small pieces of ice may be sucked or iced champagne given.

Olive oil has of late years been very much valued by physicians not merely in the cure of gall stones, but likewise in the way of their prevention. One authority gives the oil in doses of five or six ounces along with a little brandy and five drops of oil of peppermint. Two ounces of olive oil injected into the bowel have occasionally been followed by good results. Between the attacks also large doses of olive oil have been administered twice or thrice daily with a view to the prevention of gall stones. Another remedy given for dissolving them is composed of thirty or forty minims of spirit of ether mixed with the yolk of an egg. Five or six minims of the oil of turpentine administered in the yolk of an egg may be tried if other remedies fail.

Other Hints.—In so far as the patient's mode of life between attacks is concerned, plenty of open-air exercise should be taken, a sedentary habit as we have seen favouring the formation of gall stones. The diet should be plain, and the patient should rather underfeed than take a large quantity of nutriment. Foods of the nature of starch and sugar should be avoided and also fats. Alcohol should be restricted or stopped, and hot water freely sipped between meals. Salicylate of soda in a dose of fifteen to twenty grains, dissolved in a large amount of water, should be taken twice daily by way of exercising an effect on the liver secretion. Finally it may be noted that in cases in which ordinary remedies afford no relief, an operation can be undertaken by the surgeon whereby the gall bladder is opened and its contents evacuated. In the case of persons who are far removed from medical assistance, and who are subject to the attack of gall stones, it may be noted that the following mixture is recommended by a physician to be kept handy in the event of attack: Oil of peppermint, two drachms; spirit of chloroform, six drachms; spirit of sulphuric ether, four drachms; liquor of the hydrochlorate of morphia, four drachms; tincture of cannabis indica, two drachms; and aromatic spirits of ammonia up to three ounces. A teaspoonful of this mixture may be taken in a wine-glassful of water, to which a tablespoonful of whisky has been added, when attacked by pain. The dose may be repeated in say half-an-hour to an hour if no relief is obtained, subsequent doses being taken every two hours if needed.

OTHER AILMENTS OF THE LIVER

Amongst other troubles which affect this gland we find that known as *waxy* or *amyloid liver*, otherwise known as *albumenoid liver*. In this disease the liver becomes very much enlarged, and may weigh over 150 ounces, its normal weight being a little over three pounds. The ailment as a rule extends over a lengthened period. One of the chief symptoms of this disease is an anæmic or bloodless condition, whilst it is notable that other organs, such as the kidneys and spleen, may undergo enlargement. The causes of waxy liver are of doubtful nature, but it is frequently associated with diseases of an exhausting nature, and specially with tuberculosis.

Fatty Liver is a condition in which the liver is found to have undergone that process known as fatty degeneration, its normal tissues being largely replaced by fatty material. The causes of this ailment are found commonly in such states as drunkenness and tuberculosis, whilst in the obese or corpulent person the liver is also apt to exhibit this form of degeneration.

Hydatid Tumours of the Liver have already been described in the section dealing with "Parasites."

Of the foregoing ailments pain cannot be regarded as in any sense a prominent symptom. In so far as *waxy liver* is concerned it is recommended that the diet should be of a nutritious character. Tincture of iodine has been given for this condition in water in a dose of fifteen minims twice daily. In the case of *fatty liver* the obvious treatment is that of correcting the bodily state to which this condition may be due. The waters of Carlsbad and Homburg have been specially recommended for the treatment of both of these affections. In hydatid tumours of the liver the only satisfactory treatment is that of puncturing these tumours by way of removing the liquid contents of the cysts.

Cancer of the Liver as a rule is a secondary disease; that is to say it does not originate primarily in the liver itself but represents an infection derived from some other organ, such as the stomach, the womb, or breast. This disease as a rule runs a rapid course. Great pain is present, and the liver will be found to be enlarged. Evidence of the presence of cancerous growths is obtained on careful examination. The patient is apt to suffer from dropsy and jaundice, and ultimately dies of exhaustion. The treatment of this serious ailment is limited to easing the pain and supporting the strength.

Nutmeg Liver.—This disease is also known as *hyperæmia* of the liver. It usually arises from some defect of one or more of the valves of the heart, which results in the alteration of the circulation in the veins of the liver. The cells in the centre of the lobules of the liver tend to decrease in size, and to give rise to that appearance of the organ which has gained for it the name of "nutmeg" liver. In this disease the liver enlarges, that is, in the earlier stages of the ailment. Later on the liver exhibits contraction of its substance. There are disturbances of digestion represented, as well as jaundice. The face is also described in this affection as presenting usually a somewhat livid appearance. It will be understood that the treatment of this condition must first of all be directed to the removal of the heart trouble which we have seen to represent its usual cause. For the rest the treatment is mostly carried out on lines adapted to relieve the congestion of the liver; calomel given at night and followed by a saline purge in the morning being the remedies most in vogue.

Cirrhosis.—This disease is otherwise known as *gin-drinker's liver* and as *hobnailed liver*. These terms are applied to it from certain features exhibited by the organ as the result of the disease action. In the first place the term *cirrhosis*, derived from the Greek word for "yellow," has been applied to the ailment from the increased amount of yellow colouring matter found in the cells of the liver. The organ is much reduced in size, the atrophy or lessening affecting the right tube of the organ especially. The term "gin-drinker's liver" indicates that this ailment is mostly found in the subjects of alcoholism, whilst the term "hobnailed liver" is applied to indicate the peculiar appearance produced in the substance of the organ whereby the lobules of the liver are separated, and whereby they have also undergone a wasting process. The connective tissue or substance developed between the lobules of the liver increases in amount, in this way the liver coming to exhibit on its surface a large number of small projections which give to it a hobnailed aspect. It will be understood that this disease of the liver is associated in the drunkard with ailments of other organs, most notably the kidneys and spleen, whilst the stomach and digestive system also share in the general irritation of body. This disease affects males more frequently than females, the typical age extending from about thirty-five or forty years upwards to sixty years of age. The history of such cases is one of extreme indulgence in alcohol. In the early period of the ailment digestive troubles attract attention. There is dyspepsia, with retching and sickness, especially in the morning, relieved for the time being, unfortunately, by a resort to alcoholic stimulants, the use of which naturally only renders the condition worse. Blood may frequently be brought up from the stomach or may be excreted by the bowel. Dropsy ultimately appears, and a general wasting of body takes place. Jaundice is a symptom it may be noted which is not commonly seen in the case of "gin-drinker's liver." Other ailments are apt to follow in the train of the liver trouble, including a tendency to inflammation of the lungs.

Treatment.—In the treatment of this ailment the first step must be that of the patient renouncing all forms of alcohol. Spirits are especially injurious, some physicians allowing, however, a little claret or white wine well diluted with water. The diet should be plain, all rich foods being prohibited. It is of great importance that the patient should take regular open-air exercise, and also that his moral state be attended to in that every means should be taken to wean him from his fondness for alcohol. An all-important point connected with the treatment of this disease is that of securing regular action of the bowels. A remedy which has had a long and successful trial in cases of the kind under consideration aiding the return of the liver to a normal state, or at least of improving its condition, is that composed of dilute nitro-hydrochloric acid, half an ounce; dandelion juice, two ounces; tincture of nux vomica, five drachms; extract of cinchona, three and a half drachms; and infusion of chiretta up to twelve ounces. The dose is a tablespoonful taken in a wine-glassful of water four times daily before food.

It will be understood that in the treatment of this disease everything depends upon the stage at which the patient's habits are altered and appropriate remedies used. Some physicians have attained considerable success in the treatment of such cases through the giving of large quantities of milk mixed with aerated water, whilst the use of a dietary largely vegetarian in its character is also said to exert a marked effect in inducing a favourable change of habits.

Alcoholism.—With reference to the general treatment of the alcoholic habit little requires to be said in addition to the means already indicated under the heading of "gin-drinker's liver." The treatment of alcoholism divides itself into two phases. There is first the mental aspect of treatment represented by the removal of the drunkard from his accustomed surroundings, the occupying of his mind in some healthy and congenial pursuit, and the society of friends who will take the trouble to support him in his efforts to conquer his failing, strict attention being paid to every detail connected with the maintenance of a healthy life.

The second phase of treatment is that represented by the efforts of the medical man to overcome the desire for alcohol. There can be no hesitation in at once withdrawing from the drunkard all alcoholic supplies. This treatment naturally tends to cause an anxious and painful craving for the accustomed stimulant. Nevertheless, it is only mistaken kindness to attempt to cure him of his habit by merely reducing the amount of alcohol consumed, seeing that each dose he receives simply adds fuel to the fire and tends to increase the craving. It has been remarked that persons suffering from alcoholism who have been committed to jail and whose supply of drink has been at once cut short, rarely exhibit anything but improvement after the first symptoms of the craving have disappeared.

Various Methods.—The various troubles of the drunkard fall to be treated each under its own head. If he is sleepless, appropriate remedies for this condition must be administered. For his dyspepsia or indigestion, in the same way drugs tending to soothe the stomach may be given, such as bismuth, whilst strong beef tea or bovril and like fluids may be administered in order to support strength and to dull the craving for alcohol. In connection with the subject of "gin-drinker's liver" a remedy was detailed which may be used for the cure of liver and stomach troubles, and which also in some measure is calculated to allay the alcoholic desire. Another such prescription is that composed of aromatic spirits of ammonia four ounces, tincture of chinchona two ounces, liquor of the hydrochlorate of strychnine one drachm, and tincture of capsicum one ounce. The dose is a teaspoonful in half a tumbler of aerated water every hour.

Drink Cures.—With reference to so-called cures for alcoholism, usually given by means of injection into the skin, it may be said that little reliance can be placed upon them. Many of these "cures" contain strychnine, whilst others include compounds of gold. It is not an uncommon thing to find alcohol itself also represented in such cures, which are much lauded in certain quarters. The friends of patients suffering from alcoholism would be well advised if, rejecting these cures, the composition of which is kept secret, they should rely upon the means just detailed for the weaning of the unfortunate subject from his intemperate habits.

DISEASES OF THE PANCREAS OR SWEETBREAD

Regarding diseases of this organ, little that is definite is at present known. At the same time, from its intimate relations to the digestive work, certain ailments of the sweetbread are known to possess a definite relation to diseases in other organs. It was stated in connection with the subject of diabetes (vol. i.) that those cases in which the sweetbread is involved are regarded as of much more serious import than those in which this gland is unaffected. The term *pancreatic diabetes* is frequently used to indicate this variety of the affection. In diabetes the sweetbread becomes lessened in size or atrophied, whilst the functions it discharges in digestion (already fully detailed in the section dealing with the digestive processes) are necessarily liable to exhibit great irregularity. Seeing that the sweetbread juice acts not merely upon nitrogenous foods, but upon starch and upon fat as well, any derangement of the functions of this organ is certain to be followed by serious digestive disturbance. Thus if the food cannot be perfectly digested in the intestine, we may expect to find symptoms of dyspepsia present along with flatulence. Diarrhœa may be present, or the reverse condition, constipation, may be represented, whilst the matters passed from the bowel not having been properly subjected to digestive influence, exhibit quantities of fatty matters which have escaped digestive action.

Examples of Disease.—Physicians generally recognise that the sweetbread may be affected by *inflammation*, whilst it is liable also to suffer from *cancer* and from certain of those diseases, *cirrhosis* amongst them, which affect the liver. *Enlargement* of the pancreas is also known, this latter ailment sometimes arising from the blockage of the duct or tube whereby the secretion of the gland is conveyed into the bowel. The detection of sweetbread disease is one of the most difficult problems which can face the physician. He usually arrives at the conclusion that the pancreas is at fault by excluding those symptoms which he regards as more especially dependent upon disturbance of the stomach and liver.

Naturally the treatment of pancreatic disease is in a most unsatisfactory state, having regard to our want of knowledge of the causes of such ailments, and also taking into consideration the difficulty of their recognition. Where pain is present it must be treated on ordinary principles by opiates and other means, whilst the troubles of digestion may be counteracted by the administration of remedies for indigestion and especially of *pancreatin*. This latter substance is obtained from the sweetbread of the pig, and is specially prepared for administration to man. Through its use it may be believed the absence or deficiency of the pancreatic secretion of the patient may be to a certain extent made good.

DISEASES OF THE ABSORBENT SYSTEM

As has already been indicated, the *absorbent or lymphatic system of vessels* is that which is concerned not merely in removing digested food from the intestine to the blood, but also in gathering up the excess of lymph or blood which has been supplied for the nourishment of the tissues. (See p. 43.) Included in the absorbent system are the lymphatic glands (p. 44). These glands form portions of the system singularly liable to disease. As poisonous materials are readily absorbed by the lymphatics from any part of the body, the effect of the inflammation thus produced is frequently manifested first of all in the glands. In poisoning of the hand, for example, the glands under the armpit will become inflamed, just as those of the jaw become enlarged in diphtheria. Injuries to the foot or diseases affecting the generative organs will, naturally, in the same way cause inflammation of the lymphatic glands situated in the groin. Lymphatic glands are also liable to the attack of tuberculosis, this disease being specially found to affect those glands situated in the course of the lacteals or vessels carrying chyle or digested food from the intestine to the blood (Fig. 31).

Mesenteric Disease.—Infection of these latter glands (called *mesenteric glands*) is generally supposed to arise from milk containing the bacilli of tuberculosis. Whether this be the case or not, it is tolerably certain that, from one cause or another, in delicate infants tuberculosis is not infrequently found developed in this region of the body. This affection, known as *tabes mesenterica,* and popularly as "consumption of the bowels," is mostly found in children, although the disease may occur in adults also. Symptoms of the disease are exhibited by wasting of the body and by enlargement of the belly, which becomes tense and drum-like. Diarrhœa is more or less constantly present, whilst the matters discharged from the bowels are of a watery character and of an offensive odour.

Treatment.—The treatment adapted for the cure of tuberculosis infection of the lymphatic glands is simply that practised in respect of ordinary tuberculosis. The strength of the patient must be kept up by every possible means. Cod liver oil or virol is to be given after food, whilst many physicians recommend that cod liver oil or plain olive oil should be rubbed into the front of the abdomen and the trunk of the body generally, by the hand. About half an ounce of the oil should be rubbed in at each application, the body being swathed in flannel thereafter, whilst over the flannel it is recommended that a piece of mackintosh sheeting should be placed. This rubbing with the oil should be practised for four or five days running night and morning. The diet should be generous, pure sterilised milk and cream constituting its chief elements, whilst a moderate quantity of animal food may also be administered. Cases of this kind, it may be added, tend to improve rapidly and to benefit much from a removal to the seaside. Surgical treatment is also practised for the removal of the affected glands.

Hodgkinson's Disease, or Lymphadenoma.—This curious ailment, so named after Dr. Hodgkinson, who first described it in an accurate fashion, appears to consist essentially of an infection of the lymphatic glands. In addition, it is marked by the destruction of the red corpuscles of the blood, and also by the development of secondary growths or what is known as *lymphoid tumours* in the organs of the body. This disease is most common in children and in early life. In so far as its causes are concerned these are indefinite, but it is strongly suspected that its origin begins by some peculiar manifestation of such a constitutional disease as tuberculosis itself, whilst syphilis has also been credited with a share in its production. The glands of the neck appear to be those which first indicate the presence of the disease. The swelling increases, and passes to face, armpits, and groin. Later on all the glands may be affected, whilst the spleen in turn also comes to suffer. The glands in a late stage adhere together and form distinct masses, but it is notable in this disease that they neither tend to suppurate and thus produce matter, nor to break down into the cheesy condition characteristically seen in tuberculosis.

Treatment.—Physicians are accustomed to rely upon arsenic as the drug of most value here. The arsenic is either injected beneath the skin, or may be administered in the shape of Fowler's solution. In the case of an adult the arsenic must be given in large doses, beginning with five minims three or four times a day, and increased until twelve or fifteen minims are given thrice, or four times daily after food. Other remedies administered in this disease consist of cod liver oil, whilst iron is frequently combined with arsenic in the course of treatment. Finally, when the disease exhibits a tendency to locate itself and to exhibit a less general range over the body, the removal of affected glands by the surgeon has been recommended.

DISEASES OF THE SPLEEN

The spleen is an organ extremely liable to be affected in various ailments. Thus it has been shown to be connected with a variety of complaints, ranging from typhoid fever to ague. The organ has already been described both in respect of its structure and its functions. As it appears to be capable of acting as a kind of blood reservoir, relieving pressure of blood in the liver and kidneys especially, any affection of these organs may produce congestion and enlargement of the spleen.

It is thus liable to exhibit *embolism*, or that condition in which clots of blood tend to block up the blood-vessels, whilst *inflammation* of the spleen is not an uncommon disease, accompanied by severe pain at the left side of the stomach and enlargement of the organ. Directions regarding the treatment of affections of the spleen will be found included under the headings of the various diseases in which this organ is liable to be affected. The administration of quinine will frequently reduce enlargement of the spleen, whilst dialysed iron, given in a dose of thirty to forty minims after each meal, has also been recommended. Quinine in conjunction with arsenic has also been administered in cases in which enlargement of the organ is present. Physicians agree in recommending electricity, in the shape of the continuous current through the organ, for its reduction. For the relief of pain in the region of the spleen, hot poultices or hot fomentations may be tried, but as has already been remarked the ailments of this organ really depending upon other and primary diseases, these latter require to be first considered by way of arriving at a true knowledge of the direct cause operating to produce disorder in the spleen itself.

DISEASES OF DUCTLESS GLANDS

The functions of the thyroid gland have already been described as probably assisting in the manufacture of some internal secretion or other which is poured into the blood. Disturbance of this function, as has already been remarked in the section dealing with the ductless glands, is capable of producing very serious effects upon the general health at large.

Goître.—Goître is a disease characterised by enlargement of the thyroid gland. This ailment appears to be mostly caused by drinking over-hard water. It is therefore natural to find it common in districts supplied with water of this description. Compounds of lime have been credited with the power of causing goître, but it is also known to occur in districts in which the water is not particularly hard. In various parts of India, for instance, the occurrence of this disease has been attributed to the presence in the water of salts or compounds of iron. The enlargement of the thyroid gland, which exists in the neck in close relation to the organ of voice, varies greatly in size. Occasionally it may appear as a tumour of very large dimensions indeed. In England, goître is spoken of under the names of "Yorkshire neck" and "Derbyshire neck," from the fact of its occurrence in districts in these counties notable for a hard water supply. Some authorities incline also to believe that goître may be produced by other influences than the character of the drinking water. In this belief, the origin has occasionally been attributed to some poison of a similar kind to that giving rise to malarial fever. No pain is usually caused in the development of goître, but if the tumour be of large size, it may cause both pain and other symptoms through its pressure upon nerves and other structures.

Treatment.—For the treatment of ordinary goître, it is necessary that the water-supply should first of all be rigidly supervised. A change of air is a necessity in this disease, whilst the food must be of fairly rich character, including a supply of eggs, milk, and meat. In so far as local treatment is concerned, the tincture of iodine is often injected into a goître to an extent of from six to eight drops at a sitting, but it must be added that many physicians incline to believe that considerable danger is liable to attach to the use of this method. Iodoform has also been used by way of injection, and has also been given internally, the dose being about one grain two or three times a day. The services of the surgeon may require to be requisitioned for the removal of the gland. In India, biniodide of mercury made into an ointment composed of three drachms of this substance to one pound of lard is largely and successfully used. Authorities, however, maintain that this treatment is of little use in temperate climates. The ointment is rubbed in for ten minutes, and the patient afterwards sits in the sun until such time as extreme smarting is produced. Another layer of ointment is applied when the treatment is presumed to be finished. Probably the application to a goître every day of a liniment composed of equal parts of the tincture of iodine and the liniment of iodine may suffice for ordinary treatment.

Exophthalmic Goître.—This disease is otherwise known as *Graves' Disease*, whilst the name of *Basedow's Disease* has also been bestowed upon it, from the fact that both physicians accurately described its nature. This disease consists of an enlargement of the thyroid gland, accompanied, however, by a prominent development of the eyeballs, and by a highly increased action of the heart. This disease is caused largely by mental strain and sometimes by absorption of poisonous matter in the alimentary canal. The excess of secretion of thyroid fluid causes rapid action of the heart (tachycardia) and also disturbance in the adrenals and the sugar-making function of the liver. In cases of acute onset, such as were seen during the war, a patient might feel as if she were suffocated, and marked increase in the size of the thyroid might be found almost in one night. In these cases the heart becomes markedly enlarged and loud murmurs are heard all over the heart area.

Treatment.—The actual cause of this disease still remains obscure. One school of medical thought regards this ailment as dependent upon some overstimulation of the thyroid gland, thereby causing an increased amount of its secretion which is sent into the blood. In the acute condition of Exophthalmic Goitre, the principal treatment is complete rest in bed, with plenty of air and sunshine, and every effort to remove any cause of nervous upset. The best drugs for use are strophanthus and bromide to combat the nervous and cardiac symptoms. In some cases iodides have been used and may have some effect in the more chronic cases, but, as a rule, iron tonics are the more efficient in these. Good nourishing food is, of course, essential, as we find considerable wasting in many cases. Of late, various extracts such as Thyrodectin have been made from the blood of animals who have had their thyroid glands removed some little time previously in the hope that they may contain an antitoxin antidote to the poison, and success has been claimed for them. More active treatment has been tried, such as trying to reduce the size of the gland by exposing it to X-rays (i.e. Röntgen rays) and radium, while surgeons favour operations, such as removal of part of the gland, or tying the arteries serving it.

Myxœdema.—In this disease we meet with a want of development of the thyroid gland or with some marked diminution of its functions. The disease is mostly found in elderly women. The appearance of the patient is characteristic, and reminds one in some degree of the aspect presented in a case of dropsy. The face is swollen, but there is no pitting on pressure such as would result were dropsy present. The eyelids are loose and enlarged, the lips become thickened, and the hands become swollen with the finger tips expanded and flattened. Mental symptoms are also present, consisting of an apparent general deficiency of brain-action, accompanied by a want of energy and slowness of speech. There is also failure of memory. The skin at large is thickened and dry, and the secretion of the skin appears to be largely held in abeyance. The temperature is below normal. In a case not properly treated, death may result after a number of years from derangement of the functions of the kidneys, or more usually from simple collapse.

Treatment.—If these symptoms arise from the want of the secretion which the thyroid gland appears to pour into the blood, it is obvious that a line of treatment might be adopted whereby thyroid substance could be administered to the patient by the way of replacing the absent material. Dr. Murray of Newcastle-on-Tyne, following up this line of research, first used an extract of the thyroid gland of the sheep by way of skin injection. It was ultimately found, however, that the thyroid gland given as food acted in an equally satisfactory fashion; hence to-day physicians administer the dried and powdered gland given in a dose of one grain thrice daily, and increased to four or five grains three times a day. Thyroid tabloids are also prepared for convenient administration. One tabloid of one and a half grains may be given at first after each meal and at bedtime. This dose may be increased by adding one tabloid more daily till six grains are taken four times a day. The patient should be made to rest for a certain time after the thyroid extract has been administered. The essential feature of this treatment is the administration of thyroid substance in small doses at first, the dose being, as has been directed, gradually increased. After a cure has been effected small doses may be taken with greater or less regularity. Two tabloids weekly may suffice for this purpose, the progress of the case being of course duly noted.

Cretinism.—Cretinism is a condition intimately associated with ordinary goître. It may be described as a form of bodily and brain degeneration occurring in those parts of the world typically representing hard water districts. Cretinism in one sense is a form of idiocy. The body is small and stunted and the skin thickened and wrinkled. A vacant expression of face exists with thickened lips. The tongue is enlarged and the abdomen pendulous or loose, whilst the legs are deformed. The head is enlarged, and the brain power markedly deficient. In many cases a typical cretin can neither speak nor hear.

Treatment.—The most curious fact regarding this disease is found in the absence of the thyroid gland, this circumstance having prompted the treatment to that successfully followed in myxœdema, namely, the administration of direct feeding by the thyroid extract. Improvement in suitable cases speedily follows the administration of thyroid material. The treatment is commenced by giving a tabloid containing two grains of powder of thyroid gland twice daily, this treatment being persisted in until the temperature, which is low in this disease, becomes normal, and when the gain of weight approximates the body to its normal bulk. If the disease again appears to be developing the treatment must be recommenced, or be continued in a modified form. One authority describes a dose of five grains of dried thyroid material given twice a week as sufficient. This treatment may require, it is added, to be continued throughout life if signs of recurrence appear, but at the same time there can be little doubt of the immense improvement both in bodily health and in the mental faculties which follows the adoption of this interesting and thoroughly scientific mode of cure.

DISEASE OF THE SUPRARENAL GLANDS
(ADDISON'S DISEASE)

These glands, described in a previous section of this work, are situated above the kidneys, each gland somewhat resembling a cocked hat in shape. As regards their functions it was mentioned that in all probability they throw into the blood an internal secretion which has the effect of exercising a distinct effect on the muscles of the body. The absence of this secretion has the effect, therefore, of inducing certain of the symptoms characteristic of the affection.

Symptoms.—In this disease (also known as *Addison's Disease*) both glands are always affected. The patient complains of an increasing disinclination for exercise, faintness, loss of appetite, pain in the stomach, and general wasting. The most characteristic sign, however, is that of *discoloration of the skin*, which is seen in the face, neck, arms, belly, and also in the generative organs. The colour is described as resembling bronzing, and it is recorded that in some cases the departure from the normal tint of the skin has been so great that the patient has come to resemble a mulatto. This disease appears to run a course extending from a year to eighteen months, and is more frequently found in males than in females. It is an ailment characteristic of adult life. In so far as the glands themselves are concerned, it would appear that physicians regard the disease as essentially one of tuberculosis of these glands.

Treatment.—The treatment of this trouble is entirely unsatisfactory. The great exhaustion of the patient involves the most extreme care in nursing, and the prevention of all excitement and all unnecessary exertion. In a fatal case, the patient becomes half unconscious and gradually collapses. If diarrhœa is present, bismuth mixture must be given by way of controlling it. Stimulants are necessary, whilst tonics in the shape of arsenic, phosphates, iron, and quinine have all been advocated. Following out the lines adopted for the treatment of thyroid gland disease, physicians have of late been accustomed to administer an extract made from the suprarenal glands of the sheep. The dose given is stated at one drachm of the gland, or an equivalent amount of the extract. The five-grain tabloids of suprarenal substance gland form a handy mode of its administration. One of the tabloids may at first be given twice or thrice daily after food, whilst the number may be increased to three twice or thrice a day. It may be said, however, that the treatment of this ailment by such means has not afforded the marked indications of success followed by the use of thyroid material in myxœdema.

SECTION IV

DISEASES OF THE SKIN

UNDER the section on Anatomy will be found an account of the functions of the skin *in health*, and of its purely anatomical structure. It is essential here, however, to point out that in studying the *diseases* which are peculiar to that organ, it becomes necessary to subdivide the layers of the skin somewhat differently, namely according to their behaviour, or the manner in which they are affected by disease, so that from a *pathological* point of view we have—

1. The *horny layer* of the epidermis, which is practically dead, and in which we only see the results, such as desquamation, dryness, &c., of the morbid processes which are taking place in the deeper tissues.

2. The mucous layer of the epidermis and the papillary layer of the corium or true skin, which are living tissues intimately connected with each other, inflammation here giving rise to the large majority of skin diseases met with.

3. The deeper layer of the corium, and the subcutaneous connective tissue, diseased conditions of which are liable to spread to the underlying muscles or bones, and are for this reason more dangerous than those confined to the second layer.

In considering any affection of the skin there are four points which we must determine, namely : the *distribution*, the *elements* of the skin involved, the *cause*, and the *type* of the eruption.

Skin Diseases

(1) In their *distribution* over the surface of the body many skin diseases show a decided predilection for certain localities. Thus acne is most frequently found on the face or the shoulders; psoriasis on the extending surfaces of the joints; parasitic diseases, such as ring-worm, on the scalp. The position of the eruption, consequently, gives us a strong hint as to the probable nature of the disease.

(2) Next, we have to determine which *elements* of the skin are involved. Is the disease due to a general inflammation of the superficial layers of the skin, such as occurs in eczema and psoriasis; or is the starting-point in the sebaceous glands, as in acne, or in the hair follicles, as in sycosis?

(3) Thirdly, we must endeavour to discover the *cause* of the disease. Is it the symptom of one or other of the *eruptive fevers* —measles, scarlatina, small-pox? The thermometer—which should always be used when there is any doubt in the matter—will indicate whether or not there is any rise in the body temperature. Is it due to some *local irritation*, such as that produced by lice on the scalp, or the itch insect burrowing under the skin of the under surface of the wrist joint? Has the patient's *occupation* anything to do with the disease? Washerwomen and masons are subject to eczema. Workers in chemicals—such as dye-stuffs, acids, alkalies, arsenic—suffer from the irritation produced by these substances. Certain *drugs* when administered internally give rise to rashes. Thus bromide of potash causes acne. Quinine, opium, digitalis, give rise to a form of nettlerash; copaiva and cubebs to a rose-rash, like scarlatina. Finally we must ask ourselves whether or not the disease is due to the derangement of some of the internal organs. Thus disorders of the digestive system frequently give rise to eczema, nettlerash, and acne. Shingles is due to a disturbance of the nervous system. Diseases of the liver give rise to jaundice and itching. Certain kinds of food in certain individuals give rise to eruptions on the skin. Shellfish will cause nettlerash in some people. Strawberries give rise to the same affection in others.

(4) Lastly, we have to consider the *type* of the eruption. Diseases of the skin manifest themselves by certain *symptoms;* these are termed respectively objective and subjective. The former are those lesions which appear on the surface of the body, and are visible to the eye. They constitute the *type* of the disease, and may be primary or secondary.

The subjective symptoms relate to the *sensations* of the patient, and are those of which he himself can alone be aware. Such symptoms are itching, pain, a sensation as though insects were creeping over the body (*formication*), heat, &c.

The primary lesions or types of diseases of the skin are :—

(*a*) **Hyperæmia or Congestion.**—This may be an early stage of inflammation, and then the skin is red, and there is a sensation of heat or tingling ; or the congestion may be due to retarded circulation, when the affected part is of a purple or bluish colour.

(*b*) **Papule or Pimple.**—A small *solid* elevation of the skin.

(*c*) **Vesicle.**—A small rounded elevation of the skin filled with transparent fluid.

(*d*) **Pustule.**—A small rounded elevation of the skin containing pus.

(*e*) **Bulla or Bleb.**—A large pustule.

(*f*) **Wheal.**—An oval, rounded, or irregularly shaped elevation of the skin of a temporary character, such as the lesion produced by the stinging nettle.

The secondary lesions are those which are a result of the primary. They are :—

(*a*) **Scabs or Crusts.**—The shed contents of vesicles or pustules which have dried up and remained adherent to the surface of the diseased portion of skin.

(*b*) **Scales.**—Dry flakes of epidermic cells which have separated from the tissue beneath.

(*c*) **Scratch Marks or Excoriations.**—Torn points, lines, or streaks of injured skin, usually marked by dried-up blood.

(*d*) **Chap or Fissure.**—A linear crack or wound in the epidermis which reaches down to the deeper layers of the skin.

(*e*) **Ulcers.**—Irregularly shaped and sized excavations of the skin.

(*f*) **Scar.**—The new tissue which replaces that which has been destroyed.

In describing the several diseases of the skin, we might follow one or other of the classifications to be found in modern text-books on the subject; it will be simpler, however, to treat of them here under the headings of the types of primary diseases which have already been mentioned, adding to that list the diseases which specially affect the sebaceous and sweat glands, the hair, and parasitic diseases.

HYPERÆMIAS

The hyperæmias most frequently met with are *Erythema* and *Urticaria.*

Erythema consists of an inflammatory redness of the skin, occurring in limited patches. It is accompanied by a sensation of itching and tingling, and is caused by *irritation* of the skin, such as results from the application of a mustard plaster, or from the pressure of tightly fitting clothes; but most frequently it is produced by irritating secretions flowing over the surface of the skin, and its presence on the buttocks of infants—the result of inattention to cleanliness—gives rise to much suffering and discomfort.

Another form of erythema occurs where two opposing surfaces of skins come in contact with one another, as in the groin, under the breasts, between the toes. It is most commonly met with in fat people, and in neglected children. The attack comes on suddenly with redness, heat, and tingling of the skin; the surface soon becomes covered with an ill-smelling moisture, and unless steps be taken to arrest the disease, painful ulcers may form at the angle of the fold, and the condition pass from an acute to a chronic one.

A third form of erythema is the *chilblain,* which is a localised congestion of the skin commonly met with in children, more especially girls. Chilblains occur only during the prevalence of cold weather, and many individuals are subject to relapses every winter. They begin as swollen, red, shining patches on the toes or fingers—more frequently the former—and are accompanied by severe itching and pain. Sometimes nothing further happens, and the swelling disappears in a few days; in other cases blebs or blisters form. These burst, and an ulcer remains which is slow to heal.

Treatment.—In the first and second varieties little beyond strict attention to cleanliness is required. The parts should be washed and dried with a soft towel. The folds of skin are to be kept apart with a piece of lint or soft cotton. The best local application is some form of dusting powder. A mixture of two drachms of oxide of zinc and six drachms of powdered lycopodium acts excellently, or starch may be substituted for the lycopodium. If an ointment is preferred, Lassar's paste, consisting of salicylic acid, ten grains; oxide of zinc and starch, of each two drachms; and vaseline, four drachms, applied over the surface, will suffice.

For **Chilblains.**—An endeavour must be made to improve the tone of the circulation by active outdoor exercise, cold sponging of the whole surface of the body, followed by a brisk rub down with a rough towel, and a generous, stimulating diet. Medicinally, iron in some form, such as the syrup of the hypophosphites and cod liver oil should be administered. Locally, stimulating applications such as the tincture of iodine, or soap liniment should be made. Toasting the feet at the fire when they are cold should be avoided.

Urticaria, "Nettlerash" or "Hives" is an inflammatory affection of the skin, characterised by the sudden appearance on its surface of *wheals*, which are of a reddish or whitish colour, and are accompanied by sensations of burning, itching, and stinging. The wheals may disappear as quickly as they appear. The extent of surface covered by the rash varies greatly, sometimes the whole body being covered with the red blotches, whilst in other cases the rash appears in isolated patches in different parts of the body. The *cause* of the disease is sometimes obscure, but it may as a rule be traced to some digestive derangement; and is frequently accompanied by vomiting and diarrhœa. It may be produced by external irritants coming in contact with the skin, such as insect bites, jelly-fish stings, or the sting of the nettle. Certain articles of food—such as shell-fish, pork, strawberries, oatmeal—produce it in different individuals. Worms frequently give rise to it in children, and womb derangements in women. The rash itself is generally preceded by a feeling of general discomfort and a sensation of itching, the tongue is furred, and the bowels may be confined or loose. In children, in addition to the diffused redness or wheal, a small solid raised papule or pimple appears in the centre of the wheal; this remains after the wheal has disappeared, and as the top has been torn off in scratching, a scab of coagulated blood forms.

Treatment.—An endeavour must be made, in the first instance, to discover the cause, for its removal will alone cure the disease. In acute cases a purgative, and preferably a saline one, such as sulphate of magnesia, should be administered without delay; and should there be any irritating food still in the stomach, an emetic of ipecacuanha or of sulphate of zinc should be given. For some time after the attack, and until it is quite recovered from, mild aperients should be given regularly, and the food must be of the simplest description. To relieve acidity powders containing rhubarb, soda, and bismuth should be administered before meals.

Locally, means must be adopted to relieve the itching, which is sometimes almost intolerable. Of these, *lotions* in some form or other are most efficient, such as vinegar and water; alcohol, pure or diluted with water; liquor carbonis detergens, diluted with water; saturated solutions of boracic acid, or bicarbonate of soda. *Baths*, especially alkaline baths, often afford much relief. An alkaline bath may be prepared by adding four ounces each of bicarbonate of potash and carbonate of soda to an ordinary bath. All irritation of the skin by wearing rough woollen underclothing must be avoided.

PAPULAR ERUPTIONS

Prurigo is a chronic disease which begins in early childhood, and frequently continues throughout life, and is characterised by the presence of numerous irregularly distributed and intensely itchy *pimples*, or papules, which are of a pale red colour, the size of a split pea, and only slightly raised above the surface of the skin. They are situated as a rule on the back of the arms and hands, and front of the legs, sometimes on the trunk, but very rarely on the face.

As a result of the scratching the tops of the pimples are torn off, and the pimples appear black, owing to the presence of crusts of blood. The surrounding skin becomes rough and thickened, also a result of scratching. The glands in the armpits and groins are hard and swollen. The severest attacks occur in autumn, and the itching is invariably worst at night.

Treatment.—Internal medication has as a rule little or no effect on the disease ; but attention must be paid to the general health, and cod liver oil, iron and quinine, may be tried. *Locally*, the most efficient remedies are tar and sulphur, and these are best applied in the form of *baths*, but ointments containing the same drugs may also be tried. The disease, however, as has already been indicated, often proves most intractable.

Lichen is characterised by the appearance of minute, red, flattened, or raised papules, in rows or bands on an inflamed surface of skin. In the early stages the patches have a glazed appearance. After a time the pimples become covered with fine branny scales, and finally, as a result of the intense itching which is always present, and which induces scratching, crusts of blood are formed, and the surrounding skin is much thickened. Portions of skin from which the rash has disappeared are found to be *stained* a dark red or brownish colour, giving the skin a mottled appearance. The patches of disease are most frequently found upon the front of the forearm, and more especially on the front of the wrist. It occurs at all periods of life, but adults are more subject to it than children, and women than men.

Treatment.—Internally, arsenic, which should be given in small doses to begin with, is the favourite remedy, the quantity being gradually increased. The general health must be attended to, and cod liver oil and iron given as tonics. *Locally*, inunctions of ointments containing tar ; lotions, such as were mentioned when treating of prurigo, to relieve the itching, may be tried and alkaline baths.

VESICULAR SKIN DISEASES

Eczema is an acute or chronic inflammatory disease of the skin, characterised by the appearance of *erythema, papules, vesicles,* and *pustules,* accompanied by intense itching, and in some cases by a watery exudation, and terminating in skin peeling, or in the formation of *crusts* or *scabs.* Eczema is the most frequently met with of all the diseases of the skin, and is as a rule easily recognised. The difficulty of diagnosis, however, arises from the fact that all the different types of eruption may occur together or separately in the same case, so that in one region of the body we may have a patch which has become chronic, and consists of an intensely itchy, dry, red area, covered with fine scales; in another a patch covered with minute vesicles which exude an irritating sticky fluid; and in a third, scabs or crusts, formed by the *pus* exuded from pustules. An *acute* case of eczema generally begins with the appearance on the skin of a diffused red blush, which fades away at the edges. This redness is exactly like the rash of scarlatina, for if it is looked into carefully, minute spots of a brighter colour will be found scattered through the general redness; these are the inflamed *papillæ* of the skin. Very quickly after the appearance of the redness the skin becomes covered with innumerable minute *vesicles,* which burst, and convert the inflamed area into a *"weeping"* one, by the serous discharge which they pour out. This discharge is intensely irritating, and stiffens linen when dry. Or again, the vesicles may rapidly become pustular, their contents, instead of being serous or watery, are purulent or "mattery," the pustules burst, and "matter" is poured out on to the surface and forms *scabs.*

If the disease is to run a favourable course, the exudation gradually diminishes, the epidermis is restored to a healthy condition, and all that remains to mark the site of the disease is a branny peeling and the itching, which remains almost to the very end. Where the disease has become *chronic* the skin is greatly *thickened,* the surface is rough, the epidermis is very thin, and shining through it can be seen the inflamed deeper layers of the skin, which impart a deep red colour to the affected area. Deep *fissures* or cracks also frequently form which bleed, and are extremely painful. Unfortunately it is rare for a case of eczema to run an acute course, ending in recovery; as a rule, some small, insignificant-looking patch remaining—behind the ears or on the hands—and forming a focus for the recrudescence of the disease at some future period. As regards its *distribution,* eczema most frequently appears on the thinner parts of the skin, and is more

DISEASES OF THE SKIN.

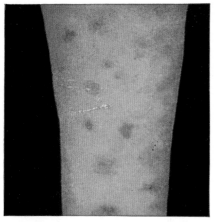

Spotted Rose Rash—Erythema Nodosum.

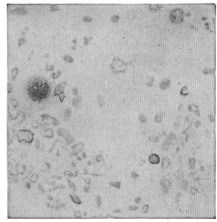

Seborrhœic Dermatitis.

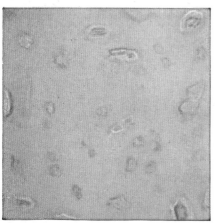

Pityriasis Rosea.

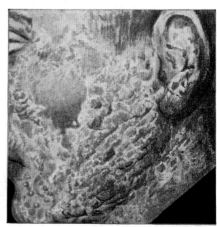

Eczema.

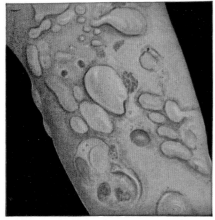

Pemphigus.

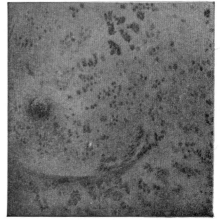

Lichen Planus Acutus.

From Drawings by EDWARD BURNET, B.A. (Lond.).

often seen as a disease of the head and limbs than of the trunk. Its most characteristic position is behind the *ears*, but it frequently appears on the face, on the head in children, and at the bend of the elbows. The rash is as a rule symmetrically disposed, so that it appears simultaneously at the back of both ears or at the bend of the elbows.

The *cause* of eczema is difficult to determine, for whilst there are many cases which are due to an *irritant* which can be easily traced, such as the itch insect, lice, chemical products which the patient comes in contact with, and the removal of which cures the complaint. There are many others in which no irritant can be discovered, and in which the only conclusion to be drawn is that there is some inherent predisposition in the patient which renders him liable to the disease. Eczema affects all ages and both sexes indiscriminately, but it differs in its character according to the *age* of the patient. In children the pustular form is more commonly met with, in young adults the typical weeping variety, whilst in old people the dry, scaly, intensely itchy form is almost the rule.

Treatment.—Eczema is a disease which is amenable to treatment; and there should be no hesitation in attempting to cure it as quickly as possible. Mothers are frequently afraid of the results of "driving the trouble in" in the case of children, but their fears are groundless, as the child, whatever its condition may be, will most certainly be better without the disease. Eczema seldom ends fatally, except in the case of a weakly infant, or of a very old person in whom the loss of sleep and want of appetite give rise to exhaustion leading to a fatal termination. Before entering into the details of treatment, certain general indications may be alluded to. As itching leads to scratching, and treatment can be of no avail so long as the latter is permitted, steps must be taken to prevent it. In the case of adults they must be prevailed upon to refrain from it, whilst in that of infants and young children the hands must be muffled, or some other form of mechanical restraint applied such as that recommended by Dr. White, who says, referring to cases of eczema of the head and face: "A skull-cap is to be made of fine old cotton or linen cloth, so as closely to fit the skull; a mask of the same material is then shaped to the face, with exactly placed apertures for the eyes, nose, and mouth, and with slits for the ears. It is to be gathered in somewhat beneath the chin and made long enough to lap some two inches at the back of the head. This in mild cases will prove to be a sufficient protection against the efforts of the infant to get at the irritated skin with its hands, and a shield against the damage inflicted by rubbing the inflamed parts against every opposing surface which offers. The protection from irritation afforded by the mask is only one of its important duties—it may be smeared with ointment, and, adjusted tightly, form an impermeable coating to the inflamed skin.   The nose and ears should protrude through their appropriate openings to assist in retaining the mask in position, which should be tightly stitched or pinned with fine safety-pins at the back of the head.   Should it be considered advisable to confine the arms, as is frequently found to be the case in strong infants, a hole is to be cut in the end of a small pillow-case large enough to allow the child's head to pass through.   This is to be drawn down over the body and arms. The back and front surfaces are then to be stitched together between the arms and body by a long darning needle, from the axilla down to the ends of the fingers, thus confining the arms in closed sleeves to the sides.   The same result may perhaps be more readily accomplished by the use of several safety-pins in place of the stitches, by which the jacket may be more readily taken off when necessary. The pillow-case is then to be fastened together by the pins between the legs from front to back, so that the arms cannot possibly be brought up to the head.   This lower fastening can of course be removed without trouble as often as it is necessary to change the napkin."

Other sources of irritation of the skin such as rough woollen clothing in direct contact with it must be avoided.   Frequent washing of the parts must be avoided, and the use of soap prohibited.   The water used for washing must be neither too hot nor too cold, and the towel for drying must be soft, and used with gentleness.   Lastly, it must be seen to that the patient enjoys a sufficient amount of *sleep*.

Drugs in Eczema.—The treatment with drugs may be divided into *local* and *internal*.   *Locally* the treatment will depend upon the stage or character of the disease, but as a preliminary all crusts and scabs must be removed when these are present, and this may best be accomplished by applying a linseed poultice to the part.   In the dry scaly varieties of the disease ointments are more applicable, whilst in the weeping forms lotions are better, remembering always that ointments are not to be rubbed in, but gently *smeared* over the affected area, and that lotions are to be frequently renewed and applied on thin cotton rags.   In acute cases soothing applications are to be made, and the best sedative is the oxide of zinc, which may be employed in the form of an ointment, or a dusting powder, or a lotion, such as the following : Oxide of zinc and starch, of each two drachms ; vaseline, four drachms (*the ointment*).   Or calamine, oxide of zinc, and glycerine, of each two drachms ; rose water, to six ounces (*the lotion*).   Or starch, six drachms ; oxide of zinc, two drachms (*the dusting powder*).

In cases where there is a copious discharge *astringents* have to be employed, and of these lead in the form of Goulard's lotion, boracic acid, and borax, are the best. In the chronic scaly dry forms preparations of tar act beneficially, and these may be applied as ointments, such as: Liq. carbonis detergens, liq. plumbi subacetatis dilute (Goulard), of each one drachm; vaseline to one ounce—the ointment. Or a lotion such as the following: Liq. carbonis detergens, two drachms; glycerine, one drachm; rose water to four ounces—the lotion. The *internal* treatment of eczema is less important than the local, but attention must be paid to the condition of the stomach and bowels, and any irregularities corrected. *Diet* does not appear to exert much influence over the disease; but in acute cases stimulants should be avoided and meat taken in moderation, whilst milky foods, fruits and vegetables may be partaken of freely. Bloodless people should have iron, and this is best given in combination with a saline aperient such as the following: Epsom salts, one and a half ounces; sulphate of iron, sixteen grains; dilute sulphuric acid, one drachm; syrup of ginger, six drachms; water to eight ounces. A tablespoonful in water to be taken half-an-hour before breakfast.

To procure sleep, which is essential, fifteen to twenty grains of bromide of potash may be taken at bedtime, but it would be well to seek medical advice before resorting to the use of medicines producing sleep.

Herpes Zoster, Zona, or **Shingles,** is an inflammatory disease which appears usually on the trunk, but may also occur on the head or limbs. It is characterised by the appearance of groups of papules, which rapidly develop into vesicles, on an inflamed area of skin. The vesicles ultimately become purulent, and drying up form *scabs.* There may be only one patch of the disease, or many may appear either simultaneously or consecutively. A peculiarity of the disease is that its appearance is preceded by *neuralgic pains;* the patches themselves are painful, sometimes intensely so, and the neuralgic pains often persist long after the skin eruption has disappeared. Whilst usually classed under skin diseases, there can be no doubt that the eruption is only the local manifestation of changes which have taken place in the spinal cord, and which have set up inflammation in the nerves supplying the affected area. This explains the pain of a neuralgic character which is so characteristic of the disease, and also the fact that the patches of disease closely follow in their distribution the line of the nerves. Herpes attacks people of all ages, and occurs most frequently in spring and autumn. One attack affords protection against succeeding ones.

Treatment.—Shingles runs an acute course and ends in spontaneous recovery, and is only dangerous when it occurs in the region of the eye, and may lead to the destruction of that organ. Internally quinine in large doses does good. *Locally,* the inflamed patches must be protected from the irritation of the clothes by being covered with pads of cotton wadding. Dusting powders, such as that of oxide of zinc and starch, or an ointment containing the same substances, may be applied to relieve the pain. Alcoholic solutions applied as compresses afford great relief. The galvanic current applied by means of sponge electrodes to the patches and along the course of the nerves, or the high frequency electric spray or effleuve, undoubtedly relieves the pain and shortens the course of the disease.

An eruption somewhat similar in appearance to herpes sometimes appears during the course of acute diseases, such as pneumonia, enteric, and other fevers, or even in connection with digestive disorders, or common colds. Its usual site is on the upper lip, but it may also appear on the nose or the ears. A feeling of heat in the region is followed by a small cluster of vesicles or blebs, which rapidly become pustular, and terminate in the formation of a scab, which is cast off without a resulting scar. The eruption is unattended by neuralgic pain, and is very apt to recur. Treatment consists in applying some salve, such as zinc ointment, and in protecting the pustules from rupture.

SCALY ERUPTIONS

Psoriasis is a *chronic* inflammation of the skin, which most frequently attacks the outer surfaces of the *knees* and *elbows*, the *head*, and sometimes the *trunk*. It is characterised by the appearance of thickened patches or *plaques*, raised above the general surface, round or oval in shape, having a dark red base, and covered with silvery scales, which are intersected by deep fissures or furrows. If the scales are rubbed off, minute *bleeding points* appear on the exposed red surface.

The disease begins as a small red spot, and quickly becomes covered with silvery scales, which are firmly adherent. It spreads at the circumference, so that eventually patches the size of a crown piece, or a dinner plate, may form. The *extent* of the disease varies in different cases ; it may be confined to patches on the front of the knees or the back of the elbows, or there may be, in addition, affected areas on the head or on the trunk. Sometimes, again, the whole body is covered with patches of varying sizes, which may run into one another. The patches often heal in the centre, leaving an inflammatory ring, somewhat like ringworm of the body in appearance; but the latter disease does not produce such abundant scales, it does not tend to affect the knees and elbows, as is the case in psoriasis, and the ringworm fungus can always be found with the aid of a microscope.

Treatment.—Psoriasis occurs as a rule in otherwise healthy or robust individuals; it gives rise to no symptoms, except slight itching in the earlier stages, and it is not infectious. As the disease is apt to disappear spontaneously, only, however, to return again at some future time, it is not possible to feel sure that the line of treatment, whatever it may have been at the time, was the cause of the improvement. *Internally*, however, *arsenic* has an undoubted influence on it, but the drug must be taken with caution, and under the direction of a medical man. The best and simplest plan is to begin with two or three drops of Fowler's solution in a wineglass of water immediately after food, three times a day. The dose may be gradually increased to seven or, eight drops, but must be discontinued for three or four days whenever the eyes begin to feel hot and itchy. The remedy may be then recommenced in smaller doses.

Locally, the scales must be thoroughly removed in the first instance by using hot baths and soft soap, and then some preparation of *tar* must be applied. The best preparation is tar ointment, which may be rubbed well into the affected parts at night, and washed off in the morning; special clothes being worn, the staining of which would not matter. An ointment containing one or two drachms of the liquor carbonis detergens to the ounce of vaseline may be substituted for the tar ointment. Dr. Pye Smith recommends an ointment composed of half a drachm of pyrogallic acid in an ounce of benzoated lard. Some skins cannot tolerate tar in the smallest quantity, so that to begin with, it must be applied to only a small area, and the effect watched.

Ichthyosis, or "fish skin" disease, is a congenital disease, which often runs in families, and is characterised by a general coarseness of the skin, not confined to any one region, but more marked on the outer sides of the arms and legs. It is due to an over production, and retention on the surface of the skin, of epidermic cells, and this condition, accompanied as it is by an almost complete absence of sweat, and by the secretion of the sebaceous glands being thick, renders the surface of the skin dry and rough, and very difficult to keep clean. In extreme cases the skin resembles the rough bark of a tree, and sometimes becomes covered with horny excrescences, which have led the owners of such skins to exhibit themselves as "porcupine men."

Treatment.—As the disease is a hereditary one, due really to a special condition, there is no actual cure for it, but much can be done to relieve the condition by strict attention to *cleanliness*, frequent warm baths, rendered alkaline by the addition of bicarbonate of soda, the use of soft soap along with the bath, to remove the scales, and render the skin soft and pliant, and inunctions with oil or some simple ointment, to take the place of the thick secretion of the sebaceous glands.

DISEASES OF THE SEBACEOUS GLANDS

Comedones are minute nodules, unaccompanied by inflammation, the size of a pin head, and having a black point in their centre, which are commonly known as "blackheads," and are caused by a blocking of the glands with sebaceous material, the black points being due to dust. Their favourite seat is the forehead, chin, or cheeks, and they occur most frequently in young people who have muddy complexions, and who suffer from constipation and dyspepsia. They are also, however, produced by inattention to cleanliness.

Treatment.—The face should be washed frequently with hot water and soft soap, or it may be steamed by being held over a basin containing boiling water. After this the contents of each comedo should be squeezed out by pressing a watch-key against it; and finally an ointment such as the following may be used :—Precipitated sulphur, two drachms; glycerine, one drachm; lard, six drachms; this is to be rubbed well into the affected area. Or the following lotion may be applied : Precipitated sulphur, three ounces; glycerine, two drachms; alcohol, one ounce; lime water, two ounces; pure water, one ounce. Shake the bottle before using.

Acne Vulgaris or "Blackheads."—This is one of the commonest of skin diseases, occurring at puberty, and characterised by the appearance of pimples on the forehead, nose, cheeks, chin, chest, and upper part of the back. It is caused by the plugging of the glands with sebaceous material (comedones), the irritation thus produced leading to *inflammation*, which may go on to *suppuration*, so that the pimples very quickly "ripen" and matter can be squeezed out of them. When this is done the inflammation dies down and a minute scar remains, but fresh pimples appear in the neighbourhood, and this may go on for years leading to marked disfigurement. As has already been remarked, it occurs most frequently on the face, back, and chest, and the most frequent period of attack is *puberty*. It is at this period of life that the hair begins to develop, and the sebaceous glands which are connected with them are unusually active, and consequently prone to inflammation. The disease is more common amongst people with fair complexions. It is frequently associated with dyspepsia and constipation, also with womb disorders. Certain drugs, such as iodine and bromine, when taken internally, and tar, when applied externally, may produce it.

Treatment.—Attention must in the first instance be paid to the condition of the stomach and bowels. Dyspepsia, if present, is to be relieved by adopting a dietary from which all highly seasoned dishes—pickles, salted meats, &c.—and stimulants are rigorously excluded, and by administering small doses of rhubarb and soda before each meal. For the constipation, which is frequently present, a tablespoonful of the following mixture, taken in half a tumbler of water half-an-hour before breakfast, should be tried: Sulphate of magnesia, an ounce and a half; dilute sulphuric acid, two drachms; sulphate of iron, sixteen grains; and compound infusion of gentian to eight ources, each dose containing a small teaspoonful of Epsom salts. *Locally*, the treatment will follow much on the lines of that laid down for comedones, sulphur in some form or other being the most efficient remedy, but mercurial preparations are also distinctly advantageous.

Whatever the application may be, it must always be preceded by a preliminary softening of the skin and emptying of the inflamed glands of their contents. For this purpose the face must be *steamed* over a basin of boiling water, then washed with a piece of flannel and soap, to open the pores of the skin, and dried with a rough towel. After this the face should be gone over carefully, and every pimple that has a yellow head should be emptied of its contents by pressing a watch-key of a suitable size against it. The face should now be washed once more, and then a sulphur lotion such as that recommended for comedones should be applied and allowed to dry on it. This procedure should be carried out every night before going to bed. In the morning any pimples which may have ripened are to be emptied, and the face again washed and dried, and then some mercurial ointment, such as the oleate of mercury, of the strength of $2\frac{1}{2}$ to 5 per cent. in vaseline, or the white precipitate ointment applied to each pimple. The sulphur after having been used for some time may give rise to considerable irritation, and when this is the case, its use must be discontinued for a time, the following lotion being substituted: Calamine, four drachms; oxide of zinc, two drachms; glycerine, two drachms; rose water to eight ounces. Either the above or lead (Goulard) lotion should be applied at night, whilst in the morning zinc ointment may take the place of the mercurial. So soon, however, as the irritation has subsided, the use of the sulphur should be reverted to. By persevering with the above treatment, acne may be cured in a comparatively short time, whereas if left alone it may continue for years.

Acne Rosacea.—This is a chronic inflammatory affection of the skin of the face, but more especially of the nose and cheeks, which commences with hyperæmia or redness of the affected area, this redness being due to slowness of the circulation, and congestion, and consequently being accompanied by coldness rather than heat of the diseased part. This, the first stage of the complaint, begins insidiously and may last for an indefinite period of time, but sooner or later it passes into the second stage, when the general redness becomes more marked, and in addition *dilated blood-vessels* engorged with blood can be seen in the surface of the skin. Finally *acne pimples* appear on the red surface—hence the name *Acne Rosacea;* the sebaceous glands become greatly hypertrophied, and the entire skin of the nose becomes thick and lobulated, its colour being a deep red or almost purple.

Causes.—The disease is met with most frequently in middle-aged men, but women who have reached the " change of life " are also liable to suffer from it in its earlier manifestations. Womb disorders are a common cause of the disease in women. It may also be due sometimes to indigestion, and there are many cases for which no cause can be discovered; but spirituous liquors taken habitually and to excess are undoubtedly a fruitful source of the complaint.

Treatment.—Constitutional treatment will consist in attacking the cause, if this can be discovered. *Locally,* in the earlier stages, sulphur, either in the form of ointment or a lotion as prescribed for common acne, affords the best hope of relief, whilst in the later stages the aid of the surgeon must be called in. By scarifying the engorged blood-vessels, or by even scraping away the hypertrophied tissue, he may do much to relieve the patient and improve his personal appearance.

DISEASES OF THE HAIR FOLLICLES AND SWEAT GLANDS

Sycosis (so named by the ancients from its resemblance to the inside of a ripe fig) is a chronic disease which affects the hair sacs of the chin, and those of the upper lip and cheeks. It is characterised by the appearance of more or less numerous pimples, which become pustular, and may be grouped together to form rounded patches. Each pimple has a hair projecting through its centre. The surrounding skin is red and inflamed, and there is a sensation of severe burning, or even of pain. All the pimples may come out simultaneously, or they may appear in successive crops. This disease must be distinguished from

DISEASES OF THE SKIN

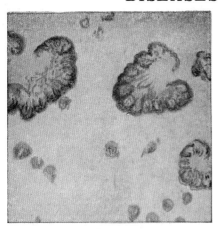

PSORIASIS.

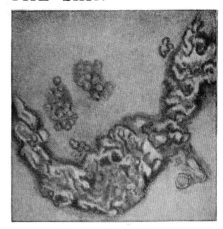

SHINGLES—HERPES ZOSTER.

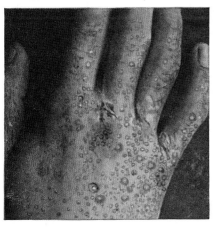

SCABIES OR ITCH.

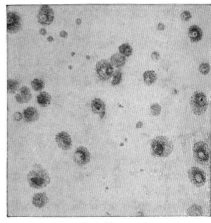

ACNE VULGARIS.

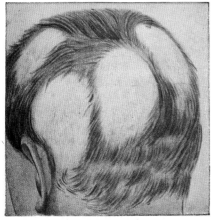

BALD SPOTS—ALOPECIA.

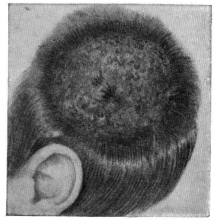

RINGWORM OF SCALP.

FROM DRAWINGS BY EDWARD BURNET, B.A. (Lond.).

ringworm affecting the same regions, which it closely resembles. · In the latter complaint, however, the hairs themselves are affected, becoming brittle, so that they break off short and loose, and can be easily extracted.

Treatment.—Local treatment alone is of any advantage in this disease, and the first step in this must always be the *clipping* as short as possible of the hair of the affected area; after this any scabs which have formed must be removed by applying poultices. The medicinal treatment will depend upon the stage of the disease. In acute cases where there is much surrounding inflammation with heat and burning, soothing applications such as zinc ointment must be made, whilst, when the affection has reached a more chronic stage, stimulating ointments or lotions containing sulphur must be applied. Sometimes the individual hairs have to be extracted, a few being taken at a time, until the whole area is cleared. Recently the X-rays have been employed in the treatment of the disease, but with varying results. Whatever the treatment, the disease almost invariably runs a chronic course, resulting in permanent destruction of the hairs, and much disfigurement.

Furunculus or Boil.—Though not invariably the case, this troublesome affection frequently has its starting-point in an inflammation of a hair sac. This inflammation leads to the death of a portion of the deep tissue of the skin, and it is nature's endeavours to get rid of this dead portion, slough, or "core" which gives rise to the succeeding train of symptoms. A boil begins as a pimple, which rapidly develops a white head, and is exceedingly painful. The pimple soon becomes surrounded by an inflammatory ring, the deeper structures of the skin become distended with fluid, which pushes up the pimple and makes it look much larger, and gives rise to an intense throbbing pain. When the boil is ripe it bursts and the "core" is expelled, this process sometimes taking two or three days, and a hole remains, which, gradually closing, leaves a scar. It is seldom that only one boil appears, there being as a rule a succession of them, which from the want of rest they occasion may seriously affect the patient's health. Boils appear most frequently on the back, and on the back of the neck and buttocks.

Treatment.—The aim of this should be to relieve the pain, and to protect the neighbouring skin from infection. Poultices relieve pain, but they also undoubtedly help to infect the surrounding skin, and for this reason should be avoided as far as possible. Cold water dressings will greatly relieve the throbbing pain, so will *lead lotion* painted over the red inflammatory ring round the boil, whilst lint soaked in carbolic oil (one to ten) and applied to the boil itself will not only relieve the pain, but, being an antiseptic dressing, will render harmless the matter which will come from the boil when it bursts, and so prevent the spread of infection. Iron tonics are called for when the attack has been prolonged, and the patient's health has suffered in consequence.

Bromidrosis.—This is an affection of the sweat glands in which the sweat has a very disagreeable odour. The disease may affect the whole body, or be confined to certain regions. The *feet* are most frequently affected, the armpits coming next in frequency. Women are more frequently troubled with the complaint than men. The horrible odour is due really to the decomposition of the fatty secretion of the skin which mixes with the sweat.

Treatment.—The results of treatment are often most disappointing, but when the disease affects the feet, improvement frequently follows the washing of them, at least twice a day, in a solution of permanganate of potash, three grains to the ounce, or in a saturated solution of boracic acid. A dusting powder such as the following: Salicylic acid, one drachm; starch, $2\frac{1}{2}$ drachms; talc, $3\frac{1}{2}$ ounces—should be freely dusted over the feet after they have been washed and dried, some of the powder being put into the stockings at the same time, and these should be changed every time the feet are washed; that is to say, at least twice a day. It has been recommended to wear cork soles which have been soaked in a saturated solution of boracic acid and then dried.

HYPERTROPHIES AND ATROPHIES OF THE SKIN

Corns are horny formations generally found on the toes, and more especially the little one. They are due to a down growth of the horny layer of the skin, which causes atrophy of the papillæ, and at the same time sets up a chronic inflammation, which gives rise to a thickened ring surrounding the conical plug. Between the toes, where the skin is generally moist with perspiration, the horny plug is soft and spongy, and only the round thickened ring is evident—this constitutes the "soft corn." As a result of the pressure caused by wearing a high-heeled, narrow-toed boot, a bag of fluid, called a cyst or bursa, forms under the corn, and this constitutes a "*bunion*," such as is seen frequently on the joint of the big toe.

Corns are produced by the irritation set up by the pressure resulting from walking in high-heeled, narrow-toed shoes. They are painful on pressure, but in addition they give rise to pain of a shooting character independent of outside irritation. Sometimes abscesses form under the corns, and then the pain is excruciating.

Treatment.—"Prevention is better than cure," and children, who frequently suffer from what may be the beginning of a lifelong annoyance, should always wear broad-soled boots—straight on the inner side, and curved to the shape of the foot on the outer—with low heels. An outline of the foot should be taken on paper whilst the patient is *standing*, and the boots built on the same lines. In advanced cases of bunions where there is much deformity, stockings should be made like gloves, with receptacles for each toe, and a short piece of leather should be let into the boot to press the big toe away from the others. Corns should be softened before being picked out with a sharp pocket-knife, and this is best done by soaking the foot in very hot water for some considerable time, or by putting on a bread and milk poultice at bedtime, and leaving it on all night. In the morning, after the corn has been removed, a 2 per cent. ointment of salicylic acid in vaseline should be smeared over the part. Soft corns may be touched with a solid stick of nitrate of silver, or covered over with flexible collodion. Tender feet should be bathed night and morning in a strong solution of salt in water, and thick woollen socks should be worn.

Warts are an overgrowth of the *papillæ* of the skin, and are very common in children. They may be hard or soft, and form raised rounded lumps, or lie flat on the surface of the skin. The common wart met with on the hands, and more especially the fingers and backs of the hands, is an elevated growth varying in size from a pin head to a split pea. Its surface is rough and covered with minute elevations. There may be only one, or several grouped together. Another variety occurs in old people, especially on the back; it is broad and flat, and almost black in colour.

Treatment.—The best plan is to cut off the wart with a pair of curved scissors, and touch the wound with a caustic such as nitrate of silver; or nitric acid or glacial acetic acid may be applied to the wart itself, care being taken to protect the surrounding skin by smearing it with vaseline or soft wax.

Alopecia or Baldness.—This ailment, due to *atrophy* or wasting of the hair bulbs, with a resulting falling out of the hair, is frequently *hereditary*. Men are more frequently affected than women —complete baldness being rare in the latter sex. Partial baldness is often accompanied by *dandriff* or "scurf," and when this is the case, the cure of the dandriff will generally restore the hair. It is in these cases alone that there is any hope of being able to arrest the process. For dandriff the one or other of the following washes may be tried, and should be rubbed into the roots of the hair at bedtime after the head has been washed with soap and soda and all the scurf removed:

Castor oil, two drachms; carbolic acid, pure, twenty grains; alcohol, two ounces. Another formula is: Tincture of cantharides, three drachms; tincture of capsicum, three drachms; castor oil, two drachms; alcohol, two ounces; spirit of rosemary, one ounce. The hair-wash (Duhring).

Parasitical diseases of the skin, due to the presence of insects and fungi, will be found treated of in the section dealing with "Parasites," page 152.

SECTION V

DISEASES OF THE KIDNEYS

Acute Bright's Disease.—This is the name given to an *acute inflammation* of the kidneys. The disease—also known as *acute nephritis*—is due to the action of *cold* and of certain *poisons* on the kidneys. The chief *causes* are :—

1. Exposure to *cold*, and more especially after a drinking bout.

2. The poison of certain *fevers*, particularly *scarlet fever*.

3. Certain *drugs* such as *turpentine, cantharides*, and *carbolic acid* act as poisons, giving rise to congestion of the kidneys, which may pass into inflammation.

4. *Pregnancy*.

Symptoms.—The onset of the disease may be sudden, and this is usually the case in attacks which are due to exposure to cold. In *children* the disease is very frequently ushered in by *convulsions*. When the disease appears during the course of one or other of the *fevers*, the commencement is usually less abrupt, and slight *puffiness* or *dropsy* of the face or *ankles* may be the first indication of its presence. The patient usually complains of *headache*, and, in the case of adults, of feeling *chilly*, the tongue is furred, the skin dry, the pulse hard and quick; and the temperature, which is never very high, ranges from 100° to 103° F. There is pain in the back, and there may be nausea and vomiting. The changes in the *urine*, however, are the most characteristic indications of the disease. Its *quantity* is greatly diminished—in some cases indeed it may be entirely *suppressed*. The *specific gravity* is high, ranging from 1.025 to 1.030.

The *colour* is always high, and the urine may have merely the appearance of "smokiness" or be of a deep porter colour. Large quantities of *albumen* are present, whilst the amount of *urea* is diminished. There is a heavy *deposit*, which consists of *blood* and *tube casts*. Finally, the patient shows signs of *dropsy*, which varies in intensity, and he becomes pale and *anæmic*.

As has already been pointed out, the disease is often very insidious in its onset, some of the most severe forms being ushered in only by slight puffiness of the ankles; but in *children*, and when it occurs during the course of *pregnancy*, an alarming series of *convulsions* may be the first indication of its presence. Bright's disease, as the result of exposure to cold, may be recovered from very quickly; but when it follows scarlet fever it never lasts less than a month, often much longer. The *risks* of the disease are the possibility of *uræmic poisoning*, of effusion of fluid into the *pleura* (or lining membrane of the chest) and *pericardium* (or heart sac).

Treatment.—The lines to follow in treating a case of acute Bright's disease are :—

1. To give the kidneys *rest*, by promoting the action of the *skin* and *bowels*.

2. To diminish the congestion of the kidneys by applying warm applications locally, and thus drawing the blood to the *surface* of the body.

The patient must be clothed in flannel and placed in bed between blankets, and kept there until such time as all the symptoms have disappeared.

The *diet* should consist almost exclusively of *milk*, and as this is often difficult of digestion, it may be diluted with water in the proportion of two parts of milk to one of hot water. The milk should always be drunk slowly in sips, and not in large draughts. Instead of water, barley-water or thin oatmeal gruel may be used to dilute the milk. Small quantities of *chicken broth* may be given occasionally. As it is desirable to keep the kidneys well washed out, the patient should be allowed to drink water freely, either pure or added to the milk. As the urine is very *acid*, it is an advantage to administer an alkali to lessen this as far as possible; and a simple way of doing this is to add a powder containing five grains each of bicarbonate of soda and citrate of potash to each glass of milk that is taken. Whey and alkaline mineral waters may be partaken of freely.

To promote the action of the skin the patient should have frequent *hot baths*, if the bath can be brought to the side of the bed. To begin with, the temperature of the water should be 100° F.; after the patient has been placed in it more hot water should be added, till it reaches 104° F. The patient should remain in the bath for from thirty to sixty minutes. He should then be rubbed dry, rolled in a warm sheet, and then in warm blankets for two or three hours to encourage the perspiration. When the hot bath cannot be given conveniently, the *hot air* or *hot vapour* bath may be substituted in the case of adults. The appliances necessary for giving these can be obtained at any instrument maker's, but may be improvised with a spirit-lamp and a tin funnel having a long tube bent at a right angle attached to it. The funnel is placed over the lamp, which stands at the foot of the bed, and the tube passes under the bedclothes, which are well tucked in at the patient's neck; the hot air is thus carried to the patient. The vapour from a bronchitis kettle may in the same way be utilised for giving a vapour bath. In the case of *children* the *wet pack* is more suitable for procuring perspiration. A blanket is wrung out of very hot water, the child is quickly rolled in this, then in a dry warm blanket, and lastly in a waterproof sheet. Profuse sweating quickly follows as a rule. The child remains in the pack for an hour, and is then removed, rubbed dry, and placed between blankets. This should be repeated every day. Whilst in the pack the patient should drink freely of barley-water or whey. It is sometimes advantageous to give a dose of the following diaphoretic mixture to encourage further the action of the skin : Sal volatile, one drachm; sweet spirit of nitre, half a drachm; mindererus spirits (solution of acetate of ammonia), four drachms; and camphor water to $1\frac{1}{2}$ ounce. The above is the dose for an adult; it may be repeated two or three times a day.

Saline purgatives to promote free action of the bowels, and thus further to relieve the kidneys, should be given every morning. For adults two or three drachms of Epsom salts dissolved in an ounce or two of water may be given early in the morning, whilst for children an ounce or two of fluid magnesia the first thing in the morning is generally sufficient. To relieve the congestion of the kidneys, by drawing the blood away from them to the surface of the body, *warm poultices* applied across the loins are both soothing and efficient, whilst in adults *dry cupping* is also useful.

In cases which begin with *suppression* of urine, hot baths, followed by the wet pack, hot poultices, free purgation, and plenty of barley-water or whey to drink, should constitute the treatment.

Vomiting is sometimes a distressing symptom, which, however, should not be arrested immediately, as it is a means by which certain irritating substances may be removed; but should it persist, a *mustard plaster* should be applied to the pit of the stomach, and the patient be given *ice* to suck, and also be encouraged to swallow pieces of it. Symptoms of *uræmic poisoning*, such as *headache, drowsiness*, or *convulsions*, must be treated by energetic purging and the wet pack, aided by the following mixture in the case of *children* : Mindererus spirits (solution of the acetate of ammonia), thirty drops; sweet spirit of nitre, twenty drops; benzoate of ammonia, five grains; glycerine, twenty drops; and water to an ounce and a half. This dose to be given to a child of five years every four hours.

During *convalescence* great care must be taken to avoid *chills*. No animal food is to be given till the urine is free from albumen; but the patient may partake of ripe and cooked fruit, and fresh vegetables. A change to a warm climate is advantageous.

Chronic Bright's Disease.—Two varieties of this disease are recognised. The one usually a sequel to an acute attack, though it may also begin insidiously, is characterised by *dropsy* as its most prominent symptom, and gives rise to what is known anatomically as the *large white kidney*. The other always begins *insidiously*, the characteristic symptoms being due to changes in the *heart* and *blood-vessels*, dropsy is *not* a prominent symptom, and the kidney is known anatomically as the *contracted* or *gouty kidney*.

When that form of the disease which is accompanied by the *large white kidney* is a sequel to an attack of acute Bright's disease, the symptoms are those of the acute affection, but only in a modified form. When, however, it begins insidiously, the first symptoms may be only those which accompany dyspepsia; following these there is marked *anæmia* and *weakness*, the face is pale, the complexion pasty, the eyelids are puffy on waking in the morning, whilst the ankles and feet become swollen towards evening. The urine is scanty, turbid, owing to presence of urates, and smoky. The deposit contains tube casts and blood corpuscles; albumen is present in large quantity. The dropsy which began with slight puffiness of the eyelids and swelling of the ankles becomes general, and is very obstinate, this constituting the most prominent symptoms of the disease. Vomiting and diarrhœa are frequent complications, the symptoms pointing to uræmic poisoning, while headache and restlessness often supervene. Recovery from the disease is very rare, more especially if it has lasted for over a year, and death is usually due to dropsy of the lungs or to uræmic poisoning.

Treatment.—The *treatment* of this form of the disease is practically the same as that of the acute disease. *Milk* should form the chief article of diet, those patients doing best who are kept on an *absolute milk* diet, if they can tolerate it. *Skim milk* agrees with some patients better than ordinary milk, and the digestibility of the latter is often increased by diluting it with a third part of water, and adding twenty grains of salt to each pint of the mixture. For the *dropsy*, hot baths and wet packs afford the best chances for relief. Saline purgatives should be administered at regular intervals to keep the bowels acting freely; the clothing should be warm, flannel being worn next the skin in all weathers. A change to, or a permanent residence in a warmer climate than that of the British Isles, is always beneficial.

The form of chronic Bright's disease, which gives rise to the *contracted kidney*, is always insidious in its onset, and no satisfactory cause can be given for it. It is chronic from the very beginning, and consists in a slow degeneration of the kidney substance, so that that organ grows old before its time. The most common age for its onset is between forty and sixty years, and males are affected twice as frequently as females. It generally occurs in men who have worked hard, eaten too much, and drunk too freely of alcohol. Sometimes, however, it is hereditary, and it may also be the result of *gout* or *lead poisoning*.

Symptoms.—These are sometimes latent, and people having the disease in an advanced form may be quite unaware of its presence; leading active lives, the sudden onset of serious or even fatal complications being the first indication of its presence. In other cases the general health suffers, the patient complains of tiredness, he is sleepless, and has to get up frequently during the night to pass his water. He complains of failing vision and headache. He suffers from indigestion and thirst, and is breathless. The urine is increased in quantity, is of a pale colour, and low specific gravity. Albumen is present in very small quantity, and may be absent from the early morning specimen during the earlier stages of the disease, but later, when the heart begins to fail, it may be present in large amount. The walls of the arteries become thickened, so that they can be easily felt, and the *pulse* is hard. The heart becomes enlarged from the thickening of its walls in the early stages of the disease, but as the muscle loses tone, it becomes dilated. The patient is subject to attacks of oppressed breathing at night, and is often found sitting up in bed and gasping for breath. The nervous system suffers, so that the patient complains of headache, has frequent neuralgic attacks, and is prone to die from apoplexy, or a "shock" as it is popularly termed; he may also suffer from dizziness, and ringing in the ears, and may become suddenly blind. Chronic indigestion with loss of appetite is a common accompaniment of the disease, and sometimes there are severe attacks of vomiting, and obstinate diarrhœa.

As has already been pointed out, dropsy is very rarely present, except towards the end of the disease, when the heart is beginning to fail, and when there may be slight puffiness of the eyelids and ankles. Bleeding from the nose is very common, and frequently the case is abruptly terminated by the rupture of a blood-vessel in the brain, a condition termed apoplexy.

Whilst this form of chronic Bright's disease is incurable—that is to say, there is no possibility of restoring the kidneys, heart, and blood-vessels to their normal condition—it is not a rapidly fatal complaint; and provided it be discovered at an early stage, and care be taken in its management, there is no reason why a man may not live an active life for many years.

Treatment.—In the early stages of the disease the most important indication is to throw as little strain as possible on the kidneys, heart, and arteries ; and to carry this treatment out the patient must lead a quiet life, free from mental worry and excitement or great bodily exertion. He must take regular, gentle exercise, keep the bowels acting regularly with the help, if necessary, of a dose of Carlsbad salts in the early morning. The activity of the *skin* must be maintained by daily tepid baths, and the kidneys must be flushed out by drinking freely of distilled water, or such mineral waters as Vichy and Apollinaris. Alcohol must be absolutely prohibited, though tea and coffee in moderation may be allowed. The *diet* should be nourishing but light, and meat should be taken only once a day and in small quantity. Farinaceous foods, fresh vegetables, ripe fruit, milk, cream, and butter should form the staple articles of diet.

Beyond the mild purgatives required to keep the bowels active, medicines are not called for in the early stages of the disease, but residence abroad during the winter months, in a warm climate such as that of Madeira or the West Indies, is of distinct advantage.

In the *later stages* of the disease, when the arteries become very much thickened and the pulse is very hard, the patient should be sweated by means of the *hot-air bath*, his bowels should be kept freely open, and the diet should be very light. For the bloodlessness or anæmia, which is also a marked symptom of this stage, large doses of iron in the form of steel drops, 20 to 30 drops three times a day, is to be administered. When the pulse becomes rapid, the urine scanty and loaded with albumen, when dropsy makes its appearance, and the patient suffers from shortness of breath, the heart has begun to fail and needs some support. The best drug is tincture of digitalis, which should be given in ten-drop doses three times a day, the bowels at the same time being freely acted upon with doses of Epsom salts.

Headache, restlessness, wandering of the mind, palpitation, and heavy foul breath, are symptoms of uræmic poisoning, and should be treated with hot baths and saline purges. If convulsions supervene, the patient should be sweated freely, and the fits controlled by inhalations of chloroform.

Uræmia.—Frequent mention has been made in the preceding pages of *uræmic* symptoms supervening in the course of an attack of Bright's disease, and it becomes necessary to explain shortly what the expression means. Uræmia is a form of *blood-poisoning* which is due to the accumulation in the blood of poisonous substances formed by the body, which substances the kidneys excrete and get rid of when they are healthy, but are unable to do so when diseased. The presence of these poisons in the blood gives rise to the following *symptoms* :—

1. *Convulsions.*—These may come on suddenly and be the first indication of the presence of the disease, or they may be preceded by headache and restlessness. The convulsions are exactly the same in appearance as epileptic fits, and often follow each other at short intervals of time, the patient being unconscious during the whole period of the attack. *Blindness*, lasting for some days, sometimes follows the fits.

2. *Unconsciousness* or *coma*, which is always present during the convulsive seizures, may also come on independently of fits, the patient as a rule complaining of headache, becoming listless, and gradually passing into a condition of complete unconsciousness.

3. *Headache.*—This is generally situated at the back of the head, and extends down the neck.

4. *Difficulty of breathing* or *dyspnœa* usually attacks the patient at night, and gives one the impression that he is suffering from an attack of *asthma*. One form of dyspnœa is known as Cheyne-Stokes' breathing, and consists in a peculiar alteration in the *rhythm* of breathing, there being pauses at intervals of a minute or so during which the respiration entirely ceases. These pauses are followed by a period during which the breathing gradually returns—shallow at first then growing deeper and deeper; this period is followed by a third during which the respiration gradually becomes shallower till it entirely ceases for a short time, and then begins again. Cheyne-Stokes' breathing is present in many cases of brain and heart disease as well as in uræmia, and is generally the immediate precursor of death.

5. *Vomiting* and *diarrhœa* are often present, either together or independently of each other.

6. Many patients suffering from uræmia become *insane*, and are the victims of delusions and melancholia.

The *treatment* of this condition consists, as has already been mentioned, in endeavouring to induce the bowels and skin to eliminate the poison which the kidneys are unable to cope with, by free purgation, and by hot baths to encourage copious sweating.

Diabetes.—See vol. i p. 140 (General Diseases).

Pyelitis, or inflammation of the *pelvis* of the kidney (page 55), is almost always due to the presence of *bacteria*, which may be carried to the kidneys by the blood. The inflammation may also spread upwards to the kidney from the *bladder*, and cause *cystitis*, while lastly this ailment may be due to the presence of *stone* in the kidney.

Symptoms.—In the early stages of the disease the patient suffers from pain in the small of the back, this pain being increased when pressure is applied to the affected side ; he also suffers from repeated attacks of feverishness, and shivering fits. When the disease becomes established pus or " matter " appears in the urine, the quantity varying from day to day, the urine being sometimes quite clear whilst at other times there seems to have been a sudden discharge of pus in considerable quantity, the discharge being preceded by a rise in the temperature and shivering fits. As a result of the purulent discharge the patient wastes, and becomes anæmic.

Pyelitis sometimes attacks *infants*, and more especially girls, the illness being ushered in by a sudden rise of temperature and fits of shivering, the child is also very restless. No cause can be discovered to account for the symptoms until the urine is examined, when pus is found to be present.

Treatment.—The diet should be simple, and consist almost entirely of milk. As the urine is almost invariably over *acid*, alkalies such as citrate of potash should be given freely, to render it neutral, and this line of treatment is particularly successful in cases occurring during infancy. The alkaline mineral waters should be drunk freely, and a drug (*urotropin*) may be tried.

Stone in the Kidney.—When the solid substances, uric acid, oxalate of lime, and phosphates, are present in such large quantities that the urine cannot hold them in solution, they may be expelled in the urine in the form of *gravel* or sand, but some of the crystals may from time to time be deposited in the pelvis of the kidney and form concretions or *stones*, varying in size from a small pea to a bean or even large enough to form a complete mould of the pelvis of the kidney.

Symptoms.—When the stone remains *stationary* in the pelvis of the kidney the symptoms it gives rise to are : 1. *Pain* of a dull aching character situated in the small of the back, and usually on the affected side, though sometimes it is on the sound side. 2. *Hæmaturia*, or blood in the urine, the quantity being increased after exertion, and diminished after a period of rest. 3. Symptoms of *Pyelitis*, namely recurring attacks of high fever, shivering fits, and the appearance of *pus* or " matter" in the urine.

When, however, the stone begins to travel and enters the *ureter* or tube leading from the kidney to the bladder, it gives rise to the most agonising pain, starting on the affected side, and shooting down to the inner side of the thigh. The pain may be accompanied by nausea and vomiting, and be so severe as to produce a condition of collapse. The face is bathed in perspiration, and the pulse is feeble. The patient makes his water frequently, and the urine contains blood. If, when a stone is passing down one ureter, and the other kidney be diseased, complete suppression of urine may result, and the patient may die from uræmia. To these symptoms has been given the name of " renal colic."

Treatment.—For the colic, hot baths, hot poultices, and hot fomentations to the small of the back, afford great relief. The patient should be encouraged to drink warm demulcent drinks such as barley-water, and it may be necessary to inject morphia under the skin, or to give inhalations of chloroform for the relief of the excruciating pain. When the symptoms cease the patient should lead a quiet life, avoiding all hurry or sudden exertion, and he should aim at passing large quantities of urine of an alkaline reaction, by drinking water freely, and also by partaking of mineral waters such as those of Vichy and Contrexeville.

Medicinally he may take half a drachm of citrate of potash in a tumbler of water every three hours, or five grains of Piperazine in water three times a day. The diet should be simple, and moderate in amount.

Tumours of the Kidney.—These may be malignant or benign. The malignant tumours grow rapidly, and sometimes reach an enormous size, especially in children.

The symptoms are pain in the back, blood in the urine, great wasting, and the presence of a tumour, which can easily be felt.

Treatment.—Removal of the growth at an early stage of its existence may be attempted, but the recoveries are very few.

THE EXAMINATION OF THE URINE

The urine is the secretion of the kidneys, and a knowledge of the changes which it undergoes as a result of disease is of the utmost importance. Whilst it is only possible in the limited space allotted to the subject here to describe these changes which are more frequently met with, and to mention the tests which can be carried out without the aid of elaborate apparatus, even this information will, it is hoped, prove of service to those who, in times of illness, cannot obtain the services of a physician.   Such information may enable them to take observations of the greatest value to the medical adviser, who may be able to see his patient only at long intervals.   A systematic examination of the urine consists in noting its *naked eye* appearances, its *chemical reactions,* and its appearance under the *microscope.*   The subject may therefore be treated under these three heads.

1. The Naked Eye Examination—Quantity.—Whilst the quantity of urine varies with the amount of fluid drunk, the amount of perspiration, and the condition of the bowels, the average amount passed in twenty-four hours may be taken to be from fifty to seventy ounces.   The quantity varies during different periods of the day, being abundant during the day and early part of the evening, diminished during the later part of the evening, and scanty during sleep. To estimate the quantity passed, a period of twenty-four hours should be taken, beginning by preference at eight o'clock of one morning, and collecting all that is passed till the same hour on the following morning, measuring the quantity passed each time in a large measure glass. The urine is *diminished* in febrile diseases, in all diseases accompanied by profuse perspiration, in acute Bright's disease of the kidneys, and whenever diarrhœa is present.   It is *increased* in diabetes, in certain forms of hysteria, and in some forms of chronic Bright's disease of the kidneys.   Drugs such as digitalis, calomel, and salicylate of soda increase the flow of urine.

Specific Gravity or Density.—This represents the amount of *solid matter* present in solution in the urine, and varies in health in inverse proportion to the quantity ; the larger the quantity the lower the specific gravity, and *vice versa.*   Taking fifty to seventy ounces as the average quantity passed in twenty-four hours, the specific gravity ranges from 1.017 to 1.020, water being taken at 1.000.   To estimate the specific gravity an instrument called an *urinometer* must be used ; this consists of a glass bulb, weighted at one end with mercury, while from the other end projects a stem graduated from 1.000 to 1.050.   The urinometer is allowed to float in the urine, taking care that it does not touch the sides of the vessel, which should be tall and cylindrical ; and when it comes to rest, the line at which the level of the fluid cuts the stem is read off, the figures giving the specific gravity of the fluid.   In disease, as in health, the rule is for the specific gravity to be in inverse ratio to the quantity, and any marked deviation from this rule is of serious import.   Thus in *Diabetes mellitus* a large quantity of urine of *high* specific gravity—due to the amount of sugar present—is passed ; and in diseases of the kidneys where the quantity of urine is diminished, serious complications are often heralded by a *fall* in the specific gravity.

Colour.—The colour of the urine depends upon the amount of *pigment*, and also upon the degree of concentration. It varies from pale yellow to dark brown even in health. As a rule, the scantier the urine passed the darker is its colour. Certain *drugs* affect the colour of urine. Rhubarb and senna make it brown; carbolic acid in the system turns it black, especially after it has stood awhile. Quinine and antipyrin darken the urine, and santonin imparts a bright yellow colour to it. Bile gives the urine a greenish tint, whilst a large quantity of blood turns it ruby red. In diabetes, anæmia, and hysteria, the urine is pale in colour. In febrile complaints it is darker in colour owing to concentration.

Reaction.—Healthy urine has ordinarily an *acid reaction*, but is subject to variations. Thus it is much less acid, or even alkaline after a full meal. In disease the urine is acid in diabetes, and in febrile conditions, especially in acute rheumatism. It is alkaline in anæmia. In chronic inflammation of the bladder, especially after a dirty catheter has been used, putrefactive changes are set up in the urine, and it becomes alkaline owing to the presence of ammonia. The best way to test the reaction of urine is to dip little pieces of blue and red litmus paper—which can be bought from any chemist—into it. Acid urine turns *blue litmus* paper *red*, alkaline urine turns *red litmus* paper *blue*.

Odour.—Healthy urine when fresh has an odour peculiar to itself, but somewhat resembling hay. When turpentine is administered internally, or even inhaled, it imparts an odour of sweet violets to the urine. When urine decomposes fumes of ammonia are given off; these can be easily recognised. Diabetic urine has a faint aromatic odour.

Frequency.—When the quantity secreted by the kidneys is large, it is voided more frequently, as in diabetes. Without there being any increase in the total quantity, the urine is voided frequently in cases of inflammation of the bladder, and stone in the bladder and kidney. When the prostate gland is enlarged the urine is voided very frequently *during the night*.

THE CHEMICAL EXAMINATION OF THE URINE

Having noted the quantity, colour, and specific gravity and reaction of the urine, it now becomes necessary to apply certain *chemical* tests to it; to discover the nature of the *solid* substances which are present in it *in solution*, some of these substances being present *normally*, whilst others are the result of disease. and may be termed *abnormal*. To carry out these tests the following apparatus and reagents will be required. A spirit lamp, some test tubes, a tall conical glass in which to collect the urine, filter papers, methylated spirit for the lamp, nitric acid, acetic acid, picric acid, liquor potassæ, Pavy's solution, tincture of guaiacum, ozoine ether. The reagents should be kept in small stoppered bottles, with the name of the reagent clearly marked on them.

Urea.—The *normal* solid constituents of urine are divided into organic and inorganic substances; the chief organic materials present are *urea* and *uric acid*, the inorganic being chlorides, phosphates, and sulphates. Urea is the most important of the normal constituents of urine; it constitutes about one-half of all the solids in the urine excreted every day. It is due to the decomposition of the nitrogenous food in the tissues of the body, and also in some degree to the waste which goes on in the tissues themselves. The excretion of urea is affected by disease. Thus, it is greatly *increased* in *diabetes*, and in all diseases accompanied by an elevation of temperature, whilst it is *diminished* in all forms of diseases of the kidney. The estimation of the amount of urea present in disease is of great importance; but the methods employed are too complicated for unskilled persons to carry out, and are therefore not mentioned here.

Uric Acid.—This organic substance is only present in normal urine in combination with potassium, sodium, ammonium, calcium, or magnesium, forming *urates*. These urates are only soluble in warm urine, so that as the latter cools they are thrown down in the form of a deposit, which quickly disappears if the urine be once more heated. From ten to fifteen grains of uric acid are excreted in twenty-four hours, the amount varying with that of urea, and always being about $\frac{1}{50}$ of the latter. The excretion of uric acid is increased in diseases of the liver, in gastric catarrh, and in acute rheumatism. It is diminished during an acute attack of gout.

Of the *inorganic* constituents of normal urine, chlorine is present in combination with potassium, sodium, and ammonium to form *chlorides*. In disease the most important change is that which occurs in pneumonia, where the excretion of these salts is greatly *diminished*. The *phosphates* present in normal urine are partly derived from the food, but to some extent also from the breaking down of tissues of the body containing phosphorus, such as nerve tissue. *Test.*—Heat a small quantity of urine in a test tube. If phosphates are present, a *white flocculent precipitate* is thrown down, which quickly disappears on the addition of a few drops of *acetic acid*. The phosphates are *increased* in cases of constipation, in febrile complaints, and in chronic nervous diseases.

Sulphuric acid is present in normal urine in the form of *sulphates,* and is derived from the breaking down of albumen which is contained in the food ; this being so, the quantity varies with that of urea and uric acid. The *abnormal* constituents of urine, or those which are present to an appreciable extent only as a result of disease, are *albumen, blood, bile,* and *sugar.*

Albumen.—This substance is never found in any appreciable quantity in healthy urine ; its presence, therefore, as an indication of disease is of the greatest importance. The commonest causes of albumen in the urine are the different varieties of *Bright's disease* of the kidneys ; and the greatest amount is present when the patient suffers from the inflammatory form of that disease, the urine sometimes becoming solid on heating. Diseases of the heart, when they give rise to an alteration in the circulation of the blood in the kidneys, are another cause of albumen in the urine. It frequently appears in the course of *febrile* complaints ; and lastly, it may appear in the urine of weakly, anæmic people, who have no heart, kidney, or feverish complaint.

It must be noted here that though kidney diseases are the commonest causes of albumen appearing in the urine, its presence is not an absolute proof of the presence of kidney trouble ; it is only a link—though an important one—in a chain of evidence.

Tests.—If the urine be not clear it must be carefully filtered before being tested.

1. *Heat and Nitric Acid Test.*—Heat a small quantity of urine in a test tube over a spirit lamp ; as the fluid approaches the boiling point a white flocculent precipitate is thrown down ; this may be either *phosphates* or *albumen.* Add a *few drops* of nitric acid. The precipitate *disappears* if it is due to phosphates ; it *persists* if composed of albumen.

2. *Cold Nitric Acid Test.*—Pour some nitric acid into a test tube. Hold the tube at an angle and gently pour in some urine, so that when the tube is held erect the urine floats on the surface of the nitric acid. If albumen be present a *cloudiness* will form at the line where the two fluids meet.

3. *Picric Acid Test.*—Use picric acid instead of nitric acid, and pour in the urine as in the last test ; if a cloud is formed, slightly heat the tube. If the cloud remains, albumen is present.

Blood.—Blood which appears in the urine may come from any part of the urinary system, and not from the kidneys alone. Its presence in small quantity is indicated by a peculiar *smoky* appearance of the urine ; whilst if present to any great extent it imparts a colour of raw meat juice or even a dark ruby red to the urine. The blood may be present as such in the urine (Hæmaturia), or only the colouring matter may be found (Hæmoglobin urea). The latter condition is apt to arise in the course of acute infectious diseases, as a result of severe burns, and in carbolic acid poisoning.

Test.—To a small quantity of urine in a test tube add a drop of tincture of guaiacum, and then about half as much ozonic ether as there is urine in the test tube. If blood pigment is present, a blue ring will form at the junction of the two fluids. The best test for blood, however, is to see the blood corpuscles under the microscope.

Bile.—The colouring matter of the bile which appears in the urine is its most important constituent, because its presence can be easily demonstrated. Urine containing bile pigments is clear and generally of a yellowish or greenish-brown colour. It *froths easily*, and the froth is of a yellow colour. Bile pigment appears in urine in cases where there is some obstruction to the flow of bile in the ducts in the liver, giving rise to *jaundice*.

Test for Bile Pigment.—Filter the suspected urine, and then let a drop of some nitric acid, which has been exposed to the light for some time, and in which, therefore, some nitrous acid has formed, fall upon the filter paper. If bile pigment is present, a play of colours, ranging from yellow, violet, blue, to green, will be seen.

Sugar.—The sugar which occurs in urine is not the ordinary cane sugar, but another variety known as grape sugar, glucose, or dextrose. It is present in normal urine, but in such small quantities that it cannot be detected by the ordinary tests. When it is present in abnormal amount it can be easily detected, and then it constitutes what is termed *glycosuria*.

Grape sugar occurs *temporarily* in such diseases as enteric and scarlet fever, gout, and diseases of the heart, but *continuously* only in *diabetes mellitus*, in which disease from twenty to thirty ounces may be passed in a day. And an important fact is that it can be detected long before other symptoms of the disease show themselves.

Tests for Grape Sugar.—There are several chemical tests for sugar, the chief among them being the copper test, which is based upon the fact that grape sugar has the property of reducing the oxide of copper to a suboxide at a temperature of 212° F. A solution of the oxide of copper is of a *deep blue* colour, whilst the suboxide is dark yellow, so that any change which takes place owing to the presence of grape sugar can be easily seen.

If albumen is present in the urine it must be removed by coagulation and filtration before proceeding to test for sugar.

1. *Pavy's Test.*—Place about an inch of Pavy's solution, which is a modification of Fehling's solution of copper, and is of a deep blue

colour, in a test tube and heat it until it begins to boil. Now add a *drop or two* of urine, and if no change occurs go on adding urine until the amount equals that of the Pavy's solution. Bring the mixture to the boil and then set it aside to cool. If sugar is present in the urine, a yellow deposit will be thrown down. The reason for heating the Pavy's solution before adding the urine is, that, if the former has been kept for some time, the oxide of copper in it is sometimes reduced on boiling, and throws down a yellow precipitate itself, and might thus give rise to a fallacy were it not tested itself in the first instance, and discarded if found to be wrong. The above is the most reliable test for grape sugar, and the best of the copper tests.

2. *Moore-Heller Test.*—A mixture containing an equal quantity of urine and liquor potassæ is boiled in a test tube. If sugar be present it is decomposed and the mixture turns a *dark brown* colour. This is not a very reliable test, but may be used as a preliminary to the copper one.

3. *The Fermentation Test.*—This test is based on the fact that grape sugar is converted by fermentation into alcohol and carbonic acid gas. To carry it out two glasses are filled with urine, and into one of the samples a small piece of german yeast, which has been well washed to remove all starch and sugar, is added. The two vessels are set aside in a warm place for twenty-four hours. At the end of that time the specific gravity of the two specimens is taken. If sugar be present, it will have undergone fermentation in the specimen to which the yeast had been added, and the specific gravity will be lower than that of the control specimen.

It has been found that every degree of specific gravity lost is equivalent to one grain of sugar per ounce of urine, so that if the total quantity of urine passed in twenty-four hours be known, it is only necessary to multiply the number of ounces passed by the number of degrees of specific gravity lost, to ascertain the number of grains of sugar excreted in twenty-four hours. Thus, if the total quantity of urine passed be 100 oz., the specific gravity of the un-fermented specimen 1.040, and that of the fermented one 1.020, then the total amount of sugar will be 20 × 100 = 2000 grains.

The annexed table may prove useful in carrying out urine testing in a systematic manner.

URINE.

Note QUANTITY, COLOUR, SPECIFIC GRAVITY.

REACTION.

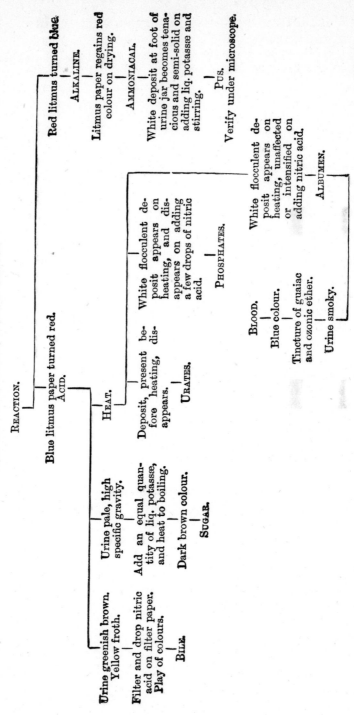

- **Blue litmus paper turned red. ACID.**
  - Urine greenish brown. Yellow froth. — Filter and drop nitric acid on filter paper. Play of colours. **BILE.**
  - Urine pale, high specific gravity. — Add an equal quantity of liq. potasse, and heat to boiling. Dark brown colour. **SUGAR.**
  - **HEAT.**
    - Deposit, present before heating, disappears. **URATES.**
    - White flocculent deposit appears on heating, and disappears on adding a few drops of nitric acid. **PHOSPHATES.**
    - White flocculent deposit appears on heating, unaffected or intensified on adding nitric acid. **ALBUMEN.**
      - Blood. Blue colour. Tincture of guaiac and ozonic ether. Urine smoky. **BLOOD.**

- **Red litmus turned blue. ALKALINE.**
  - Litmus paper regains red colour on drying. **AMMONIACAL.**
  - White deposit at foot of urine jar becomes tenacious and semi-solid on adding liq. potasse and stirring. **PUS.** Verify under microscope.

THE MICROSCOPICAL EXAMINATION OF THE URINE

Healthy urine is as a rule quite clear, amber coloured and transparent when it is first passed, and, even after it has been standing for some time, nothing more than a faint cloudiness appears near the bottom of the vessel; although, as will be pointed out later on, a thick red deposit of *urates* may occur, especially in the urine passed in the early morning by a perfectly healthy person. In disease the urine may be *turbid* when passed, or it may on standing throw down a *deposit* of the solid substances which it has held in *suspension*, and it is this deposit which has to be examined with the aid of the microscope, the knowledge gained thereby being of very great importance. In carrying out this examination the *reaction* of the urine should be ascertained in the first instance, as this will afford a valuable indication of the probable constitution of the deposit. The specimen to be examined is placed in a *conical* vessel and allowed to stand for some hours, giving the sediment time to settle at the bottom of the glass. The clear portion of the urine is then drained off, and a drop of the sediment lifted up with a pipette, placed on a microscopic slide, covered with a cover glass, and examined under the microscope.

The deposits present in urine are divided into *organic* and *inorganic*, the former being by far the more important of the two. The more important deposits are :—

ORGANIC DEPOSITS.

| Blood. | Pus. | Tube Casts. |

INORGANIC DEPOSITS.

Acid Urine.	*Alkaline Urine.*
Urates.	Phosphate of Lime.
Uric Acid.	Triple Phosphates.
Oxalate of Lime.	

Organic Deposits.—(1) *Blood.*—The *chemical* test for blood pigment is mentioned elsewhere, but red blood corpuscles themselves may be seen under the microscope. They occur in the urine in variable quantity, being few in number sometimes, whilst at others these may be in such numbers as to impart a deep ruby-red colour to the

urine.   They may be seen in their natural form as *biconcave discs*
or as swollen rounded *balls;* or again they may appear as shrivelled-
up little bodies (Fig. 46).   When the blood is so intimately *mixed*
with the urine that, even after standing for a considerable time, it
is not thrown down to the bottom of the vessel as a deposit, it may
be inferred that it comes from the *kidneys;* whereas, if the blood is
present in large quantities, and readily forms a deposit, it usually
comes from the *bladder,* the bleeding being due to the presence of a
stone or a *tumour* in the bladder.

(2) *Pus corpuscles* appear in the urine as round colourless bodies
with two or three or many dark spots in them; these are the nuclei
of the cells—pus cells being degenerated while blood corpuscles or
leucocytes.

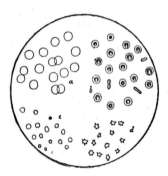

FIG. 46 —Blood Corpuscles.   FIG. 47.—Tube Casts

They occur most abundantly in cases of inflammation of the bladder
or *cystitis,* and form a thick sticky deposit at the foot of the urine
jar.   They are also found, though in smaller numbers, as a result of
inflammation of the pelvis of the kidneys, or *pyelitis.*   Inflammation
in the *urethra* may also be a cause.

(3) *Tube casts.*—These are as a rule minute fragments of *fibrin*
which had been poured into the tubes of the kidneys, and being
subsequently washed away by the urine, appear in it as *casts* of
the tubes.   They occur most frequently in *Bright's disease* of the
kidneys, and are almost always associated with *albumen* in the urine.
There are many varieties of tube casts—such as *epithelial casts*
where the fibrin has adhering to it epithelial cells which have
been torn away from the tubes of the kidneys; casts with *pus cells*
adhering to them; casts composed almost entirely of *blood,* or
having red blood corpuscles adhering to the fibrin and granular
casts (Fig. 47).

Inorganic Deposits.—(*a*) *In Acid Urine.*

1. **Urates.**—These, which consist of uric acid in combination with soda, potash, and magnesia, but most frequently with *soda*, are thrown down by the urine *as it cools*, as a deep red-brick-dust like, non-crystalline or *amorphous* deposit. Under the microscope urates appear as minute grains without any particular shape, and if the slide be slightly warmed they disappear, to appear again when it cools. Urates occur in *healthy* urine after excessive perspiration or prolonged exercise, and are then of no significance. They occur in all febrile complaints, in dyspepsia, and in diseases of the liver.

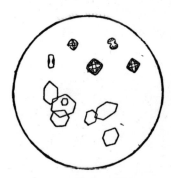

FIG. 48.—Uric Acid.   FIG. 49.—Oxalate of Lime.

2. **Uric Acid.**—This may be found in the urine as *crystals* of pure uric acid, uncombined with soda, potash, or magnesia, and is then *always* a sign of disease. The crystals may be seen with the naked eye as bright *reddish* grains adhering to the sides of the vessel, or forming a red sediment at the bottom, when they closely resemble *cayenne pepper*. Under the microscope they are seen to vary greatly in *shape*, being lozenge shaped, barrel shaped, &c. (Fig. 48), but are always of a *yellow colour*, and may thus be readily distinguished from all other crystals which appear as deposits in the urine. The presence of uric acid in its *crystalline* form may give rise to the symptoms of *gravel*, and its accumulation in the bladder, or pelvis of the kidneys, cause the formation of some of the " stones " found in these regions.

3. **Oxalate of Lime.**—This substance occurs in the urine as octahedral crystals resembling minute square envelopes under the microscope, or they may be dumb-bell shaped (Fig. 49). Its mode of origin is obscure, but as many articles of diet—such as rhubarb, spinach, beetroot, cabbage, plums, gooseberries, strawberries, tea, coffee, and cocoa—contain oxalic acid, it has been conjectured that its presence in the urine is due to an excessive vegetable diet; and cer-

tainly after partaking of rhubarb many persons suffer from symptoms which are supposed to be due to the oxalate of lime which appears in their urine. Oxalate of lime in the urine is supposed to give rise to a form of dyspepsia, accompanied by pain in the loins, an irritable bladder, nervousness and depression of spirits; but the chief danger lies in the possible formation of calculi or *stones* in the bladder, this form of stone being second only in frequency to that consisting of uric acid.

(*b*) *In Alkaline Urine.*

1. **Phosphate of Lime** may occur in the urine as a non-crystalline or amorphous, white flocculent deposit, which is not dissolved by heat—thus distinguishing it from *urates*—but disappears on the addition of a few, drops of acetic or nitric acid. Under the microscope its appearance is much the same as that of urates. Its presence in the urine is of no special significance; but appearing as it often does at the *end* of the act of micturition, it is apt to give rise to unnecessary alarm.

2. **Ammonio-Magnesian, or Triple Phosphates.**—The presence of this substance in the urine may be easily recognised by the naked eye, appearing as the crystals

Fig. 50.—Triple Phosphates.

do as bright, shining particles adhering to the sides of the vessel. Under the microscope the deposit is seen to consist of comparatively large crystals forming prisms, and having very much the appearance of crystal *knife rests*. The presence of triple phosphates always indicates *ammoniacal fermentation* of the urea in the urine, such as occurs in *cystitis* or inflammation of the bladder. A considerable part of many *calculi* or stones consist of triple phosphates. Appended is a table giving the characters of the urine in health, and in some of the commoner diseases.

In conclusion, it only remains to add that the various deposits mentioned above do not in themselves constitute disease, but are valuable indications of the morbid processes going on in the body.

THE URINE IN HEALTH AND IN SOME DISEASES

	Quantity.	Colour.	Specific Gravity.	Reaction.	Chemical Test.	Microscopic Appearance.
Healthy . .	50–70 oz.	Amber, clear	1.020	Acid	Urea, uric acid, salts	Mucus, urates?
Fevers . .	Diminished	Turbid, dark	High	Acid	Urea increased, albumen?	Urates
Heart and lung disease	Diminished	Dark	High	Acid	Albumen	Urates
Acute Bright's disease	Diminished or suppressed	Ruby red, dark	High	Acid	Albumen, blood pigment	Tube casts, red blood corpuscles
Chronic Bright's disease	Increased	Pale, frothy	Low	Acid	Albumen?	A few tube casts
Disease of liver	Normal	Greenish brown	Normal	Acid	Bile pigment, urea increased	Urates
Diabetes . .	Greatly increased	Clear, pale	Very high	Acid	Sugar . . .	
Acute gout .	Diminished	High	High	Very acid		Uric acid crystals, urates
Anæmia . .	Normal	Pale	Low	Neutral or alkaline	Albumen?	
Dyspepsia .	Normal	High	High	Acid		Urates, oxalates, phosphates
Cystitis or inflammation of bladder.	Normal	Turbid		Offensive, alkaline		Pus cells, triple phosphates

SECTION VI

ANIMAL PARASITES AND THE DISEASES THEY CAUSE

Parasites.—By a "parasite" is meant an animal or plant which lives in or upon another animal or plant. In the first place, we find certain plants existing as parasites on other plants. In the second place, many of the lower forms of animal life attach themselves to other animals in the relation of unbidden and unwelcome guests to their hosts. It may be here mentioned that the word "host" is applied to the animal or plant which acts as a literal landlord to its parasitic "guest." In the third place, we discover that certain plants may be parasitic on animals; whilst in the fourth and last place, some animals are parasitic on plants.

Some Examples.—By way of illustrating the case of a plant parasite living on another plant we may select the mistletoe, which, as most readers know, lives parasitically on the oak and the apple. It draws so much nourishment from the tree by means of its roots, but having green leaves it is able at the same time to take certain food elements of its own from the air. In the opposite direction, that of a plant parasite living upon an animal body, we find many illustrations in the shape of the microscopic *fungi* which are the causes of many skin diseases. Thus *ringworm*, an extremely common skin disease, is caused by a plant parasite belonging to the fungus class, whilst other skin troubles, and particularly some of those causing baldness, are also traceable to a like source. In one sense also, it may be said that the germs or microbes of disease which breed and multiply in our bodies, producing fevers and like ailments, may be legitimately regarded as "parasites," seeing that they have acquired the habit of taking up their abode within the human frame.

When we come to discuss the case of animal parasites existing in or upon animal bodies, we meet with a large number of illustrations, many of which are familiar enough to the ordinary reader. Thus a tape-worm, living in the digestive system of man or other animal, exemplifies the case of an animal "guest" inhabiting an animal "host." Such a parasite we term "internal," because it inhabits the interior of its host. On the other hand a parasite, such as the flea or louse, living on the skin of animals and extracting their blood by way of nourishment, comes under the class of "external" parasites.

The Evolution of Parasites.—The interesting question arises regarding the manner in which parasites have come to assume their particular mode of existence. No one can for a moment believe that animals were evolved with parasites, so to speak, ready made. On the other hand it is abundantly clear that the habit whereby an animal becomes a parasite and adopts an easy life, lived at the expense of its host, represents not an original, but an acquired habit. The proof of this statement is found in the fact that a large number of parasites are perfectly free-living and active in their young state. It is later on in their existence that, giving up as it were their habits of independence, they attach themselves to another animal and commence a life of servile dependence. The fact that an animal represents in the history of its own development the chronicle of its evolution therefore teaches us, according to the facts just stated, that the parasitic habit is one which has assuredly been acquired. At the same time it is important to note, that when an animal has taken to a parasitic mode of existence, nature demands a distinct penalty for the adoption of the dependent state. In other words, when an animal which originally was an independent being, getting food for itself and living a free existence, attaches itself to another animal, nature causes a process of *degeneration* to set in. Thus we find to-day that when parasites, which begin life possessing eyes, organs of movement, a digestive system, and the other belongings of animal life, commence their period of parasitic existence, these organs degenerate, decline, and finally vanish away. In this way nature teaches us the lesson that the only healthy life must be the independent one, so that when an animal loses all need for the exercise of its own powers in the way of movement or food-getting, it sinks to the low level of existence exhibited in the state of the parasite.

EXTERNAL ANIMAL PARASITES

Dealing first with external parasites, we find these to be represented, as far as man is concerned (leaving out those lower plant forms responsible for skin diseases, &c.), by insects of various kinds. The common flea (*Pulex irritans*) is probably the best known of the insect parasites which affect man. Lower animals each possess their own species of fleas. Those infesting the cat, the dog, the rabbit, the fowl, and other animals, differ from the species which causes annoyance to man. The flea is a wingless insect possessing a very long pair of hinder legs. The mouth is of what naturalists call the suctorial type, and possesses organs adapted for piercing the skin and for withdrawing blood therefrom. It need hardly be remarked that the adult flea is alone the insect which infests the human body. It is an insect which passes through the three stages of *larva* or *caterpillar* (or "maggot"), and *chrysalis* (or *pupa*), this last finally giving origin to the *imago* or perfect insect. It appears that in summer the young flea may become full grown in from twelve days to a fortnight.

The Chigoe or Jigger.—This flea is a peculiar form or species limited to tropical America. It is interesting to man from the fact that the female flea, becoming of enormous size from the development of eggs, burrows beneath the human skin. The usual seat of perforation is beneath the toe nail. This species attacks also dogs and mice, and appears to have been introduced into Africa by human agency. The presence of the insect in the human tissues gives rise to a large amount of irritation which may extend to ulceration, and may even, it is said, produce death itself. Surgical means have to be adopted for the removal of the parasite, the negroes being extremely skilful in removing this pest.

Lice.—There can be no doubt that whilst fleas may be troublesome enough parasites, they are not so commonly associated with dirt and unhealthy conditions of body as are lice. Three species of these insects are known to occur in man. The first is the commonest species, and is known as the "head louse," from the fact that it generally infests the scalp. It is known as the *Pediculus capitis*. The second species infests the body generally, and is known as the "body louse" (*P. vestimenti*). The third and last variety is known as the "crab" louse (*Phthirius inguinalis*). The body louse and head louse resemble each other fairly closely. The crab louse, on the other hand, has a much broader body than the other species, its two hinder legs being much broader and thicker than the front pair, whilst their claws are extremely strong, enabling the insect to retain a firm hold of the body. These latter infest the region of the pubis and adjacent parts. This insect is from the $\frac{1}{28}$th to the $\frac{1}{10}$th of an inch in length. It sometimes extends its range to the armpits and breast.

Phthiriasis or the "Lousy Disease."—A very curious feature in connection with the presence of these insect parasites on the human body, is that apparently well known to the Greeks of old, whereby certain human beings appear to be chronically infested. From time to time in the course of history various distinguished persons have been said to suffer from what is apparently some peculiar condition of body favouring the continual development of lice. There is a legend to the effect that Herod himself was afflicted with this peculiar ailment. An old author makes the statement that "Divers persons have come to their ends, being devoured by lice." Physicians accustomed to treat skin diseases have noted such cases. Notwithstanding every care and attention being paid to bodily cleanliness and changing of clothes, the parasites appear to return and to continue their development. In some recorded cases all remedies have apparently proved useless. The late Sir Erasmus Wilson held that these lice creep from the outside skin into the follicles or skin glands and make these last their breeding-places. It seems, however, extremely peculiar that, notwithstanding the application of ointments and lotions which have the effect of killing off the parasites under ordinary circumstances, lice should continue to multiply in certain individuals. The eggs of these creatures are extremely minute bodies, which may be contained in the air. The only rational explanation which occurs is therefore that of supposing that some particular state of the skin exists in such cases, whereby the development of the eggs obtained from the air is readily encouraged. It is noteworthy in connection with this latter idea, that after fevers and other exhausting diseases, patients are liable for a time to exhibit the development of lice.

The Demodex.—This name is applied to a curious little mite which is known under the scientific name of *Demodex folliculorum*. It lives naturally in the follicles or sacs of the hairs, especially inhabiting the wings or sides of the nose. It is a curious fact that probably every individual harbours little guests of this kind. They vary in length from the $\frac{1}{70}$th to the $\frac{1}{100}$th part of an inch. As a rule they give no trouble whatever, but if they increase in numbers and cause any irritation of the sides of the nose, they may be removed by washing the part with a weak solution of corrosive sublimate.

The Itch Mite.—The disease known as *scabies* or *itch* is caused by the presence in the skin of a mite known as the *Sarcoptes scabiei*. The mite is somewhat tortoise shaped. It is the female mites which alone burrow into the skin. The male mites are not parasitic in this latter sense, but appear to exist on the skin surface. Within the skin-burrow the eggs are laid, and the young insects escape after development and burrow into the skin afresh. The most common seat of attack is between the fingers. The disease may spread over the body, although the face is very rarely attacked. Naturally we find that the irritation produced by the presence of these mites under the skin gives rise to an eruption associated with painful itching, this latter condition becoming worst when the skin is warm. Itch is naturally a contagious disease, from the fact that contact with an infected person conveys the mites from one body to the other. In children it is said that where itch is present the eruption is most frequently to be found on the ulnar or little finger side of the wrist, on the buttocks, and on the ankles.

Treatment.—For the destruction of fleas various powders are used. Most of these contain the plant substance known as *Pyrethrum*, which has accordingly been popularly known by the name of "Flea bane." There can be no doubt that the exercise of great cleanliness is necessary to rid a house or its belongings of these insects, seeing that as in the case of like parasites the presence of dirt constitutes a condition favouring their development. Insect powders can be obtained ready made from any chemist.

In respect to the *treatment of lice* the remark just made concerning cleanliness applies with even greater force to the case of these insects. They are typically found wherever dirty conditions prevail, no better illustration of this fact being found than the case of children whose hair is not properly attended too. To rid the body of head lice or of the crab louse carbolic oil may be used of the strength of one to eight. Some authorities recommend a 5 per cent. solution of oleate of mercury. It is well, however, before applying any remedies that the parts should be thoroughly washed with soft soap and warm water and that the hair should be cut short. A favourite ointment for the cure of lice is the ointment of *stavesacre*. The use of this ointment must be persisted in for a considerable period. Ordinary petroleum oil has been also extensively used with success in public institutions. A weak solution of corrosive sublimate is also recommended as a remedy to destroy what is known as the "nits" or eggs of lice. The hair after being washed with soap and water may be soaked in vinegar or a solution of borax and well combed. For the destruction of crab lice an ointment of white precipitate of the strength of twenty-five grains to the ounce of lard may be used with success. It is of extreme importance as part of the cure of lice where these parasites are present in great numbers, that the body clothes should be efficiently disinfected by moist heat in a disinfecting chamber. The use of warm baths and of Izal soap is also to be commended as means to be included in the general practice of bodily cleanliness.

The Treatment of Itch.—The substance most commonly used for the treatment of itch is sulphur ointment. This is composed of two drachms of sulphur, one drachm of carbonate of potash, and one ounce of lard. This ointment should be applied over the affected parts after a hot bath for at least three nights. Powdered sulphur in some cases is also rubbed into the skin and well sprinkled on the under garments. Where any delicacy of skin exists another ointment may be employed. This latter is composed of prepared storax two drachms, and lard one drachm. It should be applied after the fashion of the sulphur ointment. The caution may be here given that all garments of a person on whom itch has attained a general development should be carefully disinfected.

INTERNAL PARASITES

The internal parasites afflicting man are drawn from various groups of the animal kingdom. They mostly belong to that class of animals popularly known as "worms." Some of them are more or less closely related to ordinary worms, but the majority belong to other and separate groups of the animal kingdom.

The Guinea Worm.—The guinea worm is known scientifically as the *Filaria Medinensis*. It occurs in Africa and India. In length it varies from one to three feet, its diameter being about the $\frac{1}{10}$th part of an inch. By some authors it has been stated that this worm represents the "fiery serpent" mentioned in the Old Testament which afflicted the Israelites. Plutarch the historian in the eighth book of his "Symposiacom," dating from about 140 B.C., states that "People taken ill on the Red Sea suffered from many strange and unheard of attacks; amongst others worms, like little snakes, came out of them, which gnawed away their legs and arms, and when touched again withdrew themselves, coiling themselves up in the muscles, thereby giving rise to the most insupportable pains."

With regard to the development of this curious parasite it would seem that the worm, like most other parasitic forms, demands two "hosts" for its perfect development; that is to say, it does not attain its full development in the first animal to the body of which it gains access. We shall find this to be a peculiarity of other parasites, the tape worms included. From the eggs of the guinea worm developing in man's body there are produced embryos (or young) which pass into water. In the water each embryo enters into the body of some fresh-water flea. Here it undergoes a certain amount of development, and the idea of man's infection now prevalent is that this half developed worm is swallowed through the water-fleas being obtained in the drinking water. Obtaining thus entrance to man's body the worm then develops fully. If this mode of infection be credited the worm can only reach the body surface by boring its way from the internal parts. Other authorities appear to lean to the belief that the young worm itself or the embryo from the water-flea finds its way directly into the body through the skin. Whatever be its mode of entrance it gives rise to swellings and sores chiefly found upon the feet and legs. A good deal of constitutional disturbance is also present. The presence of the worm is marked by a boil or pustule, which when it breaks discloses the head of the worm. The essence of the treatment here is to extract the worm carefully so that its body may not be broken, in which latter event there is liable to be a fresh infection of the body from the eggs or young contained in the parent worm. The usual method is to secure the head of the worm by means of a thread, and to fasten this thread to some object around which day by day the worm can be carefully coiled, until it is completely removed, otherwise a surgical operation may be adopted for the more speedy removal of the parasite. One authority states that tincture of assafœtida given in doses of thirty drops thrice daily is a remedy for guinea worm. The precautions to be taken against attack are summed up in the advice that the feet should be well covered and kept dry whilst bathing in pools, while marshes in tropical districts should be avoided.

The Filaria Worm.—The worm known under this name, to give it its full title, is the *Filaria Sanguinis hominis*. It appears, however, that the worm itself is only the young stage of a species known as the *Filaria Bancrofti*. The latter form occurs in the lymphatic vessels of persons affected with two diseases known as *chyluria* and *elephantiasis*. The young filaria is found in the urine and also in the blood when the patient is asleep. The average length of this parasite is the $\frac{1}{75}$th part of an inch. It appears to be enclosed in a sac. In so far as the history of this worm is concerned, we find that the F. Bancrofti or mature worm apparently dwells in a lymphatic vessel, the young passing into the lymph, which in turn is carried to the blood. It is these young which abound in the night time but pass into a resting state during the day.

This curious fact is explained by the relation of these parasites to the mosquito, within which they pass a certain stage of the development. The mosquito mostly attacks man at night, and in the act of biting its human victim the young filarias, attaching themselves to its proboscis, are conveyed to the insect's stomach. Such of them as attain to full development inside the insect's body pass out into water. It is from this fluid that man is infected either in the act of drinking water, or, as some believe, by the young filarias penetrating the skin. Once lodged in the human body the worms pass to the lymphatics and become fully developed, giving rise in their turn to the young forms which are conveyed to the blood. The prevention of this parasite is really a matter of seeing that all water in infected districts should be thoroughly boiled before use, by way of destroying any possible parasites it may contain.

The Bilharzia.—This parasite, scientifically known as *Bilharzia hæmatobia*, occurs in Egypt, South Africa, and other tropical regions. In length it measures about a quarter of an inch, its particular habitat in the body being the veins of the large bowel, the bladder, and kidney. Its presence gives rise to indigestion if the liver be affected and also the passing of blood in the urine. In this latter fluid the eggs of the parasite are met with. They average the $\frac{1}{150}$th part of an inch in length. The mode of infection here is chiefly through drinking water. When the eggs escape from the human body they appear to pass into fresh water crustaceans or water fleas, so that the drinking of water containing these latter forms infects man. By way of *prevention* against attack, it is recommended that all drinking water should be carefully supervised and should be boiled or well filtered before use, whilst unwashed vegetables in infected districts should be avoided. Bathing in canals or still water must be prohibited. Injections of salvarsan have been tried, but the results, though good, proved to be only temporary. Very lately complete cures are claimed following injections of sodium antimony tartrate.

Dochmius or Anchylostomiasis Worm.—This worm, known as the *Dochmius duodenalis*, has of late days attracted very considerable attention in Britain from the fact that it has attacked the mining population of certain districts, having probably been brought to Britain by miners from Poland and Italy. The worm itself is found in Egypt and in certain parts of Italy. In length it is about half-an-inch, and it is found attaching itself in large numbers to the lining membrane of the small bowel. The developed eggs of these worms *pass from the patient's body* and appear to develop where the temperature is high and the soil wet. The young worm appears to be much longer than the adult. Infection here arises from drinking water, seeing that the young worms escape into the water from the soil and thus infect the individual. This disease produces great disturbance of the system, marked by the presence amongst other symptoms of a peculiar kind of anæmia, which is liable to prove fatal in extreme cases.

The treatment which has been proposed for this disease is the administration of thymol. The dose is thirty grains given in the morning, and a similar dose two hours afterwards. The thymol is usually given in brandy, whilst two hours after the second administration a full dose of castor oil is given. It is recommended that this treatment should be repeated in a week's time.

Round Worms.—The "round" worms are so named in contradistinction to the *flat worms,* amongst which latter are included the flukes and tape worms. Two varieties of round worms are commonly found in man, whilst others less common have also to be regarded as disease-producing parasites.

Thread Worms.—What is known as the small "thread" worm (*Oxyuris vermicularis*) (Fig. 51) is commonly found in the rectum or lower bowel. It is especially common in children, in whom it gives rise to symptoms marked by feverishness and irritation of the lower bowel and anus, a depraved appetite, and, as is the case where other worms are present, a good deal of irritation of the nose is found. The average length of this worm, which is the smallest of those infecting the intestine of man, is about a quarter of an inch, the female worm being larger than the male. This parasite produces enormous numbers of eggs which pass from the bowel and undergo development outside the body. At the same time it is important to note that as the eggs of these parasites may lodge under the nails of the patient and be thus conveyed to the mouth reinfection is liable to occur. The eggs are also liable to be conveyed in polluted drinking water and by unwashed vegetables.

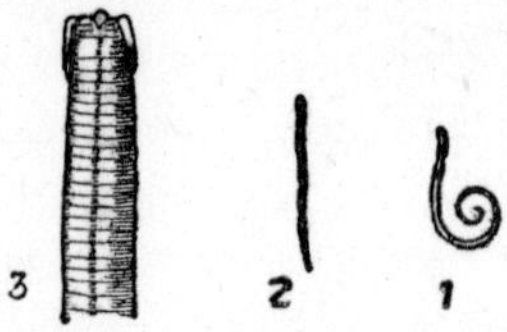

FIG. 51.—Thread Worm.
1, Male; 2, Female; 3, Head magnified.

The **Treatment** of thread worm is that of administering an enema or injection of salt and water. Other substances have been used as injections such as infusion of quassia or lime water. Half an ounce of perchloride of iron to a pint of water also makes an excellent remedy for an adult. If these means fail to relieve the patient, two grains of santonin may be given in two drachms of syrup of senna. If need be, a dose of castor oil may be administered an hour or two afterwards; but the senna itself usually produces the desired effect of moving the bowels.

The Round Worm.—This parasite is termed the *Ascaris lumbricoides* (Fig. 52). In shape it resembles the ordinary earth worm. It is of a pinkish white colour, the female being ten or twelve inches long and the male half that length. Several of these worms may be found in the bowel at the same time. They are common in children and inhabit the small intestine. One danger attaching to the presence of round worms is found in the fact that occasionally they may pass upwards into the stomach, or worse still, may penetrate the intestines and thus cause fatal inflammation. The symptoms here are similar to those produced by the presence of thread worms. For their cure two grains of santonin may be given with syrup of senna as described in the case of thread worm. This dose of two grains will suit a child of three years of age and upwards. One authority recommends that the santonin should be mixed with butter and spread upon a slice of bread, two grains of calomel being sprinkled on the butter. If santonin be given

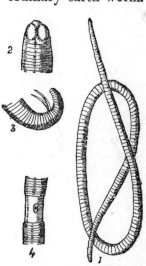

FIG. 52.—Round Worm.

1, Adult Worm; 2, Head; 3, Tail of Male; 4, Middle of Female Body, from Side.

simply with a dose of castor oil its action will generally be found most efficient. If given with the senna, castor oil will not be needed. The main object of giving either the calomel, senna, or the castor oil is to induce free action of the bowels.

The third worm is known as the *Trichocephalus dispar*. It is extremely common in hot climates. The eggs passing from the body of man develop in water or damp soil. Infection proceeds from such polluted water. The worm attaches itself chiefly to the lining membrane of the first part of the large intestine or "cæcum."

The *Pentastoma* also belongs to the family of round worms and occurs in the liver, other species also being found in the lungs. This parasite measures about one inch in length. It is found in Africa and the West Indies. Its presence is apt to give rise to serious symptoms.

The Trichina Disease.—This disease is caused by a minute worm known scientifically as the *Trichina spiralis* (Fig. 53), so called from the spiral manner in which it lies embedded in a cyst or sac in the muscles of affected persons. The history of the discovery of the trichina worm forms in itself an interesting chapter in science. In dissecting rooms there had been occasionally noticed in the muscles of the chest small white particles, many of which were of a gritty or limy nature. In 1835, the late Sir James Paget, then a medical student, discovered the white specks in question to represent small worms of rounded shape. Later on Professor Owen (afterwards Sir Richard Owen) described the worm and gave it the name it now bears. The further history of the trichina worm refers to certain mysterious outbreaks of illness occurring in Britain, in Germany, and

FIG. 53.—Trichinas in Muscle, each enclosed in a Cyst.

elsewhere. The cause of these outbreaks was variously interpreted. The symptoms of the ailment exhibited a somewhat indefinite character, and when numerous cases occurred the illness was variously referred to typhoid fever, acute rheumatism, and even to poisoning. No fewer than twenty-six epidemics of the disease in question occurred in Germany between 1860 and 1865. In one of the most typical of these epidemics occurring at Hedersleben in 1865, three hundred and fifty persons were seized with the mysterious disease, and of these one hundred died. It appears that on the 25th October of the year just mentioned a pig was killed and sold; a few days afterwards the mysterious epidemic made its appearance amongst those who had partaken of the flesh of the animal.

In this country epidemics of the trichina disease have not been common, probably for the reason that in Britain raw or imperfectly cooked pig's flesh is not a common article of diet. Still, cases of trichina disease (otherwise known as *Trichiniasis*) have occurred in Britain. An outbreak took place in Cumberland, for example, in 1871, whilst other cases have been subsequently recorded. The symptoms of the disease produced by the trichina worm consist of general derangement of the system, accompanied by fever, prostration, and by muscular pains. The origin of the latter symptoms will be made clear when we understand the manner in which the life-history of the trichina is ordered.

The worm, as has already been remarked, is enclosed in a capsule or sac, being coiled up therein in a spiral manner. Each of these little sacs is about the $\frac{1}{70}$th part of an inch in length. It is therefore just visible and no more to the naked eye. When the worms first gain access to the flesh of an animal they are immature (Fig. 54); that is, they exist in a young or imperfect state of development. The length of the worm itself is about the $\frac{1}{35}$th part of an inch. The perfectly developed female worm attains a length of about $\frac{1}{8}$th part of an inch, whilst the male in the same state averages the $\frac{1}{18}$th part of an inch in length.

The History.—The trichina worm is found not only in man but in rats, cats, pigs, and other animals. It is of course flesh-eating animals which are most liable to harbour this parasite, seeing that it can only be acquired by the second animal eating the flesh of that in which the trichina lies in its immature state. In man a common source of the disease is represented by his eating pork containing the immature trichinas (Fig. 54). What happens in a case of infection may be described as first consisting in the dissolving of the sacs or capsules in which the immature trichinas are contained. The young worms are thus set free in the stomach. In from two to four days each of these young worms has become fully developed within the intestine or bowel. The result of this production of the two sexes of the worm is the development in the bowel of immense numbers of young trichinas. These

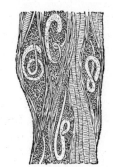

Fig. 54. — Immature Trichinas in Muscle.

young are probably liberated from the bodies of the female parents in from seven to eight days after the infected meat has been eaten. Now comes the essential feature of the trichina disease. Immense numbers of young are produced. One estimate gives from 30,000,000 to 100,000,000 of young trichinas as the number produced as the result of an ordinary infection. Soon after their production, the young brood of trichinas begin to migrate from the digestive system. They bore their way through from the digestive system in order to reach the muscles of the body. A period from eight to ten days seems to be required for the completion of this change of abode. We may thus reckon that a period of from fifteen to sixteen days is required for the full development of the trichina disease. We now are able to understand the special symptoms this disease exhibits. The passage of millions of these minute worms from the digestive system to the muscles is attended with severe pains and with prostration and the other features which mark epidemics of this character. The muscles in which the young brood chiefly take up their abode are the *diaphragm* or "midriff," the muscles between the ribs (*intercostals*), the muscles of the neck, those of the organ of voice and of the eye, and less frequently the biceps and triceps of the arm. Once settled down in the muscles, the young brood of worms ultimately develop the capsules or sacs (Fig. 53) in which we saw the worms to be enclosed within the flesh of the pig. If a portion of human flesh thus infected were to be eaten by another animal, the history just detailed would be repeated, and we thus note, as in the case of other parasites, that the trichina worm requires two "hosts" for its development, and cannot become a mature worm in the host to whose muscles it has migrated.

The Source of Infection.—Seeing that the source of infection in this disease can only come from the flesh of an infected animal, it may be taken for granted that the pig (in the case of man) is the one species to be feared in connection with this ailment. The source from which the pig derives its trichinas is a doubtful matter, but having regard to the miscellaneous feeding which that animal exhibits —due to no fault of its own—we need not feel surprised if amongst the miscellaneous articles which the pig may occasionally eat, the dead bodies of rats or other animals which have been infected with trichinas are represented. The further history of the worms once imbedded in human muscle is one of degeneration. After some time each worm gradually becomes converted into a little limy particle. We can therefore understand that if the individual who is attacked by the trichinas survives the period of pain and prostration caused by the passage of the young worms from the digestive system to the muscles, he will not be further troubled.

Prevention.—In the case of the trichina worm, as will also be found in the case of tape worm infection, the great means of prevention is represented by the thorough cooking of pork. It has been ascertained that the freezing of pork and processes of salting and pickling have no effect in killing the trichinas embedded in it, but if on the other hand meat be exposed to the temperature of boiling water for say half-an-hour the parasites in it will be destroyed. One authority says that thirty-six minutes' boiling for every two pounds or so of trichina-infested meat will undoubtedly kill the parasites. There is illustrated here one great rule for the prevention of parasitic infection derived from flesh, namely, the efficient cooking of all meat. In addition, it may be added that the rigid inspection of flesh, and especially of pork, must undoubtedly tend to lessen the chance of acquiring the malady we have been considering.

Tape Worms.—The parasites included under this designation are familiar enough. They exhibit length and breadth with only a minor degree of thickness. Scientifically they are called *Cestodes*, a name derived from the classic word for a "girdle" or "belt." Each tape worm presents itself to view to the eye of the naturalist as *a colony of animals*. It is in point of fact not one animal but an aggregation of similar units. Each unit is represented by a "joint" of the worm. This joint in the common species is of elongated shape and is known as a *proglottis* (Fig. 55, *c*), the whole worm itself being called a *strobilus*. If we investigate the constitution of a tape worm from a general point of view, we find it to consist of three distinct parts. These are, first, the minute head (Fig. 55, *a*, and Fig. 56), by means of which the worm attaches itself to the lining membrane of the bowel or intestine within which it lives. To the head, secondly, succeeds a slender portion called the neck (*b*). Succeeding the neck, we find small and imperfectly formed joints. As we pass backwards, we find the third portion of the worm to consist of fully formed joints or *proglottides* (*d*).

The Process of Budding.—The manner in which this curious organism is developed can be readily understood when we have regard to the fact that the head and neck constitute the source of its origin. The joints are budded off from the neck extremity, the youngest joints are therefore those next the neck, the most mature and oldest joints being those at the opposite or tail end of the worm. This process of budding giving rise further to what we may call "colonial" beings is represented in other groups of the animal

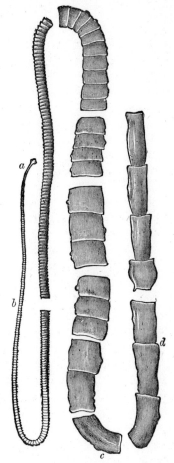

FIG. 55.—*Tænia solium.*—Tape Worm derived from Pork, showing—*a*, Head; *b*, Neck; *c*, a Detached Joint; *d*, Three Detached Joints.

world, but it is a process which is typically seen in the parasites under consideration. With respect to the size of tape worms, they may vary materially in this respect. A common length in the case of the ordinary tape worm (*Tænia solium*) (Fig. 55) is seven or eight feet, but this extent may be greatly exceeded when we have regard to the fact that the intestine or bowel of man measures twenty-six feet in length, so that we can readily understand how, under favourable circumstances, a tape worm by continuous budding may grow to an enormous length. At the same time, we have to take into consideration the fact that the oldest of the joints of the worm are perpetually dropping off as new joints are being produced by budding from the head and neck. It is the passage from the bowel of the cast-off joints which, of course, forms the one distinctive symptom indicating the presence of this parasite in the digestive system.

Development.—In order to understand the life history or career of a tape worm, we must first bear in mind the rule applicable to other parasites, namely, that these animals demand two "hosts" for their development. The first host which receives the young worms does not develop the perfect parasites. They require to be trans-

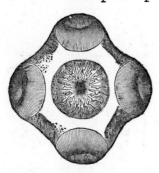

Fig. 56.—Head of Tape Worm magnified, showing Hooks in the Middle and Suckers at the Edge.

ferred to the body of the second "host," which must eat the flesh of the first in order that the full life history may be completed. We may naturally begin the consideration of tape worm development with the minute eggs which are contained to the number of many thousands in each mature joint of the worm as it exists in man. In this description we select the common or pork tape worm (Fig. 55) as illustrative of these parasites' life histories. Each egg is about the $\frac{1}{700}$th part of an inch in diameter. If we reflect upon the fact that each joint of the tape worm

contains many thousands of eggs and that a full-grown tape worm numbers many hundreds of joints in its constitution, we may feel appalled when we consider the number of eggs to which a single parasite may give origin. It is the fact that these eggs require to pass through a complicated cycle of development which materially lessens the chances of their development and in the course of which by far the greater majority undoubtedly perish, which constitutes nature's mode of limiting their propagation.

The eggs in the case of the common tape worm escaping from the body of man are swallowed by a pig. This animal represents the first "host." In the pig it will be understood the egg has no chance of becoming a mature tape worm. The egg is a small body, and within it can be seen a little embryo possessing six horny hooks at its head extremity. Swallowed by the pig, these embryos are liberated from the eggs, and bore their way from the digestive system of the animal to take up their abode in its muscles or flesh. Arrived in the muscles each embryo settles down and develops around its hinder part a bladder-like expansion. In this stage of its development the young tape worm is known as a *scolex* or *cysticercus* (Fig. 57), whilst it has also been known as a *cystic worm* and as a *bladder worm*. The average size of the bladder-like cyst is that of a small pea; occasionally, however, it may be of larger size. If the pig happens to have received a large dose of tape worm eggs, the animal becomes much affected by the passage of the embryos from the digestive system to the muscles. It exhibits symptoms of fever and of general disturbance of its bodily functions. These symptoms cease when the embryos have settled down in its flesh. A pig thus affected is said by the veterinary surgeon to be troubled with

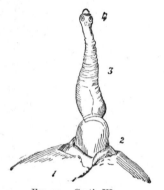

FIG. 57.—Cystic Worm.
Head (4); Neck (3); and Bladder
or Cyst (1 and 2).

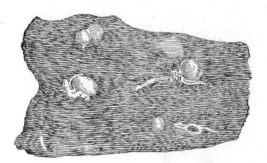

FIG. 58.—"Measly" Pork showing Young Forms
of Tape Worm.

"measles," and the flesh of such an animal is described as "measly pork" (Fig. 58). It is this pork which forms the great source of tape worm infection by this species of worm in man.

The Further History.—Let us now suppose that a portion of measly pork in an imperfectly cooked state is eaten by man. This event naturally forms the commencement of the second epoch or era of the worm's life history. Passed into the human stomach, the immature tape worm gets rid of its bladder-like expansion. The already formed head and neck of the bladder of the worm (Fig. 57) constitutes the head and neck of the future tape worm. The head attaches itself to the lining membrane of the bowel in man. Next begins the process of *budding* from the neck forming the joints, and it only requires time for the complete and perfect tape worm to be thus produced. The period occupied in this process, on an average, may be set down at four months.

The following table may be found to summarise the various stages in this curious development :—

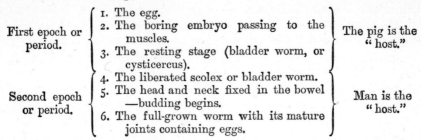

| First epoch or period. | 1. The egg.
2. The boring embryo passing to the muscles.
3. The resting stage (bladder worm, or cysticercus). | The pig is the "host." |
| Second epoch or period. | 4. The liberated scolex or bladder worm.
5. The head and neck fixed in the bowel —budding begins.
6. The full-grown worm with its mature joints containing eggs. | Man is the "host." |

Some Other Histories.—From the account just given of tape worm development, it will be seen that the young stage of each tape worm residing in the first host must be eaten by its second host. It is of course possible that the animal which naturally forms the second host of the tape worm may, by swallowing the egg, convert itself into the first host. This, however, rarely happens. It has been said that, in the case of the common tape worm, the "cystic" form, or "bladder" worm, takes up its abode in the muscles of the pig. The muscular system, however, is not the only part of an animal in which the young tape worms may reside. Thus these cystic worms may be found in the brain, in the eyeball, and in other parts of the animal frame. In one case, that of the young form of a tapeworm of the dog, called *Tænia cœnurus*, the cystic worm may attain the size of a hen's egg. When it occurs in the brain of the sheep, it gives origin to a disease of that animal known as "staggers." In the same way the young form of another tape worm passes its early stage in a first host represented by a fresh-water fish, as will hereafter be described. A tape worm of the dog, *Tænia marginata*, spends its youthful stage in the sheep and other domestic animals, and yet another parasite of the dog has for its first host hares and rabbits. Just as the cat obtains one of its tape worm parasites by eating the mouse, in the same way a tape worm found in the fox passes its early life in a species of field animal known as the "vole." But perhaps the most extraordinary example of what has been called "the vicious cycle of parasitism" is that seen in the case of the dog. This animal is affected with a tape worm called the *Tænia cucumerina*, a worm, by the way, which may also occur in its full-grown condition in man. The young form of this tape worm passes the first stage of its life in the louse, living on the dog's skin, into which, in the form of the egg, it passes from the dog's intestines. The animal infects itself further by the swallowing of the louse with its contained tape worm embryo previously derived from its own body. The

The Broad Tape Worm

"vicious cycle" in this case is therefore represented within the body of one and the same animal.

Amongst other tape worms which are liable to occur in man is the *Tænia mediocanellata,* otherwise known as the "beef tape worm." In all probability this species represents the most common parasite in Britain and Europe. The worm has as its first host the muscles of the ox, and more rarely those of the sheep. In about sixty days after infected meat has been eaten, the mature joints may be discharged from man's bowel. This tape worm is one of the largest found in man, and may attain a length of over twenty feet. The head, like that of other tape worms, possesses suckers wherewith it adheres to the lining membrane of the bowel, but it has no hooklets, as is the case with the common or pork worm (Fig. 56).

Another species of tape worm, but one not common in Britain, is that known as the *Bothriocephalus latus,* otherwise known as the *Broad tape worm* and as the *Russian tape worm* (Fig. 59), from the fact that while uncommon in Britain it is frequently found in Russia, Poland, Switzerland, and sometimes in Ireland. It has also been found in Japan. This is the largest tape worm infesting man. It may grow to a length of twenty-five feet, its mature "joints" numbering over three thousand. The joints in this species are wide, that is when measured from side to side, but are short when compared with the oblong joints of other tape worms. The head of this species has neither hooks nor suckers, but is deeply grooved on each side. The reason for the peculiar geographical distribution of this worm is readily found when we have regard to the mode of infection. It is necessary, of course, for man to eat the first "host" in which the worm passes the preliminary stages of its existence. The broad worm is found to pass its earlier stage in the body of fresh-water fish, of which the pike is an example. As such fishes in a dry and uncooked state are frequently eaten by inhabitants of the countries in which this tape worm occurs, infection is limited to such regions.

FIG. 59.—Head and Neck of Broad Tape Worm.

FIG. 60.—*Tænia echinococcus,* showing the four joints.

A Dangerous Tape Worm.—Whilst the presence of any tape worm in the body undoubtedly gives rise to symptoms of ill-health, at the same time the ailment cannot be regarded as a rule as a dangerous one. The case is, however, very different when we come to consider the history of a special tape worm found in the dog, and known as the *Tænia echinococcus* (Fig. 60). This is an extremely small species of tape worm. In its total length it averages a quarter of an inch long and consists of four joints only. The head has a double row of hooklets and four suckers for adhesion to the intestine of the dog. The head measures in width the $\frac{1}{100}$th part of an inch. Only the last of the four joints is capable of producing eggs, which are of spherical shape. The great interest attaching to this worm is found in the fact that man unfortunately tends to appear as the first "host" of this parasite, although other animals, such as oxen and horses, may be infected.

Hydatids.—When the eggs of this dog tape worm are swallowed by man or other of the animals mentioned, instead of each developing

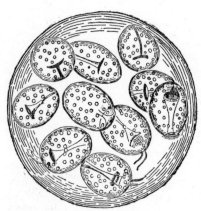

FIG. 61.—Cyst of Hydatid Tape Worm showing Secondary Growths.

into a little cystic worm it gives origin wherever it may rest—in the liver, lungs, brain, or kidneys—to a body called a *hydatid*. Inside this hydatid we find produced, by a process of budding (Fig. 61), other embryos which project from the sides of the cyst. Hence we find a tumour formed filled with a straw-coloured fluid containing a large proportion of salt to be formed. We can readily understand that if more than one such hydatid tumour is formed in the case of an organ like the liver, very serious destruction of the liver tissue may in this way be brought about. Each of the little embryos developed by budding inside the hydatid varies in length from the $\frac{1}{600}$th to the $\frac{1}{100}$th part of an inch. It possesses four suckers and a circlet of hooks.

We are now able to perceive the dangerous nature of the small tape worm of the dog, for if man swallows the eggs of this parasite they will tend to produce in his body *hydatid tumours*, involving serious risk of life. The dog no doubt obtains his infection from cattle and sheep, and from the hydatids produced in their bodies through these animals swallowing the eggs of the worm. In cases where dogs are fed on the offal of slaughter-houses infection of these animals is extremely frequent. Infection is also liable to occur in man from his close association with infected dogs, and also from drinking water into which the eggs of this tape worm have escaped. Uncooked vegetables in the shape of lettuce, for example, may also be regarded with suspicion, in that the eggs of this tape worm are liable to infect them. It may also be added by way of prevention that dogs should not be encouraged to lick the faces or hands of their owners, inasmuch as they may in this way convey parasites they have obtained from contact with other and infected dogs.   It is a wise law which enacts that no dog may be kept in a slaughter-house, as through the observance of this rule risk of infection can be largely avoided.

Prevention of Parasitic Infection.—With regard to the prevention of parasitic infection, there are four rules capable of being readily put into practice, the observance of which undoubtedly protects man from infection by the parasites just described.   The first rule enacts that *all flesh meat should be thoroughly cooked*.   If meat is kept at the boiling temperature for a certain time until its substance is permeated by the heat, the danger of infection contained in the meat may be avoided.   Hydatids are killed at a temperature of 170° F.   It has already been noted that infection is most common in countries where meat is eaten in a smoked or uncooked condition.   A physician has remarked that the habit of prescribing for various digestive ailments raw meat has resulted in an increase of cases of infection by the tape worms derived from uncooked beef and mutton.

A second rule advises us *to pay great attention to the purity of drinking water*.   Whilst ordinary supplies such as those of towns and cities may be regarded as thoroughly safe, water derived from wells, springs, and ponds cannot be so regarded, inasmuch as many chances exist of contamination by manure from the surroundings, such contaminating substances being liable, as we have seen, to contain the eggs of parasites.   Where any doubt exists regarding the purity of water-supply, the rule should be followed to use either a Berkefeld filter or to boil the water thoroughly before use.   The third rule concerns *the care with which all vegetables should be treated in the matter of cleanliness, and especially those vegetables which are eaten uncooked*.   The fourth and last rule concerns *the health of our dogs*. If a dog be noted to be passing worms of any kind he should be at once treated by the veterinary surgeon.

The Cat.—In this connection it might be well to add the information that *the cat is an animal liable to suffer from diphtheria* and to be infected from man, whilst in turn the cat can convey the disease to the human subject.   This fact has already been noted in the section of this work dealing with diphtheria (vol. i.).   Any cat exhibiting symptoms of throat trouble with sneezing and running at the nose, should be carefully isolated and kept apart from association with human beings so as to determine the necessity, in event of its becoming worse, of mercifully killing it so as to prevent the spread of this terrible ailment.

Treatment.—The treatment of round and thread worms has already been described. For the treatment of tape worm a somewhat different plan has to be practised. It is well to mention here that a great number of cases fail to be speedily cured because the strict directions of the physician are not adhered to. In the second place it must be clearly understood that *no case of tape worm can be regarded as cured unless the minute head is brought away with the joints.* If the head and neck alone be left attached to the lining membrane of the bowel they will be capable, through the process of budding already described, of giving origin to a new worm, so that in many cases a patient from whose bowel has been discharged several feet of a worm and who imagines himself to be cured is apt to feel thoroughly disappointed when after an interval joints begin again to be discharged.

Treatment of Tape Worm.—The remedy upon which most reliance is placed for the cure of tape worm is the *extract of male fern.* An authority lays great stress on the fact that disappointment in the treatment of tape worm by this drug depends upon the extract not being freshly prepared or on its not having been taken from an active root stock of the fern. The mode of treating a case of tape worm resolves itself into ensuring that the stomach and bowels are as empty as possible. To effect this end the patient is usually advised to fast for a period of eight hours before taking the medicine. In other cases a dose of castor oil or of Epsom salts taken three hours before its administration may effect the same end. At bedtime, the liquid extract of male fern is taken. The dose is a drachm, although ninety minims in the case of a strong man may be taken with safety. The extract should be given in a drachm dose, to which are added one drachm of powdered gum arabic and one ounce of peppermint water. Another formula consists of : Seventy-five minims of the liquid extract of male fern, one yolk of egg with a little chloroform water and simple syrup to make up a two ounce mixture. Presuming this dose has been administered at bedtime after an eight hours' fast, in the morning a full dose of castor oil should be taken. A meal of mashed potatoes is recommended to be taken in the forenoon. After this treatment the worm will probably be expelled. Careful search should then be made to ascertain if the head and neck are present. If not, the same treatment should be repeated after an interval of say three days. If the extract of male fern causes nausea and sickness as above prescribed, the chemist should be instructed to place this substance in capsules containing ten or fifteen minims each. Four or six of these capsules may be taken for a dose in place of the draught above described.

Other remedies for tape worm include turpentine. The objection to this remedy is that it must be given in a fairly large dose and the amount required is apt to induce serious irritation of the kidneys. *Kousso* has also been prescribed, this substance being infused in boiling water in a quantity of four drachms. The infusion is swallowed when it has become cold. The rhind or bark of *pomegranate* taken in the form of a decoction is also effective. From one to two ounces of the decoction may be taken each hour after fasting until three doses have been swallowed.

It may be well to add that all tape worms or other parasites passing from the bowel should be duly burned by way of avoiding any distribution of the eggs and of thus preventing fresh infections.

VEGETABLE (SKIN) PARASITES

Tinea Trycophytina, or Ringworm.—This is a highly contagious disease, and produced by a vegetable parasite or fungus, which infects the epidermal layer of the *skin*, and attacks the hair. Its characteristic appearance differs according as it appears on the body (*tinea circinata*), on the head (*tinea tonsurans*), or on the hairy parts of the face (*tinea sycosis*).

Ringworm of the Body.—This ailment begins as a small pimple or patch covered with scales, and if looked at carefully minute vesicles will be seen at the margin. As the patch grows at the margin the centre becomes paler and less scaly, and eventually a red, slightly raised, scaly *ring* is formed, hence the name. There may be only one patch or several, and sometimes contiguous rings run into one another, and form a scroll pattern over the affected area. The exposed parts of the body, such as the face, neck, and forearms, are the regions most frequently affected ; and the disease may be contracted from some of the domestic animals, such as the horse, dog, and cat. Ringworm is sometimes mistaken for a certain variety of psoriasis or for eczema, but if a few of the scales be soaked for a few minutes in a solution of caustic potash, and then placed under the microscope, the fungus will be easily discovered.

Treatment.—Ringworm of the body is the easiest variety to cure, as there are very few hairs to be infected, and local applications alone are needed. What these are to be will depend upon the age of the patient. In children, simply washing the parts thoroughly with soap and water, and applying an ointment composed of half a drachm of ammoniated mercury in an ounce of simple ointment, is as a rule sufficient. In older people, an ointment consisting of from one to three drachms of hyposulphite of sodium in an ounce of simple ointment, should be firmly rubbed into the affected area night and morning. Sulphur ointment or the ammoniated mercury ointment may also be used ; whilst sometimes painting the ring with a strong tincture of iodine or with glacial acetic acid quickly effects a cure.

Ringworm of the Head.—This is a chronic disease which may run an indefinite course unless treated with perseverance and care. It begins as a small red scaly pimple, which spreads at the margin, and very soon a rounded greyish patch covered with fine scales is formed. The hairs are soon affected, so that they lose their gloss, become brittle, and break off short, the end of the stump having a ragged uneven appearance, many of the hairs fall out, so that the affected area is practically bald, with only a few stumps projecting here and there. Occasionally minute patches of the disease break out in several parts of the head simultaneously, and then are very difficult to discover.

Treatment.—This, to be efficient, must be systematic, and may be divided into three lines : (1) To protect other members of the family, for the disease is highly contagious ; (2) to localise the disease to the affected area, and prevent it spreading to other parts of the head ; and (3) to attack the disease itself. The first indication is carried out by providing the patient with his own brushes, combs, and towels. The second, by washing the head frequently with some parasiticide, such as a saturated solution of boracic acid, or a 2 per cent. solution of carbolic acid, and by cutting the hair very short. The third by applying a parasiticide to the affected area, and *extracting the hairs* growing in it ; this latter can be easily done if broad-bladed sharp forceps (epilation forceps) made for the purpose are used, a few hairs being taken out at a time. After each time that some of the hairs have been extracted some of the ointment should be well rubbed in, and in any case this should be done twice a day. Any of the following parasiticide preparations may be used : Boracic acid, twenty grains ; sulphuric ether, one drachm ; rectified spirit, to one ounce. This lotion should be painted on with a brush night and morning, and is suitable for delicate skins. Or sulphur ointment, four drachms ; nitrate of mercury ointment, one drachm. These two are to be mixed together, and then one drachm of pure carbolic acid is to be added ; or one drachm of carbolic acid may be added to an ounce of glycerine, or to an ounce of simple ointment, to form an ointment. In chronic cases *Coster's paste,* consisting of two drachms of iodine and one ounce of oil of pitch, may be painted on with a brush, and allowed to remain on till the crust falls off, when it may be reapplied.

Tinea Sycosis, or Ringworm of the hairy parts of the face and neck. is a contagious extremely chronic variety of the disease. It begins as a small, red, scaly pimple, which spreads at its margin, setting up inflammation in the hair follicles and deeper layers of the skin, so that a typical case shows a rounded, raised, hard, lumpy, patch of disease, which shows points of suppuration, and in which the hairs become brittle, break off short, and fall out, or may be easily extracted. Its usual site is below the jaw or at the back of the neck. It is sometimes difficult to distinguish between tinea sycosis and the non-parasitic variety of the disease, which has already been described. The sensation of burning, however, is much more marked in the latter, the hairs are not primarily affected, and consequently do not become brittle, nor can they be easily extracted, and there is not the same amount of inflammatory thickening and lumpiness of the surface which is so marked a characteristic of ringworm.

Treatment.—This consists in keeping the parts closely shaved, in extracting all the hairs growing in the affected area, and in the careful persistent application twice a day of a parasiticide, of which corrosive sublimate is the best and may be painted on as a lotion two or three grains to the ounce of water, or a 1 per cent. solution in tincture of Benzoni. If an ointment is preferred, one comprising a drachm of hyposulphite of sodium in an ounce of simple ointment can be recommended. The Röntgen rays have proved efficacious in some cases. Whatever the form of treatment is, it must be persevered in for a considerable time.

Favus, or Honeycomb Ringworm, is a comparatively rare contagious disease due to a vegetable parasite, the *Achorion Schönleinii*, and is characterised by the appearance on the scalp of separate, or confluent, circular, cup-shaped, yellow crusts, usually perforated by hairs. The disease begins as a general scaly inflammation, followed very quickly by the formation of the characteristic crusts, which emit an odour like mice, and which when removed are found to be friable, crumbling away between the fingers; they consist almost entirely of the fungus. The hair becomes affected very early in the course of the disease, and falls out or breaks off short.

Treatment.—Consists in removing the crusts by first softening them with poultices; careful extraction of the hairs, and the application of a parasiticide, such as the corrosive sublimate lotion already mentioned; or sulphurous acid, or a sulphur ointment containing two drachms of sulphur to the ounce of simple ointment, twice a day.

Tinea Versicolor, or Chloasma, is a contagious disease due to the growth on the skin of a vegetable parasite, the *Microsporon furfur*, and is characteristic by the appearance on the trunk of brownish yellow, irregularly shaped patches, which are covered with fine branny scales and are often itchy.

Treatment consists in thoroughly washing the parts with soft soap and water, and then rubbing in turpentine, or a solution of hyposulphite of sodium a drachm to the ounce of water. As the disease is contagious, it is well to examine all the members of the family, and cure them all at the same time.

Impetigo.—A contagious variety of this disease is frequently met with in children, and sometimes attacks adults. Some observers have found a vegetable parasite closely resembling the *trycophyton* as seen in ringworm of the body, and to this they attribute the affection, whilst others, equally careful, have failed to discover any parasite, so that the question as to the parasitic nature of the disease remains an open one. Impetigo resembles *eczema,* and, indeed, many cases of *pustular eczema,* which may or may not be due to the presence of *pediculi,* are wrongly termed impetigo. There are, however, a certain number of cases characterised by the appearance, on the more exposed parts of the body, but more especially on the face and hands, of groups of *vesicles* the size of a split pea, unaccompanied by itching. These vesicles soon become pustular, and eventually bright yellow scabs form, which are raised above the surface of the skin, and are surrounded by a ring of inflammation. When the scabs dry and fall off a red mark remains, which gradually fades away. The contents of the vesicles are *extremely infective,* so that the disease not only spreads from one part of the body to another, but may attack all the members of a family, and, indeed, one case may infect a whole street or school, the disease usually occurring in epidemics. Impetigo may be distinguished from pustular eczema by the absence of itching and by the bright yellow scabs.

The *treatment* consists first in softening and removing the scabs by the use of poultices or washing with hot water, after which an ointment consisting of ten grains of ammoniated mercury in an ounce of lard is to be applied. Attention must be paid to personal cleanliness, and to the general health.

Excessive Itching, or Pruritus, is often due to other causes than skin troubles. It characterises some kidney-troubles, one very annoying form affecting the genitals of women. The treatment resolves itself into the discovery of the special cause. A lotion made by adding a little liquor carbonis detergens to tepid water often acts admirably. The glycerine of borax is also a useful remedy for outward application.

SECTION VII

THE ANATOMY AND PHYSIOLOGY OF THE EYE

BY way of introduction to the consideration of diseases of the eyes, and following out the rule adopted in this work of giving an account of the natural structure of organs and parts before proceeding to consider their diseases, we may now proceed, in accordance with this plan, to discuss the anatomy and physiology of our organs of vision. The eye is situated in a special cavity of the skull known as the *orbit* (Fig. 63, 2). The composition of this eye-cavity has already been referred to in connection with the description of the bones of the skull. In this cavity the eye reposes on a delicate cushion composed of fat (Fig. 62, Q). It is this bedding which, in a fashion, renders the eye less likely to sustain shock, whilst the overhanging part of the orbit also tends to its further protection from injury. When through old age, or it may be through disease, the amount of fat in the bed of the eye is diminished, we

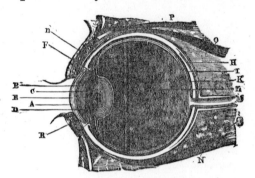

FIG. 62.—Section of the Eye.

A, Transparent Cornea ; B, Aqueous Humour ; C, Pupil ; D, Iris ; E, Crystalline Lens ; F, Ciliary Processes ; H, Sclerotic Coat ; I, Choroid Coat ; K, Retina ; L, Vitreous Humour ; M, Optic Nerve ; N and R, Eye-muscles ; P and O, Eyelid Muscles ; Q, Orbital Fat.

then obtain the sunken appearance of the eye characteristic of both of these states. Each eye is further protected by its eyelids, which are folds of skin lined with mucous membrane similar to the membrane which lines other cavities and regions of the body. Towards the inner surface of each lid we find a line of small glands developed. Each gland opens on the edge of the lid. These are called *Meibomian glands.* They supply a secretion which serves to keep the edges of the eyelids moist where they come in contact. What is termed a *Meibomian Cyst* consists of a distension of one of these little glands by its own secretion, its outlet having, by some means, become blocked. They will be referred to later as Cysts of the Eyelids. The eyelashes are situated on the edges of the lids. It is notable of these hairs that they are susceptible of extremely quick growth, and when an eyelash is lost the *hair follicle* or sac is capable of soon reproducing a new hair.

The Conjunctiva and Tear Glands.—The special name given to the membrane lining the lids is the *conjunctiva*. This is really a continuation of the skin of the body, and, after being distributed to the inner surface of the lid, it is reflected over the eyeball. In the case of an ordinary inflammation of the eye, as will be hereafter explained, the blood-vessels of the *conjunctiva* become much engorged. In such a case the inflammation is naturally called *conjunctivitis*. Connected with the eyes, as accessory parts, we find the *tear glands.* Each *lachrymal gland*, as the tear gland is called, is placed to the outside of the eyeball, and lies practically in the upper and outer corner of the orbit (Fig. 63, 3). This gland secretes, or manufactures, the tears from the blood which is supplied to it. The tears largely consist of water and certain minerals, of which salt is probably the chief. Hence the poetic phrase, "Salt, salt tears," is applicable enough as a scientific description of this fluid. The tears are poured out upon the surface of the eyeball from small ducts opening on the inner side of the upper eyelid. This fluid flows over the eyeball, and is primarily intended for the purpose of keeping the eyeball moist and clean, and also of washing off the surface any irritating particles which may gain access thereto. Near the inner angle of the eye we find two small openings, each leading to a canal (5). These canals are found to pass between the eye-cavity and the bridge of the nose. Here we find a small *lachrymal sac* or bag-like structure (7), which receives the waste fluid. The tears finally pass into a tube called the *nasal duct* (8), which leads directly into the nostril, so that the nostrils constitute, as it were, the drainage canals of the eyes. In certain eye troubles, to be afterwards described, the nasal duct is liable to be blocked up, causing an overflow of the tears from the eyes themselves. When we cry and when the tears roll down the cheeks, we see the results of mental emotion producing an increased flow of the contents of the tear glands, so that the nasal duct, for the time being, is unable to carry off the excess.

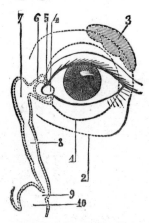

Fig. 63.—The Tear Glands.

1, Outline of the Globe of the Eye; 2, the Orbit; 3, Lachrymal Gland; 4, the Caruncle; 5, Tubercle and Superior Lachrymal Point; 6, Lachrymal Canal, Superior; 7, Lachrymal Sac; 8, Canal or Duct to Nose; 9, Inferior Opening of Nasal Duct; 10, Lower Opening of Nose.

The Eyeball.—The eyeball and its contents may be best described if we look at a section of the organ to start with (Fig. 62). The whole structure of the eye may very well be compared to a photographer's camera. In both we find an apparatus for receiving and condensing or converging the waves of light, which, proceeding from objects, enable us to see them. In both we find means for focussing the apparatus, so as to adapt them for purposes of receiving images situated at varying distances. In both we discover a sensitive plate or apparatus upon which the images are received, whilst in both we find means for excluding vagrant or wandering, or at least unnecessary, light waves. This likeness to the photographer's camera has struck all physiologists, and we shall be able in detail to note more fully how the resemblance in question is carried out. The eyeball may be described to be a hollow globe or chamber, containing in its interior certain definite structures. In the first instance, we find that its shape is due to the fact that the outermost coat (*sclerotic*) (Fig. 62, H) is of dense structure, and thus gives the eyeball its shape. This coat or layer is denser or thicker at its hinder part than in its front portion. In colour this *sclerotic* coat is white; hence, when we talk familiarly of the "white of the eye" we mean to indicate this particular layer. In the front of the eye the sclerotic becomes transparent, and presents us with what we may call a circular window known as the *cornea* (A). Popularly the *cornea* is known as the "*sight*" of the eye. Whilst the *sclerotic* possesses both blood-vessels and nerves, the *cornea* wants the former, but contains an abundant supply of nerves. With regard to its microscopic structure we note the *cornea* to exhibit many highly interesting features. Chief amongst these is the fact that it may be described as a thoroughly living structure, seeing that it contains a large amount of living matter or *protoplasm*. Physiologists therefore incline to the belief that this particular constitution of the *cornea* makes up for the want of blood-vessels, in that it maintains its living and highly characteristic appearance not so much in virtue of blood supply, but because it itself contains living material. The *conjunctiva*, continuous with *d*, Fig. 64, which we have seen to cover this sclerotic coat, is only very loosely attached to it, but becomes altered in appearance when it is continued over the cornea itself, losing all its blood-vessels, and blending intimately with the underlying corneal tissue. The second coat of the eyeball and that lying inside the sclerotic coat is known as the *choroid layer* (Fig. 62, I). The choroid represents the dark coat of the eyeball, this character being given to it by the numerous cells containing black colouring matter with which it is supplied. In addition, this latter coat is well supplied with blood-vessels adapted for the nourishment of the adjacent parts. In front the choroid coat ends close to the point where the sclerotic coat, as already described, merges into the cornea. Here we find a number of processes known as *ciliary processes* (F, Fig. 62). These possess a distinct relation to certain other structures included in the eyeball, and perform certain important duties in connection with the eye's work.

The Iris and Eye-humours.—In the front of the eyeball we find other parts which require to be duly noted. In the first place comes the *iris* (D), which may be described as a kind of curtain. It is the coloured part of the eye, and, as we look at it, we see that the particular colour of an individual's eyes is thus explained. In the centre of the iris is a hole known as the *pupil* (C). To the ordinary eye this appears as a round black spot. In reality, through the pupil we are looking into the interior of the eyeball. Immediately in front of the *lens* we find a space which we may call the *anterior compartment* of the eye (B). This chamber is filled with a fluid called the *aqueous humour*, a term applied to it from the fact that it largely consists of water and minerals. Behind the lens is a larger chamber which we may call the *posterior compartment* (L) of the eye. This is completely occupied by a jelly-like substance known as the *vitreous humour*. It does not appear to exercise any important function as regards sight, but may be regarded as a structure which, practically filling the greater part of the eyeball, enables it to maintain its characteristic shape.

The Pupil's Movements.—The *iris* has been described as a kind of curtain with a hole (the *pupil*) in the middle of it. This curtain possesses certain remarkable powers of contraction, due to the fact that it contains muscular fibres of an involuntary nature. There are in reality two sets of these fibres, the outer set running round the edge of the pupil, whilst the other set may be said to resemble somewhat the arrangement of the spokes of a wheel. It is through the contraction of these muscular fibres that the pupil is enlarged to allow more light to enter the eye, or contracted so as to avoid injury of the eye through too great an amount of light being present. We can readily notice these movements of the pupil if we cause a person to stand in front of a bright light. The pupil is then seen to be contracted. If now we shade the eye with our hand the pupil will be seen to expand. These changes are much more characteristically seen in an animal like the cat. Animals accustomed, as are carnivorous creatures, to hunt by night, generally have more distensible pupils than other creatures.

The Lens (E).—Lying immediately behind the pupil of the

eye we come upon another structure called the *crystalline lens*. This structure has been compared to an ordinary magnifying glass. In shape it is convex, or bulges out on each face or aspect, the convexity being less in front than behind. This is a clear and transparent structure, destitute of all colour, and of a crystal-like appearance. As the years of life pass on, however, the lens tends to become of somewhat denser consistence, and acquires a yellowish tint. In this condition vision is not necessarily interfered with, but if, as sometimes happens, particularly in old persons, the lens becomes opaque, instead of presenting us with a clear glass appearance, and shows a structure resembling that of ground glass, we then say that the individual exhibiting this peculiarity suffers from *cataract*. This subject will be referred to in connection with diseases of the eye. It may only here be mentioned that an operation can be successfully undertaken for the cure of this disease. The opaque lens is removed from the eye, and in such a case it is filled by watery fluid, which itself not being sufficient for direct vision, is made available by the use of appropriate glasses.

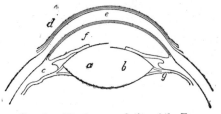

FIG. 64.—The Accommodation of the Eye.

a, Lens, with front advanced for near sight; *b*, Lens at rest; *c*, Ciliary Muscle; *d*, Corneal Outer Layer; *e*, Cornea; *f*, Hinder Corneal Layer. (The Iris is the line on each side of the Lens in front.) *g*, Suspensory Ligament of Lens.

The Accommodation of the Eye.

—As will be understood from the description of the parts of the eye already noted, the crystalline lens lies in close relation to the iris in front, and to the vitreous humour behind. The lens is an extremely important structure in respect of the fact that to alterations in its shape are due the wonderful power we possess of focussing the eye for different distances. Thus, in a moment, from reading a book at a distance of say twelve or fourteen inches from the eye, we are enabled to focus our gaze upon say a church clock half a mile away. This focussing, which in the case of a telescope or opera-glass requires a considerable amount of trouble, is accomplished in our eyes instantaneously and involuntarily. The part played by the crystalline lens can be readily understood. It may be described as being contained within a kind of sac, known as the *suspensory ligament* (Fig. 64, *g*). It is due to the action of this *suspensory ligament* that the alteration in the shape of the lens enables us to focus the eye, as has been described. The ligament is attached to the *ciliary process* (*c*) already described in connection with the choroid coat of the eye. In the natural condition of matters the lens is kept somewhat flattened by the tension or pull exerted by the ligament. Close by, and surrounding the point of union of the cornea, the ciliary processes, and the choroid layer, we find a number of muscular fibres of involuntary kind which are known collectively as the *ciliary muscle* (c). If we now suppose this muscle to contract, it tends to advance or to pull forward the suspensory ligament. The result of this action is that the pressure on the lens is decreased, and being of an elastic nature it at once bulges outwards, or, in other words, becomes more convex than before. The manner in which these actions accommodate the eye for sight at varying distances may now be understood. If we are looking at an object near at hand the ciliary muscle comes into action. As a result the lens bulges forwards, or, as has been described, becomes *more convex* (a). The waves of light are more refracted, and the image of the near object is thus duly formed in the eye. If, however, we look at a distant object the reverse procedure takes place. The ciliary muscle ceases its action, whilst that of the suspensory ligament comes into play. The result is that the lens becomes more flattened and the eye is adapted for regarding a more distant object (b). We thus see that when we regard any such object, the accommodating powers of the eye are not brought into play, the front surface of the lens being kept in its flattened position by the action of its capsule and of the suspensory ligament. Looking, as has been described, at a near object, the ciliary muscle comes into play, diminishes the tension of the ligament, and causes therefore the lens to become more convex. In the case of the photographer's camera, as has been well remarked, it is adapted to varying distances by moving the sensitive plate backwards and forwards, whereas in the case of the eye the sensitive plate, to be presently described, remains in the same position, and the adaptation is carried out by the change in the *shape* of the lens itself.

The Retina.—Another structure of extreme importance remains to be described in connection with the eye. This structure corresponds to the sensitive plate of the photographer's camera. It is known as the *retina* (Fig. 62, K). It consists practically of an expansion of the *optic nerve* (M) of the eye, or that which conveys the impressions received by the eye backwards to the brain. The *retina* practically lines the eyeball on its inner surface, and rests on the *choroid* coat (I). In front it comes in contact with the *vitreous humour* already described. This membrane is naturally of very delicate structure. As a rule it can be stripped off from the adjacent parts, but exhibits one point of attachment where it joins the optic nerve. This optic nerve enters the eyeball not quite at the middle of the back-surface, being inclined very slightly towards the inner side, or that of the nose.

The Elements of the Retina.—It is not necessary here to enter into extreme detail as to the microscopical structure of this wonderful layer. Amongst the elements of the *retina*, however, may be mentioned two sets of bodies known as *rods* and *cones*. Physiologists regard those *rods* and *cones* (Fig. 65, *a*) as the essential terminals, if we may so term it, of the nervous elements of the eye. The particular condition known as *colour blindness*, which consists of an inability to distinguish certain colours, appears to arise from a deficiency in the development of the *rods* and *cones*. For such a condition of course there is no cure. It is necessary also to observe that as regards the retina we find opposite the centre of the pupil of the eye a spot of yellowish colour of somewhat oval form. This is known as the *macula lutea*, or *yellow spot*. In the centre of this spot there is a central hollow or depression, known as the *fovea centralis*. Here the retina is of an extremely fine nature. It would appear that it is not sensitive to an equal degree in all its parts to the light waves on the reception of which our vision depends. In the yellow spot, therefore, the sensitiveness is probably most highly developed, and we may conclude that objects can be most distinctly perceived when the light waves proceeding from them fall directly on this part of the retina. At the yellow spot the cones of the *retina* are specially developed.

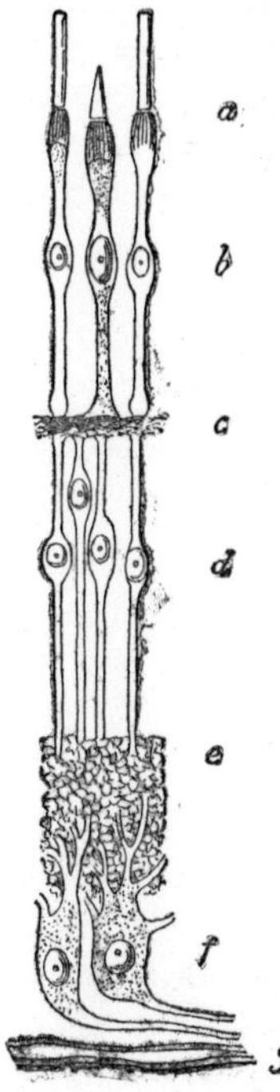

FIG. 65.—The Rods and Cones of the Retina.

a, Rods and Cones; *b*, External Granular Layer; *c*, Inner Granular Layer; *d*, Internal Granular Layer; *e*, Molecular Layer; *f*, Large Nerve Cells; *g*, Fibres of the Optic Nerve.

The "Blind Spot."—At the spot where the optic nerve expands to form the retina we find a point at which the eye seems to be totally non-sensitive to the influence of light. This spot is known as the *blind spot*. It would appear that light waves have no effect in stimulating it in any way. Here the rods and cones of the retina are absent, this latter fact tending to show the difference between the blind spot and other sensitive areas of the retina. A simple experiment may be quoted by way of demonstrating the existence of this blind spot. If we close the left eye, holding out the arms to the front, doubling the fingers but keeping the thumbs in contact with each other and upright, and then look steadily in a good light at the left thumb with the right eye, we may note a peculiar feature when the right arm is slowly moved outwards. Thus, if this experiment be properly performed, when the thumbs are separated for a distance of about six inches the right thumb cannot be seen. If, however, it be moved further away it again comes into view, or when brought back and placed in contact with the other thumb. Here we see that at a certain distance all the rays of light from the thumb fall on the blind spot of the retina, and thus produce no sensation on the sight; whilst an alteration of the position of the thumb, bringing the light waves to other parts of the retina, restores the power of vision. The same experiment may be performed in another way by taking a piece of cardboard three or four inches long, and by making a small cross at one end and a much larger cross at the other. If this piece of cardboard be held before the eyes and the left eye shut, whilst the right eye is closely fixed on the small cross, the larger cross will disappear according as we move the board to or from the eye.

Eye Movements.—The movements of the eyes are carried out by means of six small muscles (Fig. 62, R and N show two of the six), the eyes being capable not merely of being moved from side to side, but of being rolled in the socket in various directions. *Squinting*, as will be hereafter shown, is due to the fact that a divergence of action exists between the muscles of the two eyes. It has already been noted that all our sensations of sight are due to the fact that light waves given off by the objects we see pass into the interior of the eye and are condensed or concentrated by passing through the various structures of the eye. They are finally arrested on the retina as the eye's sensitive plate as the part on which the images of things seen are formed. The transmission of these images from the retina to the brain, where further modifications must take place, resulting in the last act of all, namely, the appreciation or consciousness of all we see, leads us into fields of speculation regarding brain work to which further reference cannot be made here.

How we See.—It is curious to note that the images of things seen are found to be received in an upside-down fashion by the retina, and that, notwithstanding this, we have the consciousness of perceiving objects in their natural position. An eminent authority on the eye remarks on this point that "much ingenuity has been expended at various times in endeavours to explain how it is that inverted images upon the retina produce the erect condition of the objects which the images represent. The most probable of these explanations is that the nerve elements of the perceptive layer of the retina, which consist of rods or cones, being in their long axes directed towards the centre of the eyeball, naturally refer the impressions which are made upon each of them to the direction from which the light proceeds. Thus the cones of the upper portion of the retina, being directed downwards,

STRUCTURE OF THE EYE

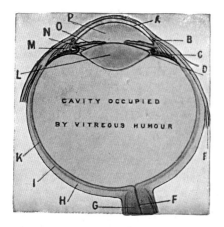

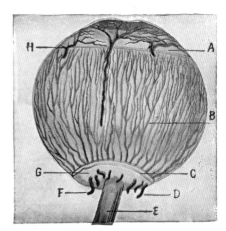

A. Cornea
B. Canal of Schlemm.
C. Ciliary Process.
D. Canal of Petit.
E. Internal Rectus Muscle.
F. Canal for Central Artery.
G. Optic Nerve.
H. Sclerotic Coat.
I. Choroid Coat.
K. Retina.
L. Crystalline Lens.
M. Ciliary Body.
N. Posterior Chamber.
O. Iris.
P. Anterior Chamber
(Aqueous Humour)

A. Ciliary Muscle.
B. Long Ciliary Arteries.
G.C. Sclerotic Coat.
F.D. Short Ciliary Arteries
E. Optic Nerve.
H. Anterior Ciliary Artery.

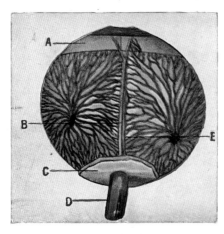

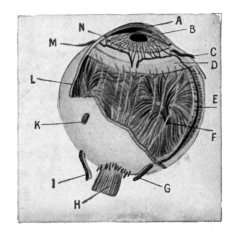

A. Ciliary Muscle.
B. Ciliary Nerve.
C. Sclerotic Coat.
D. Optic Nerve.
E. Long Ciliary Vein.

A. Cornea.
B. Pupil.
C.M. Anterior Ciliary Arteries.
D. Ciliary Muscle.
E.G.I. Long Posterior Ciliary
Arteries.
F.K. Venæ Vorticosæ.
H. Optic Nerve.
L. Sclerotic Coat.
N. Canal of Schlemm.

FROM DRAWINGS BY EDWARD BURNET, B.A. (Lond.).

and receiving the rays of light from below, naturally refer or trace them to objects at a lower level than the eye; while those of the lower portion, being directed upwards and receiving rays of light from above, naturally refer or trace them to objects above the level of the eye. In this way it can readily be understood that the inversion of the retinal image may be self-correcting when it is regarded as a source of the sensory impressions which are communicated to the brain." Another authority, dealing with the same question, asks: " Why is it that objects do not appear to us to be upside down? This is easily understood when we remember that the sensation of sight occurs not in the eye but in the brain. By education the brain learns that the tops of objects excite certain portions of the retina, and the lower parts of objects other portions of the retina. That these portions of the retina are reversed in position to the parts of the object does not matter at all any more than does it matter when one's photograph arrives home from the photographer that it was the wrong way in the photographer's camera. One puts it the right way in the photograph album." It has also been well remarked that the sense of touch must have exerted a very considerable influence in the education of the brain towards the proper appreciation of the position of external objects. If for example we wish to touch any part of an object outside us, the image of which exists on the lower portion of the retina, we naturally raise the hand, or if we wish to touch any object or part of an object, the impression of which is received on the right side, the right hand must be passed to the left side, and *vice versâ*.

Single Vision.—Yet another point of interest in connection with the eye is that which leads us to consider the question why we have single vision while we have two eyes. There is no doubt whatever that a double image is produced of each object seen, one image on each retina. It is therefore an easy matter to disturb this singleness of vision, and to produce double vision. The simplest experiment of this kind is that of pressing the eyeball with the finger to one side, in which case a double image of an object looked at will be seen. Very much on the principle that when the two barrels of a binocular glass are acting equally and perfectly we gain a clear sight of the object looked at, whilst even a slight irregularity in the movement of the two barrels of the glass will produce blurring of the vision, so we may assume that it is only when the image of any object is received or falls upon an exactly corresponding part in each retina is single vision possible. In persons who are troubled with *squint*, it might be assumed that, owing to the irregular action of the one eyeball as compared with that of the other, double vision would be apparent. This would be the case but for the fact that persons troubled with a squint practically look at objects with the straight eye, and learn to neglect the image formed on the squinting eye. This misuse of the eye is caused by the difficulty of focussing with both eyes, when there is irregularity of the sight (astigmatism) or long sight (hypermetropia). At the very earliest signs of squint a child or infant should be taken to an ophthalmic surgeon, and the necessary glasses must be worn constantly, or the child will lose the power of seeing with that eye.

Subjective Sight.—What have been termed *subjective sensations of sight* are those which appear to proceed from some irritation or other of the eyes themselves. Thus what are popularly known as "*seeing sparks*," or flashes of light, produced through some irritation of the eyeball, as when it receives a blow, have no real or outward existence, and are due to the irritation in question. These bright sparks are called *phosphenes.* Another example of such internal disturbance, giving rise to curious sensations, are what are called *muscæ volitantes.* These are popularly described as "floating specks" before the eyes. They appear to be produced by certain minute particles, probably contained in the humours of the eye; whilst in certain liver troubles, for example, and also in that variety of headache termed *migraine,* curious figures may appear, this again being due to some internal irritation of the organs of vision. Furthermore, if we suppose that such irritation proceeds directly from the brain, we may reach a state of matters in which the person may actually conceive that he sees objects or figures outside of him which have no real or active existence at all. A popular explanation of *ghost-seeing* is that which refers the production of the spectral figures to an irritation of the brain, whereby there is projected from the brain outwardly upon the retina of the eye images or memories, it may be, of things or objects once seen. An individual affected thus, is said to suffer from hallucinations. These latter are common in sane persons, and are also seen in the case of the drunkard when attacked with *delirium tremens.*

About Colour.—In relation to the exercise of the sense of sight, a few words in conclusion may be permissible regarding the relation of colour to the eye. Ordinary light, as most readers may be aware, is really composed of several different kinds of rays. These rays are red, yellow, green, blue, indigo, orange, and violet. The reason why any bodies appear to us coloured is owing to the fact that certain light rays are allowed to proceed through them, whilst others are intercepted by them. Thus if we speak of red glass, the sensation in virtue of which we term the glass red is due to the fact that the glass allows only red rays to reach the eye, the others being intercepted. In the same way, if any body or object intercepts all other rays save yellow and certain of the red rays, it will appear orange-coloured to the eye. It is also found that blends of certain light rays, called *complementary colours*, will give a sensation of white. Thus orange and blue will produce white, as also will green and purple, and yellow and indigo blue. How the colour is perceived by the eye is a somewhat difficult matter to explain; but the theory has been very fully worked out by certain physiologists. · Assuming that there are three fundamental colours—red, green, and violet, and that these produce the impression of white, they presume that there are three sets of nerve fibres in the eye, each capable of responding to one of the colours in question. It is supposed that when all three fibres are equally stimulated, sensation of white is perceived, whilst a sensation of red will arise from the excessive stimulation of the fibres sensitive to that colour, the other fibres not responding to the stimulation in question.

Another interesting point connected with the functions of the eye, and with the manner in which colour perception is carried out, is that called *after-images*. A familiar illustration of this phenomena is found, for example, when, after gazing at objects in a bright light, we seem to retain the impression or picture of the things seen after our eyes are turned away from them, or when the eyes are closed. Sometimes these images appear in their natural colours and tints, in which case they are called *positive after-images*. On the other hand, we may experience the sensation of *negative after-images* when the light and shade are reversed, as for example when a window appears dark and dark objects white. This latter result is brought about apparently through gazing at the object for a longer period than that which results in the production of the positive images.

DISEASES OF THE EYES

The eye is such an important organ, and the loss or impairment of its functions is of such serious consequence to the individual, that it is essential to know something of the common diseases to which it is liable; their causes, symptoms, how they may be avoided, and how they may be treated when they occur. This Section is not intended to enable any one to treat for himself the serious diseases of the eye, such as, for instance, *iritis* (inflammation of the iris), but is written in the hope that by giving a simple description of these ailments the reader may escape the serious consequences of neglected diseases, and that he may successfully treat those of minor importance, but which are frequently the cause of no little annoyance and discomfort. The general lines upon which the more serious eye affections are here treated may be briefly stated, partly as a matter of scientific interest, and partly with the idea that if this work should be in the possession of any one stationed miles away from a doctor, and yet having a medicine chest, he may be able to mitigate suffering, or even save the sight of an eye. Diseases which require the use of the ophthalmoscope (an instrument for looking right into the eye), such as inflammation of the retina, will be only briefly mentioned, as their detection requires much technical skill and practice.

Injuries to the Eye.—On account of the excellent protection afforded by its socket (Fig. 63, 2), the eye usually escapes injury from blows with things such as cricket balls, and nothing further than a "black eye" follows. It may, however, be burst by such an accident, or the retina may get displaced by the concussion; therefore after any very serious blow it is advisable to consult a doctor. The best immediate treatment is to apply a compress of lint dipped into pure cold water to the eye, and secure it in position by a handkerchief or bandage.

Black Eye.—When the soft tissues about the orbit are forcibly struck, the small capillaries (or minute blood-vessels) are injured, and allow the blood to diffuse into the loose tissue under the skin. The colour of the skin is due to the alteration that takes place in this blood before it is reabsorbed. It used to be a common remedy to apply a piece of raw beef, and firmly bind it to the injured eye. If this was done immediately after the accident it did good in limiting to some extent the amount of blood diffused into the tissues, by the mechanical effect of the cold and pressure. We do not apply raw beef, but we carry out the same idea in a more cleanly way. We fold some lint up into a pad of several thicknesses, wring it thoroughly out in *cold* water, and firmly bandage this on. After a "black eye" has once formed the cure must be patiently left to nature.

Small Bodies in the Eye, such as particles of coal dust. should be removed at once, as they cause great discomfort if allowed to remain. A great many devices exist for this purpose, such as taking a pinch of snuff, but none are so good as removal by manipulation. When you see any one with one of these little bodies in the eye, first of all look at the cornea or "sight" of the eye (Fig. 62, A) to see if it is there, then pull down the lower lid and afterwards turn up the upper lid. This latter can be very easily done, thus : Seat the patient in a chair, stand at the back of him, and take the lashes of the lid firmly between your thumb and finger of one hand. With the other hand lay a small instrument (a match will do) along the lid, *tell the patient to look down* and gently draw up the lashes, while you press down the upper part of the lid with the match. In this way the upper eyelid will be everted or turned upwards, so as to disclose its under surface. Having done this and found the offending particle, you can remove it with the edge of a moistened handkerchief. If much irritation is complained of afterwards, bathe the eye with a little warm water, or drop into it a few drops of this solution of cocaine hydrochlorate :—Cocaine hydrochlorate, four grains ; distilled water, one ounce.

Scratches of the "Sight" (the "watch-glass" of the eye) usually cause much pain. The treatment consists in bathing the eye with warm water, shading it, and using the cocaine drops. If not quickly bettered, see a doctor, as atropine drops will be needed, and these should only be used when ordered by the doctor.

Lime in the Eye.—Wash out with weak vinegar and water (not plain water), or sugar and water. In factories where this accident, and burns of the eye from "flashes" are frequent, a great deal of unnecessary pain might be saved if a mixture of castor oil and cocaine (eight grains of the cocaine (the alkaloid) to the ounce of castor oil) was kept handy and a little put into the eye before going to the doctor.

Small pieces of metal occasionally go right into the substance of the eye-ball, especially where men have to work at lathes. No time must then be lost in seeing an eye surgeon, who, if the substance is iron or steel, may be able to extract it with an electro-magnet. If allowed to remain for any length of time, destruction of the eye-ball is almost sure to follow.

The number of eyes that are lost by small pieces of metal penetrating them, and the amount of reduction of visual power that is occasioned by constantly getting small foreign bodies, such as emery (so largely used nowadays) on to the sight, has led many ophthalmic surgeons of experience to suggest that persons following occupations which render them liable to these accidents should wear protective glasses. Were this done, the toll of eyes blinded every year would be markedly diminished. A good glass would entirely prevent the emery from getting on to the "sight" and would stop 99 per cent. of all little missiles that fly up into the eye. Of course, if a man is a boiler-maker say, and a piece of a rivet flies into his eye, the case is serious, for no glass would save him from injury ; but what we want to emphasise is that the great majority of such accidents would be obviated by the use of *plane* glasses. The objection that they confuse the sight can have no weight, because numbers of artificers have become alive to the protection they afford, and work in them quite comfortably and securely. The danger of the glass breaking is infinitesimal, and should not deter any from using this simple precaution.

Before leaving the subject of injuries, just one word may be said about what is known as *sympathetic* inflammation. When one eye is so seriously injured that severe inflammation occurs in it, there is great danger of the other eye becoming affected, in sympathy, as it were. This terrible complication may occur within a few weeks to six months, or more, after the accident, and often total blindness is the result. To avoid this, the only way is not to wait too long before removing the eye that is injured; and to know what eye to attempt to save, or when to excise it, requires the skill and experience of a specialist. This operation is often objected to by the patient if he can see anything at all with the injured eye; but if he refuse treatment, valuable time may be lost. It is much wiser to take the advice, which at least will insure to him good vision in one eye, than run the risk of losing both.

Glass Eyes are usually put in about one month after the eye is removed. They are subject to much wear and tear, and must not be worn after they get rough. People wearing glass eyes should observe the following rules :—

1. Always remove the eye at bed-time, and wash and dry it.

2. Put a morsel of pure vaseline into the socket every morning. This makes the eye move easily, and prevents irritation.

If irritation occurs, wash out the socket with a little boracic lotion (half a teaspoonful of boracic acid to half a pint of warm water).

"Sore Eyes."—Just around the lashes, on the margins of the lids, a little redness and inflammation frequently occur. The lashes tend to fall off, and little scales collect around. The condition is popularly termed "*sore eyes.*" Its causes are, straining of the eyes by working in a bad light, &c., or from debility. It also is caused by defective sight, and should then be relieved by suitable spectacles. The best treatment is to remove all the scales by bathing the lids two or three times a day with warm soda and water (half a teaspoonful of washing soda to a pint of water), and then to apply a little weak mercury ointment, composed of four grains yellow oxide of mercury, and one ounce vaseline. The general health must be improved by fresh air, good food, and cod liver oil if necessary.

A Stye is a small abscess at the margin of the lid at the roots of the eyelashes. It is often very painful, and styes frequently tend to recur. The treatment is to apply warm boracic fomentations by means of clean old linen, to be wrung out of the following lotion :— One teaspoonful boracic acid; one pint hot water. When a definite little white abscess forms, just open it by the prick of a clean needle. At night a little boracic ointment should be put on the edge of the lids. Attend to the general health.

Cysts of the Eyelids.—These feel like little peas under the eyelid. They seldom reach any size, but there may be several of them. They can be easily opened by a doctor without any pain, if cocaine be first put into the eye, and as they are opened on the inner aspect of the lids they leave no visible scars.

Ingrowing Lashes and turning in of the lids frequently occur, especially in elderly people. The treatment is to remove the lashes that turn in. To do this, seize the lash with a small pair of forceps such as one often sees in a manicure case, and gently but firmly pull it out. If more than one or two lashes have to be removed, cocaine will first have to be put in, but you had then better let a doctor perform the little operation. Should they persistently grow in, they can be altogether destroyed by the electro-cautery or electrolysis.

"Watery Eyes."—This ailment is caused by some obstruction to the tube that drains the tears from the eye into the nose (Fig. 63, 5, 6, 7, 8, 9). The tears then run down the cheek. This requires a little operation for its relief, a probe being passed down the tear-duct. Associated with this condition a little swelling often forms at the inner angle of the eye (near the nose), and if this is gently pressed a little milky fluid can be squeezed out. Should this get inflamed an abscess or collection of matter will occur.

The treatment is to bathe the eye two or three times a day with boracic lotion (teaspoonful to a pint of water). If the little swelling is there, gently press on it to empty it. Should an abscess occur apply warm boracic fomentations, and see a doctor, for if it bursts it frequently leaves an unsightly scar, whereas a small incision would prevent this, and also give relief to the pain.

Diseases of the Conjunctiva.—The conjunctiva is the thin membrane covering the white of the eye and also the inside of the lids. When inflamed the condition is called *conjunctivitis* or *ophthalmia*.

Simple Conjunctivitis is caused by draughts, dust in the eyes, working by a bad light, or "roasting" the eyes over a hot winter fire, excess of tobacco or alcohol, &c. It is characterised by a "gritty feeling in the eye," pain, a sticky discharge, and a red eye. Both eyes are generally affected, and the lids stick together in the morning. The disease is commonest in the spring and autumn, and often runs through a whole household, showing infection to be conveyed by towels and like objects. A peculiar form of this affection occurs in young and weakly children who are just recovering from a fever, such as measles. In them, in addition to the general redness, you see a little yellowish-red spot often quite close to the "sight." It is called a "phlyctenule," and the child often fears the light so much that he will close his eyelids so tightly that it is almost impossible to see the eye.

Treatment.—Bathe the eyes several times a day with the warm boracic lotion, and if there is much pain and discharge put in a few drops of the following :—Sulphate of zinc, one grain ; hydrochlorate of cocaine, four grains ; distilled water, one ounce. Anoint the edges of the lids with a little vaseline to prevent them sticking together during the night. Such things as tobacco and stimulants had better be avoided, and smoked glasses may be used to protect the eyes from the wind or from too dazzling a light.

In the "*phlyctenular*" *form* in children a little of the yellow oxide of mercury ointment placed *inside* the lids night and morning is good local treatment. Use a shade for the eyes. The child in this, as in most other inflamed eye conditions, will mope in dark corners ; this he must be induced not to do. Give him a good broad shade ; you can make one easily out of stiff brown paper with tape threaded through holes in the upper corners and tied behind the head. Make him go out into the open air. At the same time give him a teaspoonful of cod liver oil and malt extract three times a day after food—in a word, do everything to improve the general health.

Purulent Ophthalmia.—This is a form of conjunctivitis of much more serious type than the foregoing. Here we get much swelling of the lids and conjunctiva, and the eye is bathed in a profuse yellow discharge. It is usually due to direct infection of the eye by a gonorrhœal discharge from the male or female generative organs. In the adult this usually occurs by means of the finger or through towels soiled by the discharge. A child may be infected from the mother as it is being born into the world.

Special reference must be made to this grave disease in children. Although the infection occurs at its birth the eyes are usually only noticed to be very sore on the third day after. The lids get swollen, and on separating them a yellow discharge is seen. When this occurs at once take the child to a doctor. Delay is dangerous, if the child's sight is to be retained. The eyes must be well washed with boracic lotion every hour or so, and the lids kept free from accumulation of the "matter." The doctor will prescribe drops usually of silver nitrate solution (two grains to the ounce of water), and this must be properly got into the eyes. Ointment is usually used, also to anoint the edges of the lids. This prevents sticking of the lids, and retention of the discharge in the eye. This condition accounts for nearly twenty-five out of every hundred cases of blindness in the country, and it is truly awful to contemplate the number of children that are doomed to total darkness every year by what is entirely a preventable disease. It is not saying too much to state that blindness from this cause would be as rare as it is now common if a few simple

DISEASES OF THE EYE.

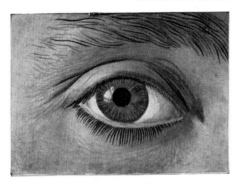

NORMAL EYE—IN HEALTH.

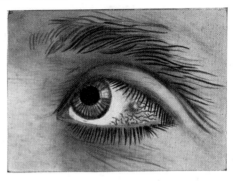

PUSTULAR INFLAMMATION OF THE CONJUNCTIVA.
(*Pustular Conjunctivitis*).

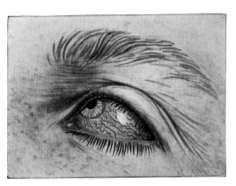

EPISCLERITIS.

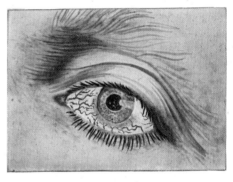

INFLAMMATION OF IRIS.
(*Serous Iritis*).

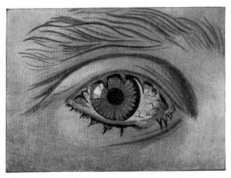

ECZEMA OF THE MARGIN OF THE EYE-LID.
(*Blepharitis*).

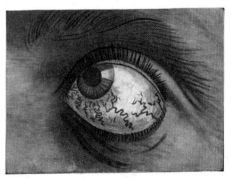

GLAUCOMA.

precautions were followed at the time of a child's birth. The essential rules are :—

1. As soon as a child is born its eyes should be carefully wiped, and gently washed over with some boracic acid lotion. Don't touch the eyes with the water you use for washing its body.

2. If the child's eyes·show any tendency to be inflamed on the third day, go to a doctor with it at once. Do not *poultice* the eye, for this is a most dangerous and reprehensible practice. It is a disgrace to the country that such ignorance exists of the terrible results of this all too common disease which entails such a penalty on the helpless victim, and if this article should only be the means of emphasising the nature of the disease and especially the means of prevention, much wretchedness will be prevented thereby. *Never poultice the eyes when there is any discharge. In fact poultices, as a rule, are bad in eye diseases.* When *moist* heat is required, it should be applied by lint wrung out of the hot boracic lotion.

It is a good working rule to regard *every* disease of the eye *in which there is a discharge, as contagious;* and with this point in view it will be well, at this juncture, to give a few cautions to those who have to deal with them.

The towels and washing materials, &c., of the patient should be kept strictly for him, and carefully boiled and disinfected after use. The linen used for wiping the discharge away should be burnt at once. It is also well to be careful not to use *soiled* towels in public lavatories, baths, &c. Cases of infection often occur in this way. Do not use sponges for bathing the eyes at all. Do not hug and kiss a baby suffering with discharge from the eyes, and when attending to the condition carefully wash your hands afterwards. Use only brown paper shades which can be easily renewed. Never buy an expensive shade and put it by for future use, after it is no longer required. Such a shade is a possible means of infecting any other eyes for which it may be used.

Diseases of the Cornea (Fig. 62, A, Fig. 64, *e*).—The cornea, as previously stated, is the clear part of the front of the eye, or, as it is sometimes called, the "watch-glass" of the eye. It is eminently essential for good sight that this should remain clear. It seems almost a special provision of nature that this part of the organ should be so exceedingly sensitive, as the discomfort caused by a very minute irritant impels even the most careless to seek to remove it, whilst if left it is liable to set up inflammation which may lead to much more serious results than if the foreign body were on the "white" of the eye.

Injuries of the Cornea often occur from the lodgment of little pieces of metal chippings, and emery, in those whose occupations render them liable to these little accidents. Sparks from engines when riding in a railway carriage facing the engine are also a fruitful cause of this ailment. Such bodies cause great pain and irritation, and soon set up an inflammation of the tissue in which they lodge. The part is so very sensitive that it is always desirable, where possible, to place a few drops of the cocaine solution (four grains to the ounce) into the eye a little before attempting their removal. To remove such a body, seat the patient on a chair and facing a good light, and standing at his back separate the lids with the forefinger and thumb of the left hand. Now direct him to look at something opposite and so keep his eye steady. Then with the point of a clean sharp instrument just pick the particle off the cornea. If it is imbedded some distance in the substance of the sight it will require proper "cocainising" and skill to get it out, and you had better make no attempt to remove it, but send the patient to a doctor at once. After a wound of the cornea from any cause a few drops of castor oil give great relief. The oil lubricates the lids as they move over the injured surface, and if four grains of the cocaine (alkaloid) are dissolved in each ounce of the oil, the comfort given by this application will be found great indeed.

In any injury from burns, or otherwise, you may as a "first aid" method put in a little cocaine, or cocaine and oil, but in all injuries of this structure, other than trivial ones, it is wise to lose no time in seeing a doctor, for where the loss of substance or the injury is considerable atropine will have to be used, and it is unsafe for any one but a qualified man to use this powerful but most useful drug.

Whenever the "sight" of the eye is injured (except in the case of those injuries which only just take off the superficial layer of the cornea), the injured part heals by "scar-tissue" as in the other parts of the body, and *not* (and this is the important fact) by a regeneration of the clear corneal tissue growing into and filling up the wound or ulcer. Now this "scar-tissue" differs from the corneal tissue, in that it is opaque or whitish in colour, and it can thus be readily understood how even a slight wound of the cornea may cause serious impairment of sight.

Ulcers of the Cornea may be produced by injuries. They also occur in such a serious disease as purulent conjunctivitis, as a complication; but they are especially common in young weakly children who are just recovering from some fever or debilitating illness.

Symptoms.—The chief symptom of this affection, as of all *corneal* ones, is the dread of light, and in young children they sometimes so tightly screw up the lids that it becomes necessary to give them chloroform before a satisfactory examination of the eye can be made. If, however, you can see the eye you easily perceive the ulcer by the loss of "polish" over it, and you will also notice that the eye is red and "waters" readily.

Treatment.—This ailment certainly requires the care of a doctor with special knowledge of eye troubles, and the child or adult should be taken to see a specialist at once. It is here that atropine is an essential part of the local medication. It is usually employed in the form of ointment or drops—four grains of the sulphate of atropine to the ounce of distilled water. A good broad double shade of stiff paper tied on with tapes, and well protecting the eyes from side lights, is beneficial and comforting, and can be easily made at home. Pay special attention to the general health. The child is not to "mope" indoors, but must take proper exercise in the open air, unless of course ordered otherwise by the doctor in charge of the case. Children nearly always improve under a course of cod liver oil and malt extract. One or two teaspoonfuls to be given two or three times a day after food, combined with a little syrup of iron if an anæmic or bloodless state exists.

Milky Spots on the "Sight" are, as already remarked, the result of old ulceration, and although the faint ones may become a little less noticeable in time, yet there is no application which will remove them. There are some ophthalmic surgeons who "tattoo" these white spots with Indian ink, and thus render them less disfiguring, but it must be left to a specialist to decide upon the advisability of such a procedure in each case. In this connection it may be stated that there used to be a custom of prescribing a lotion (Goulard's lotion) containing *sugar of lead* as an astringent application in any inflammation of the eye. This lotion is still used by "quacks," and sometimes as a popular remedy. We may say at once that any lotion *containing lead should never be applied to the eye* except under medical direction, for this most important reason, that should there be any injury of the "sight" or the slightest ulceration of it, the lead is very liable to get into its substance, and become deposited as *white lead* (albuminate of lead) in the clear watch-glass of the eye, thus producing a permanent opacity in it. Therefore avoid lead lotions altogether.

Inflammation of the Substance of the Cornea.—There is just one more common disease of the cornea which we may note. It is an affection which is commonest between the ages of six and sixteen, although it may occur much later in life. The *causes* of it are usually either inherited syphilis, or it may occur in weakly children of a consumptive tendency

Symptoms.—It manifests itself by the cornea becoming hazy or like "ground-glass," but there is no ulceration of its surface. The eye is often very red, there is great dread of light, and the discomfort of these young patients, as they screw up their eyelids and take the opportunity of avoiding every ray of sunlight, is very piteous to see. The disease, as said before, usually occurs in those children who start life with a constitution warped by inherited disease. This ailment is frequently associated with general defects of bodily development or nutrition, although this is by no means always the case.

Treatment.—This requires the experience of an eye surgeon. It may be added that great patience is required both from patient and friends, as the disease usually runs a very chronic course. The treatment, if persevered in, will well repay everybody concerned. The child's general health must be very carefully attended to. Proper exercise in the open air should be insisted upon with a good broad shade, or dark-tinted "goggles" when the eyes are improving. A change from town to country for a time is often attended with most gratifying results, and cod liver oil with malt extract, if preferred, is always an advisable part of the treatment.

Iritis.—This disease is inflammation of the *Iris* or *coloured part of the eye* (Fig. 62, D, and Fig. 64). It is a most serious ailment, and one that demands prompt and efficient treatment. It is only mentioned here to emphasise its importance, and no one unskilled in the treatment of eye affections should undertake such a case if special treatment can be obtained. It is usually caused by "cold," especially in people with a tendency to rheumatism or gout. Another great cause is venereal disease, especially syphilis and gonorrhea.

Symptoms.—The eye is red and painful, the pain frequently shooting above the eye and into the nose. The redness differs from that of conjunctivitis in that it is most intense round the "sight" of the eye, there frequently being an intense purplish-red halo around it. The *pupil is usually smaller* than that of the other eye, and often irregular in shape. If shaded from the light it does not dilate or expand so easily as that of the unaffected eye.

Dangers.—If you will refer to the picture showing a section of the eye (Figs. 62 and 64), you will see that the *iris* or *coloured part of the eye* is a thin muscular diaphragm or curtain in front of the *lens*. It lies quite close to the latter. This proximity to the important lens makes iritis a serious complaint, and for this reason : when any tissue of the body gets inflamed it tends, sooner or later, to adhere to surrounding surfaces. This is exactly what the inflamed iris does to the clear lens if left untreated, and it not infrequently "blocks" up the pupil, and renders the eye practically useless. The main treatment depends upon the use of a certain drug dropped into the eye, which will make the pupil large. This drug is *atropine.*

Atropine is the essence, as it were, of the belladonna plant, and no doubt some of us have known ladies who, more anxious about their looks than their health, have occasionally used the tincture of belladonna as eye-drops in order to give a "full eye." This effect is produced by virtue of the power the drug has of causing the pupil to dilate to a large size. We need hardly say that this practice is fraught with many evils, to say nothing of inconvenience, for when using this substance in the eye anything looked at closely has a blurred appearance, for the simple reason that the "focussing" power of the eye is temporarily paralysed If the practice is persisted in, this focussing power becomes weaker and weaker, as in the case of any other unused muscle, and serious disturbance of vision and of general health may follow.

The Treatment of Iritis must be undertaken promptly to be successful, and it will consist of the application of atropine dropped into the eye two or three times a day. Dry or moist heat may be frequently applied in the form of compresses (*not poultices*), and if the pain is severe or the pupil not dilating well, one or two leeches applied to the temple of the affected side may give wondrous relief. For this pain also, antipyrin, in five grain doses, is often most beneficial. The other eye must be protected from bright light by a shade or smoked glass. Appropriate remedies must be used for the disease that has caused the iritis : *e.g.* salicylate of soda if the disease is of rheumatic origin, or mercury if it is due to syphilis.

Diseases of the Lens.—*Cataract* is nothing more nor less than an opacity of the lens of the eye. Look at the picture of the eye and see where the "lens" lies (Fig. 62, E). This structure, normally as transparent as a magnifying glass, becomes more or less like opal. It is most common in people past middle life, but occurs often in children. They may be born with the ailment. It may also be brought about by injury or disease, *e.g.* diabetes. In old people the sight gradually fails, usually in one eye first, and in the course of months (or sometimes years) they cannot see any object with the most affected eye, *but they can always recognise light from shade*, otherwise disease must exist elsewhere. No treatment has any effect upon this condition except an operation. The surgeon removes the lens, and afterwards prescribes strong convex spectacles. In the adult, operations for cataract are not usually done so long as the individual is able to see to do his work with one eye ; when that fails, however, the other is usually ripe for operation. The operation is quite painless, and is done under cocaine as a rule, chloroform being unnecessary. In *children* the operation is undertaken at any time, according to the discretion of che surgeon, as the cataract being a *soft* one, it is not "extracted," in the ordinary sense of the word, but is broken up by a needle pushed into it. It often requires several *needlings* as they are called, before the lens matter is removed. Therefore parents of children undergoing treatment must be patient. We may add that in many cases an ordinary observer cannot see anything wrong in eyes that are almost blind from cataract, whereas, on the other hand, most people have an entirely wrong idea regarding the ailment, and not a few imagine they suffer who exhibit no symptoms at all. The moral is, don't worry about cataract at all.

Glaucoma must be mentioned, because it is a disease of the eye that demands quick recognition and prompt treatment, otherwise the eye will be ruined. It is caused by some obstruction to the ordinary ways in which the fluid secreted in the eye gets out. Consequently the tension of the eye increases, it becomes more or less hard, and in a very short time this back pressure acting on the retina (which is the nervous curtain or layer of the eye, and forms its inner coat) (Fig. 62, K) destroys its function, and blindness results. It is mostly a disease of advanced age and is more frequent in women than men. Gout seems to be a predisposing cause in some instances, but it most commonly occurs without anything apparent to account for it.

The attacks may be *acute* or *chronic*. In the *acute form* the eye is red and the patient complains of great dimness of vision. Pain in the head is present. The patient not infrequently vomits, and the disease has thus been mistaken for a sick headache. Another very common and most important symptom is, that on looking at a light (a candle flame, for instance), it is seen to be surrounded by a halo of coloured light or "rainbows," as the sensation is called. It should be added that whenever a patient past middle age complains of this last symptom, even if unassociated with the others, he will be wise to go at once to the best eye doctor he knows, as it is frequently the first thing one notices in a *chronic* attack of glaucoma. With regard to the pupil it should be noted that it is usually *larger* in the affected eye than in the other, and also that when a strong light is thrown into it, the pupil gets smaller very slowly. There is *no home treatment* for this disease. The only safe resort is to have an operation performed, the results of which, on the whole, are fairly encouraging.

Tobacco Blindness.—It is not generally known that excessive tobacco smoking materially injures the sight, and yet cases are quite commonly seen in hospital practice of patients becoming practically blind from this cause. The darker and stronger brands of tobacco are the most injurious, and among the lower orders, where "twist" and "nail rod" are the common kinds used, the disease is of course more frequent. The patient complains of gradual failure of sight, and glasses do not improve it. When he comes to be examined by a specialist it is found that he has not got proper perception of colours, especially red. This does not mean that the sufferer is entirely colour blind, but in some positions if a speck of red or blue be held before him he thinks they are white.

The remedy is twofold. *First, prevention* by avoiding excessive smoking of all kinds, but especially of dark strong tobacco. If the disease has already appeared the only cure is to stop the use of tobacco *absolutely*. If this is done the sight recovers itself in a few weeks' time, but if the smoking is persisted in, it goes from bad to worse, and the sight is permanently and seriously damaged.

Colour Blindness.—This is a curious and inborn condition in which the retina or nervous network of the eye fails to appreciate the distinctions between the various colours. There is no remedy for it, but it entails no drawbacks except to one who wishes to enter the services or become a railway servant. It can be readily understood how this incapacity to distinguish the colours of signals or of lights at night would be highly dangerous to the public.

Squint or Strabismus.—A squint occurs when the axes of both eyes are not parallel, so that an observer looking at the "squinter" sees one eye turned in or out as the case may be. At first the eyes squint alternately, but eventually it settles in one eye, and the squinting eye often becomes useless. This last condition occurs from the fact that if both eyes were looking at an object (those eyes not being in the same axes) the image would be formed on different parts of the retina in each eye and thus double vision would ensue. This happens where the squint occurs in an adult, from paralysis, but in the young, instinct leads them to ignore the image in one eye, and thus after months or years it becomes practically blind.

The Causes of Squints in young children are defective sight, especially if associated with weakness or debility. Worms, convulsions, and other causes play a part in its production. The paralytic type may occur after diphtheria, whooping-cough, apoplexy, &c.

Treatment.—By far the greater number of these patients are young children whose squint depends upon the fact that they have defective sight. As a rule, if the child is "long-sighted" the eye turns inwards, whilst if "short-sighted" it turns outwards. In these children, if they are provided with glasses which correct their defect of vision, a great many of them cease to squint, and some few as they grow older can manage afterwards without glasses, except for close work. At any rate they mostly improve very much, and if after wearing glasses for a year or so they still squint, the surgeon will consider the desirability of performing a slight operation, which consists in dividing the little eye muscle (Fig. 62, R and N) which is pulling too much.

A point of great importance, however, is that treatment must be commenced as early as possible, especially if the desired result is to be obtained without resorting to operation, also in order that the squinting eye may not grow useless and the individual become to all intents and purposes "one-eyed."

Defects of Vision.—In effect the eye is often likened to a camera in which the place of the sensitive plate is taken by the retina (Fig. 62, K), which, as we know, is the nerve-layer of the eye. The lens in front of the camera condenses all the rays that come into it and throws the image of any object on to the sensitive plate. Now we know that when that plate is at the "focus" of the lens we get clear defined images of objects in front of the camera. This represents the normal eye (Fig. 66, 1). Now let us consider what happens if we push in the bellows of the camera and so shorten it. In this case we get the plate nearer to the lens than its "focus," and so the image is indistinct. This represents the *long-sighted eye* (3). Again, if we pull out the bellows we get the plate further away from the lens than its "focus," and in this case also we get a "blurred" image. This represents the *short-sighted eye* (4).

In *long-sighted* people (3) the eye is too short, the focus of the eye being in this case behind the retina. The *symptoms* are very variable according to its degree. Patients as a rule first com-

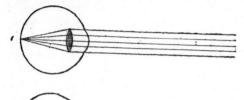

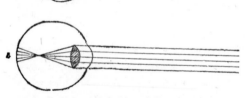

FIG. 66.—How the Light Waves fall on Different Eyes.

1, Emmetropic Eye, rays falling on Yellow Spot of Retina ; represents Normal Eye at rest. 2, Normal Eye in Near Vision, Lens more curved in front. 3, Hypermatropic Eye (Long Sight), rays passing behind Retina. 4, Myopic Eye (Short Sight), rays passing in front of Retina.

plain of fatigue in the eyes after using them much. Reading becomes blurred and tiresome, and they are compelled to hold their book further away from the eyes. The eyes after a time become red and irritable, and a *chronic conjunctivitis* is sometimes induced. In children a squint is often produced, and the eye usually turns inwards.

This kind of sight does not as a rule tend to get worse, but glasses for reading are required much earlier than in those who have a normal eye. The *treatment* is to get spectacles with a bi-convex lens in order to bring the image of the objects on to the retina.

In *short sight* (4) the eye is too long, and so we get blurred images. In this case, however, near objects are held closer to the eyes, and so good images are thus obtained, but the distant vision is much impaired. Unlike "long sight," this condition is not inborn, but is acquired. It usually begins at an early age, when the eyes are being used for much near work, as in school children, in whom it often tends to get worse and worse. In many cases the stretching of the coats of the eye causes serious disease inside the eye, and the sight becomes worse than ever. The educational period of life is the most dangerous for this ailment, and the defect is encouraged by the close application that modern methods of education entail. In Germany, where the school training is even more exacting, a very large percentage of the population are short-sighted, and it has been estimated that if the present increase goes on, nearly the whole of the German nation will become short-sighted in a measurable number of years. There is no doubt a strong hereditary tendency to short sight, and it would be wise to examine the children of all short-sighted parents before they begin their school-life.

Treatment.—The rays are brought on to the retina by placing bi-concave spectacles in front of the eyes, and so clear images are produced ; but this is by no means the end of the story. Great care must be taken to stop the progress of the "myopia," as this short sight is called, and glasses alone fail to do this.

Children who show this tendency to hold their work close to their eyes, or who cannot see distant objects well, should have their sight examined without delay. To compel these children to strain their eyes in order to keep pace with others favoured with perfect vision, is unfair and cruel. Teachers of the young should be on the alert to detect such cases, and should also see that all children hold their work at correct distance, and also that the schoolrooms should be well-lighted and properly ventilated.

Short-sighted children should be placed in the front row of

their classes, if required to see the black-board. Books for their use should be printed in good clear type.

With short-sighted children "home-work," especially in the winter evenings, should be forbidden, and all poring over books discouraged. If the child is pale and weakly, everything possible to improve the general health should be done, and in this particular fresh air and exercise are imperative.

An application of the same principles applies to short-sighted adults, and, where possible, an individual with a marked degree of short sight will do well to choose some calling in which close application to books and writing is not essential.

Astigmatism is an abnormality of sight which depends not upon the length of the eyeball, but upon the symmetry of the cornea or "watch-glass" in front of it. In astigmatism this is not equally curved in all directions, and so rays going through it are not all brought to a focus on the retina. Some of them may be, but not all. This gives indistinct vision, especially for reading, as some letters are seen more distinctly than others. A very slight degree of astigmatism is also sufficient to cause severe and persistent headaches, and people who find that after much reading they suffer in this way should remember the latter fact.

Treatment.—Lenses which only magnify or reduce in one meridian are employed to correct this condition.

Diseases of the Retina.—The retina is sometimes displaced by a blow on the eye, and it also may become spontaneously detached. These are serious cases, and even in skilled hands the treatment often fails to give much relief to the serious defect of vision which is thereby occasioned.

Inflammation of the Retina occurs in such general diseases as chronic kidney disease and diabetes. It is a serious complication, and can only be detected by one accustomed to the use of the ophthalmoscope.

Old Sight.—When speaking of the eye as compared with a camera, it is at once understood that the plate of a camera "sees" all things for which it is "focussed," and no others, perfectly, so that if we are taking a landscape, and at the same time hold a pen about a foot in front of the lens, only a blurred image of the pen will be seen on the plate. Now the eye by a beautiful little muscular mechanism automatically alters its focus, and in this way, we see, has an enormous advantage over a camera. This little muscle alters the focus by making the "lens" of the eye more or less convex, and the eye is thus enabled to quickly alter its focus, so that it can take in all the details of a landscape, and in a moment alter its focus

In order to examine a pen (Fig. 64, *a* and *b*, and Fig. 66, 2). It cannot, however, see both perfectly at the *same time*. This act by which we alter the focus of the eye is called "accommodation." Now this power of accommodation, present at its height at the age of twelve, gradually gets less and less until between sixty and seventy, when it is absent altogether. This is due to gradual failure of the little muscle and also to the loss of elasticity of the lens. The want of it usually becomes noticeable about the age of forty-five, when people find they cannot see their book or work so well, and have to hold it farther from their eyes. About this age *weak convex* glasses are necessary for near work and reading, and these usually require strengthening about every four or five years.

In conclusion, we should like to warn people who suffer from defective sight from going to an uneducated optician and choosing glasses by "rule of thumb." A great deal of absolute harm is brought about by this practice, and many a person goes on from year to year wearing spectacles which, although he may imagine are the best he can get, are entirely unsuited to his sight. The best and cheapest way in the end is to go to an eye-specialist and obtain a proper prescription for suitable glasses, and then have them "filled" by the best optician he knows. In the case of the poor, they can always get the services of an eye-surgeon at one of the eye departments of our hospitals, so that glasses properly adapted for each individual sight are within the reach of all.

Care of Glasses.—It is essential for good sight that not only must the glasses be optically correct, but they must be kept bright and free from scratches. Therefore never let the lenses be placed downwards when you remove the spectacles from the nose, but let them rest on the rim and the ear-pieces. This will effectually preserve the glasses, and prevent much annoyance and expense.

The "bridge" of the frame should fit the nose "like a glove," and if it causes any irritation, don't make it unsightly by wrapping wool or cotton round it, but take it back to the optician, and don't be satisfied until it is made easy.

It is a common thing for mothers to "pack" the bridge of the baby's glasses with wool from the first, but this is unnecessary, often does more harm than good, and, moreover, is unsightly. If the frames are of steel, an occasional application of a little vaseline will prevent the perspiration and moisture causing them to rust. Should the lenses get dirty and greasy, washing them in strong warm soda and water, or with ammonia, is the best thing. Protective "goggles" that have been worn during an inflammation of the eye should be well washed with strong ammonia and water, and afterwards placed in a solution of carbolic acid (1 part of acid to 20 parts of water) for some hours. Afterwards put a little vaseline on the rims.

SECTION VIII

AMBULANCE OR "FIRST AID" WORK

INTRODUCTION TO THE SUBJECT

THE rise and progress of the movement for rendering "First-aid" to persons in distress, and who have suffered from the effects of accidental injuries, forms one of the marked features of the last century. No more beneficent movement has probably ever been chronicled in the history of humanity, especially in relation to the great question of "man's duty to man." The foundation of all successful ambulance work is naturally found in the adequate training of those who profess to render assistance in cases of injury. Unless such training is afforded, and, what is more to the point, properly appreciated, no success can possibly be attained in First-aid work. A typical course of ambulance instruction must include first of all a knowledge of the *anatomy and physiology of the body.* The amount of instruction of this kind is such as may be obtained in any elementary course of lectures on physiology, supplemented by clear demonstrations by aid of diagrams, and by the examination of the bodies of any lower animals, or by aid of models of the anatomy of the human frame. In this way the student first of all acquires a distinct knowledge of the organs of the body whose welfare he may be called upon to guard in cases of injury. After such a systematic course of instruction a training may be given regarding the various classes of injuries and the best modes of treating them.

It must be distinctly understood that in the vast majority of cases the duty of the ambulance student is that of placing the patient under such conditions that pain may be saved, if not life itself, pending the arrival of the medical man. It is true that in some untoward circumstances where medical aid is not possible of being had, the ambulance student may require to undertake further duties. It is therefore the object of this section of the work not merely to indicate the treatment proper to be followed in the case of various accidents and emergencies, but likewise in appropriate cases to detail the further measures which, in cases of extreme emergency, any layman may be called upon to bring into practice.

A few general hints may here be given regarding the general principles on which ambulance work may be conducted, leaving the more particular details proper to each class of injury to be treated in the succeeding sections of this work. The rules according to which first-aid help can be successfully rendered may be said to follow the lines of ordinary common sense. It is needful in the first place to warn the ambulance student that whilst other people may lose their heads in face of an accident, he of all persons must endeavour to keep as cool as possible. Excitement on his part will render him probably unfitted to give that aid which may imply the saving of life itself. In the second place it is his duty to prevent all crowding around the patient, and by enlisting the services of bystanders to keep the patient as free from annoyance as possible, whilst in connection with this part of his duty he should be able to direct the efforts of persons willing to help, in the way of removing the patient safely and quickly to some place where appropriate treatment can be carried out.

The next rule impresses upon us the duty of at once sending for medical assistance. It is a notable fact that, in many cases, to send for the doctor after an accident has occurred is a matter which escapes the attention of the bystanders. In sending for the doctor try to give him some indication of the nature of the accident, so that possibly he may arrive better prepared to render assistance than if he were left in ignorance of the nature of the emergency. As far as possible the circumstances under which the accident occurs should be duly noted— for example the position in which the body has been found, and other details such as a person of ordinary intelligence can readily appreciate. If the ambulance student happens to find himself in the presence of a crime, he may be able to give valuable information to the authorities from his simple observation of the circumstances of the case as they appear to him on his arrival on the scene.

It is not necessary here to enter into detail regarding the treatment of ambulance cases at large, seeing that the details applicable to one case may not be applicable to another. As a rule it is of importance to place the patient in an easy position on the ground, and in the vast majority of cases, the rule should be followed that all clothing should be loosened from his neck and chest. Whether the head should be kept high or low is a matter for recognition of the particular ailment or accident from which he is suffering. A very important matter in connection especially with the case of broken bones, for example, is that of seeing that the patient is not roughly lifted to his feet, or moved in any way at all, until he can be gently and carefully carried to a place of safety. It will be readily understood that the act of setting on his feet a man who suffers from a broken bone in his leg would have the effect probably of driving the broken end through the skin, and of converting a simple accident into a very serious one.

Finally with regard to the administration of stimulants by way of recovering persons, this is a point which may be made the subject of a general observation. There are a large number of persons in this world who seem to regard a bottle of brandy or whisky as the one recognised remedy to be administered in all and sundry emergencies. Later on it will be shown that in certain emergencies (as in the case of a man stricken with apoplexy) the giving of stimulants may produce a fatal result. Therefore the caution is extremely needful in recognition of the tendency to rely upon stimulants for the general treatment of all accidents and emergencies. We might here say that, when in doubt, give no stimulants at all. Any good effect which may be produced by a stimulant may be in all probability far more readily and more safely produced by keeping the patient warm. This last feature indeed is one of the most important points in connection with the treatment of "shock," which accompanies or follows almost all accidents.

SIGNS OF DEATH

It is of importance to the ambulance student as well as to all who come in contact with illness to be able as far as possible to appreciate *the signs of death*. So far from this being an easy matter to decide, especially at a period soon after death is supposed to have occurred, it is sometimes extremely difficult to positively say whether vitality has ceased or not. So forcibly have certain persons been impressed with the notion that the signs of death are not always correctly interpreted, that they insist upon the probability of a considerable number of cases of *premature burial* having been represented both at home and abroad. Such cases are naturally more frequently represented in times of epidemics where, large numbers of persons perishing, and especially in warm countries, early burial becomes a necessity. That, however, premature burial is at all a frequent occurrence may be strenuously denied.

It may be said that practically the only sure and infallible sign of death is that seen in the *putrefaction or decomposition of the body*. The rate of putrefaction naturally varies very much, a great deal depending on the state of the body, on the disease which has caused death, on the surrounding temperature. on the presence of moisture or

exposure to the air, and on other conditions. The occurrence of putrefaction is more rapid in air than in water. In damp earth it probably
takes place least rapidly of all. In the case of an ordinary death the
signs of putrefaction will probably begin to be noticed about the third
day. They commence as a rule on the belly or abdomen, a greenish
hue of the skin being then noted. Added to the appearances which
succeed, indicating the advance of putrefaction, we naturally find the
characteristic and disagreeable odour which characterises bodily decay.

Physicians are accustomed in doubtful cases to rely not on one
sign of death but on a combination of them. As will be shown in
the section dealing with the apparently drowned, life may be present
when all signs of the heart's action have ceased and when the pulse
cannot itself be felt. In this condition the heart must be working,
but in such a feeble way and at such low pressure, so to speak, that it
gives forth no physical sign of its activity. Cessation of breathing
may also take place without death having occurred, a condition we see
likewise represented in the half-drowned man. In all probability the
action of the lungs ceases long before that of the heart.

Popular modes of ascertaining whether death has occurred or not
in relation to breathing are represented by holding a cold looking-
glass before the mouth and nostrils by way of seeing if the surface is
dimmed with moisture, whilst a cup filled with water may be placed
on the chest, close observation noting whether the surface of the water
is at all disturbed by any movement of the chest-walls. The cooling
of the body forms another indication of the probable presence of death;
yet in some instances of sudden and fatal cases of cholera and yellow
fever the heat of the body may be retained for a considerable time.
A body which may be cold before death may exhibit a rise of temperature after death from the radiation of its internal heat. It is said that
at an average temperature and without clothing, a dead body will cool
at the rate of about one degree Fahrenheit per hour.

Another characteristic of death is the gravitation of the blood in
the blood-vessels to the lowest parts of the body. These parts in consequence become discoloured, constituting post-mortem lividity. Thus
the buttocks, back, and other dependent parts sooner or later exhibit
discolorations of a livid hue. These signs usually make their appearance in from eight to ten hours after death has taken place.
Rigidity of the body is also another point to which the attention of the
observer may be directed. This condition owes its origin to the fact
that after death the muscles become stiffened through the coagulation
or clotting of the muscle juice. In ordinary cases it begins in the
neck and face, and gradually extends from above downwards. When
putrefaction ensues, and this muscular rigidity vanishes, it will dis-

appear in very much the same order. After exhausting diseases muscular rigidity sets in very soon, whereas in the case of a person dying suddenly, if at the time in full health, the rigidity is longer delayed in respect of its onset. In some cases, however, the muscles may assume a rigidity immediately on death taking place. Soldiers in the battlefield who have been instantly killed have had their bodies set into rigid positions, which have had the effect of suggesting that life is still present. When death occurs from poisoning by strychnine, a similar result is seen. The other signs which may be relied upon by way of convincing us that life has ceased are found in the skin becoming of an ashy pale colour, whilst all the tissues lose their elasticity and firmness. The eyeball sinks, probably on account of the loss of so much of its fluid, and the front of the eye or cornea, instead of being bright and glistening, becomes opaque. Naturally, there is no reaction of the pupil of the eye to light, and no sign is given when the skin is irritated.

It will be observed that many of these signs may be represented in cases where animation has simply been suspended. Therefore the greatest possible care must be taken before deciding that a person is really dead, and especially where death has taken place suddenly, or under circumstances which appear to render a fatal result unlikely of occurrence. After all is said and done in connection with this subject, we may fall back upon the opinion already expressed, that the only positive and certain sign of death is that of commencing putrefaction and decay of the body.

ON BANDAGING

The bandage (Fr. *bande*, a tie, a long narrow piece of stuff) is the most ancient, the simplest, and the most widely applicable of surgical appliances. It is principally used for the following purposes :—
1. To give rest and support.
2. To retain dressings in position.
3. To fix splints.
4. To apply pressure at any given point.

There are two varieties of bandages :—
1. The roller.
2. The triangular.

The roller bandage consists of a strip of calico or other material, varying in breadth from an inch and a half to six inches, and in length from a yard and a half to six yards, according to the region of the body on which it has to be applied, and is rolled up firmly to facilitate its application. This bandage can be efficiently applied by the practised surgeon alone, and is only suitable for the *permanent* treatment of injuries. Its disadvantages in the *emergency* treatment of injuries are that it is difficult to apply; the art of being able to do so efficiently requiring a considerable amount of practice. Its unskilful application may do harm, and, lastly, it is seldom, if ever, at hand when needed. For this last reason, if for no other, it became necessary to adopt some simpler form of bandage which could be more easily and rapidly applied, which would be practically as efficient as the roller bandage, and have the further advantage of being readily obtainable. All these requirements are fulfilled in the *triangular bandage*, which was first introduced by Mayor of Lausanne, but did not come into general use till Esmarch of Kiel again drew attention to it, and with such success that it has always been known as Esmarch's bandage. The triangular bandage is made by taking a piece of calico of 40 inches square and cutting it across diagonally, thus getting two bandages each somewhat similar in shape to the diagram below. For descriptive purposes the base, or longest side of the triangle A, is known as the *lower border*. The two shorter sides B B are the

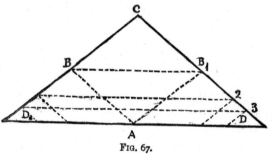

FIG. 67.

side borders. The angle C opposite the lower border is the *point*, and the remaining angles D D are the *ends*.

This bandage may also be bought with diagrams printed on it, showing clearly how it is to be applied to different parts of the body. The advantages of this bandage are self-evident. In the first place it is readily obtainable, for a large pocket-handkerchief needs only to be folded across to improvise one; it is easily and rapidly applied, as will be seen when the several methods of using it are described; and, lastly, it can be easily removed, and the importance of this point will be readily recognised if the fact is borne in mind that the treatment in an emergency is purely temporary, that whatever appliances have been used, they must be taken down again by the surgeon, and the more quickly this can be done the better will it be for the comfort of the patient.

There are three modes of applying the triangular bandage: *unfolded, folded broad,* and *folded narrow.*

To fold the bandage broad, the point is brought down to the

centre of the lower border, and then the bandage is folded once more, working in the same direction.

To fold it *narrow* it is to be folded a *third* time, thus making the narrow fold half the breadth of the broad fold. The dotted lines 1, 2, 3 (Fig. 67) indicate the folds of the bandage. To fasten the bandage the ends must be knotted together, the "sailor" or *reef knot* being invariably employed (Fig. 68, A), as it is less liable to slip than the "granny" knot depicted in Fig. 68, B. In fastening the bandage, remember that the knots must always be placed on the outer side of the injured limb, in order that they may be the more easily undone with the minimum amount of movement of the limb

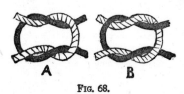

when the permanent dressings are being applied; that the knot must never press directly on a *wound* nor on a *bone* which has only a thin covering of soft parts, as for instance the *shin bone;* that to prevent a knot pressing on the *skin*, it must be placed on a fold of the bandage, or a *pad* of cloth must be placed between it and the skin to protect the latter from injury; that when *splints* are employed, the knots must always rest on the splint.

FIG. 68.

Before passing to the consideration of the methods of applying the triangular bandage to the various regions of the body, it will be convenient to give a description of the methods of forming the different varieties of *slings* which are used for supporting the arm.

1. *The large arm sling.*—Take an unfolded bandage, throw one end of it over the shoulder of the sound side, the body of the bandage lying across the patient's chest, and the *point* behind the injured elbow; next bring the injured arm across the patient's body, in front of the bandage, and hold it there with the thumb pointing upwards, and the angle formed by the forearm and upper arm slightly less than a right angle. Then take the other end of the bandage, and bring it forward over the forearm and up to the shoulder of the injured side, and knot the two ends on the shoulder. Lastly, take the point and bring it round to the front of the elbow, and pin it to the body of the bandage, as shown in Fig. 69. This sling is used in cases where it is considered necessary to support the elbow.

2. *The small arm sling.*—Take a bandage *folded broad*, throw one end of it over the shoulder of the *uninjured side*, allowing the body of the bandage to lie across the chest. Next take the injured arm and bend it across the chest, placing the wrist across the centre

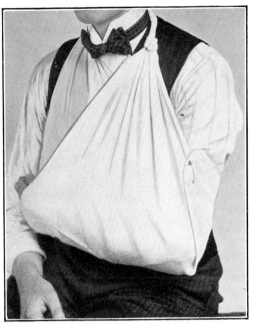

FIG. 69.—THE LARGE ARM SLING.

FIG. 70.—THE SMALL ARM SLING.

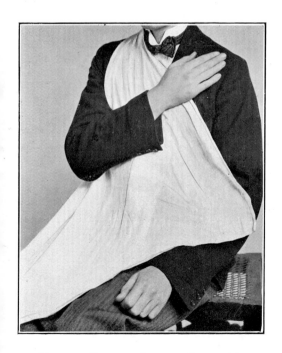

FIG. 71.—SLING TO SUPPORT ELBOW (1).

FIG. 72.—SLING TO SUPPORT ELBOW (2).

of the bandage with the thumb pointing upwards. Finally bring the lower end of the bandage over the front of the wrist, and up, to, and on the shoulder of the injured side, and knot the two ends on the shoulder. This form of sling is used in cases where it is desirable that the elbow should hang free, as in fractures of the *upper arm* (Fig. 70).

3. In cases where it is considered necessary to support the elbow, and at the same time to have the arm at an acute angle, use a " St. John " sling, made as follows :

    (*a*) Lay an unfolded bandage across the chest over the injured limb with one end on the uninjured shoulder and the point beyond the elbow on the injured side.

    (*b*) While steadying the injured limb pass the lower end of the bandage under it, across the back, and tie the ends somewhat loosely in the hollow *in front of* the sound shoulder.

    (*c*) Fold the point over the elbow of the injured limb and secure it by one or two pins.

Improvised Slings.—Should occasion arise for the use of a sling, and the only apparatus available be two small handkerchiefs, then one of them should be folded like a cravat, and tied loosely round the neck ; the other one is used unfolded, a corner being passed through the " cravat " and tied to the opposite corner, thus forming a support in which the injured arm is laid.

In the event of there being no handkerchiefs suitable for the formation of a sling available, the sleeve of the coat may be pinned to the coat or the flap of the coat on the injured side can be turned up, and brought over the front of the injured arm and pinned to the breast of the coat, thus forming an admirable and efficient support for the arm.

The triangular bandage as applied to the various regions of the body for the purpose of retaining *dressings* in position.

Bandage for the Palm.—Fold the bandage *narrow*, place the centre of it on the palm, carry the two ends over to the back of the hand, cross them there, and bring them round to the front of the wrist ; cross them once more and carry them to the back of the wrist and knot them (Fig 74). This bandage may be used to apply *pressure* in bleeding from the palm.

Bandage to Cover the whole Hand.—Take an unfolded bandage and lay it on a table, place the injured hand palm downwards on the bandage with the wrist on the centre of the lower border and the fingers directed towards the *point* of the bandage. Next fold the bandage over the fingers and the back of the hand, and carry the point up the forearm (Fig. 75). Now take the ends, and crossing them on the back of the hand carry them to the front of the wrist; cross the bandage here once more, and bringing the ends to the back of the wrist knot them, covering the knot by folding down the point and fixing it with a pin, as indicated in Fig. 76.

Bandage for Wounds of the Arm. — Dress the wound. Take a bandage *folded broad*, place the centre of it over the wound, carry the ends round the limb, and bring them back again to the same side on which the wound is, and knot them, taking care that the knot does not press directly on the wound. Place the arm in a sling.

Bandage for the Elbow.—Fold a bandage *broad*, and lay the elbow on its centre, carry the ends forward to the front of the joint; cross them and carry them to the back of the forearm; cross them and carry them once more to the front of the joint; cross them for the third time and knot them on the outer side of the upper arm. The crossings should fix the upper and lower edges of the bandage, and it is well to bend the elbow prior to applying the bandage (Fig. 70, Lesser Sling).

Shoulder Bandage.—Take an unfolded bandage, lay the centre of it on the shoulder with point upwards towards the neck, and the lower border reaching to the middle of the upper arm. Take the two ends, cross them on the inner side of the arm, bring them back to the outer side and knot them. Next put the injured arm into a small arm sling, and pass the point of the bandage under the sling at the shoulders, fold it over and pin it to the bandage on the top of the shoulder (Fig. 77).

Bandage for the Sole of the Foot.—Fold a bandage *narrow*. Place the centre of it on the sole of the foot, bring the ends forward and cross them on the front of the foot, carry them round the ankle to the back of the leg. Cross them here, and bring them to the front, where they are knotted (Fig. 78).

Bandage to Cover the whole Foot.—Place the foot in the centre of an unfolded bandage, with the toes directed towards the point; fold the point upwards over the toes and the front of the instep. Cross the two ends on the front of the foot and carry them to the back of the ankle. Cross them here, and in doing so secure the lower border of the bandage; bring the ends round to the front of the ankle joint and knot, covering the knot by folding down the point over it and pinning it as shown in Fig. 79.

FIG. 73.—SLING TO SUPPORT ELBOW (3).

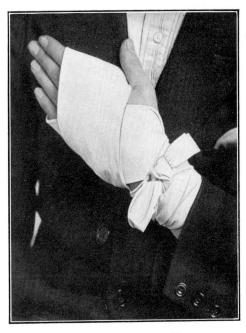

FIG. 74.—BANDAGE FOR PALM.

FIG. 75.—BANDAGE TO COVER THE HAND (1).

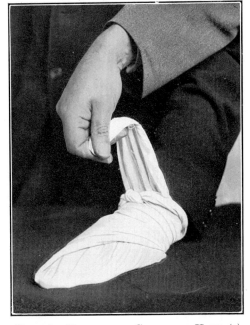

FIG. 76.—BANDAGE TO COVER THE HAND (2).

How to Bandage for Injuries

Bandage for the Knee.—Fold a bandage broad, and lay it across the joint, with its centre resting on the knee-cap. Carry the ends to the back of the joint; cross them and bring them to the front of the lower part of the thigh; cross them and take them once more to the back of the joint; crossing them here finally, and bringing them to the *outer* side of the leg below the knee, where they are knotted (Fig. 80).

Bandage for the Hip.—This bandage is similar to that for the shoulder. A narrow folded bandage, carried round the waist in the form of a belt, and knotted in front, taking the place of the sling in the former case, preventing the bandage from slipping down. A second *unfolded bandage* has its point passed under the " belt," and pinned as in the accompanying illustration, with the lower border reaching to the middle of the thigh; the two ends are now taken and carried round to the inner side of the thigh, crossed and brought back again to the outer side where they are knotted (Fig. 82).

Bandage for the Chest.—To fix dressings or retain a poultice in position, take an *unfolded* bandage, lay it on the chest with the point over one shoulder, and the ends passing round the body to the back—the two ends are knotted together here (Fig. 83). The point is now drawn over the shoulder, and knotted to one of the ends (Fig. 84).

Bandage for the Breast.—To support an inflamed breast, or retain dressings in position, take a bandage folded broad, and hold one end on the shoulder of the uninjured side. Carry the bandage over the breast that needs to be supported, and bring the end under the arm on the injured side, across the back to the top of the shoulder on the uninjured side; carry it round the front of the shoulder, under the armpit, and round again to the front of the joint, where the two ends are to be knotted.

Bandage for Broken Ribs.—Take two or three bandages folded broad and firmly bind the chest with them, having the centre of one of the bandages over the seat of injury, and the ends knotted at the opposite side of the chest. *See* Fracture of Ribs.

Bandage for Scalp Wounds.—Take an unfolded bandage, place the centre of it on the top of the head, allowing the lower border to fall forwards across the forehead and reach to the root of the nose—the point resting on the back of the neck. Gather up the ends and carry them backwards above the ears, cross them at the back of the head, as low down and as near the nape of the neck as possible, to prevent the bandage slipping up, and bring them forward again, and knot them on the centre of the forehead; then take the point and make traction on it to obtain the requisite amount of pressure, and fold it upwards and pin it to the centre of the bandage on the top of the head (Fig. 81).

An admirable bandage for retaining large dressings, starch poultices, &c., on the head may be formed from a large *square* handkerchief. Fold it so that one portion of it is about four inches broader than the other. Lay it on the head with the narrow portion uppermost; take the corners of this portion and knot them under the chin; then take the inner and broader portion, fold up the side over the forehead, pull on the ends to get the handkerchief to fit closely over the head, and carry the corners to the back of the neck, and knot them there.

Bandage for the Eye.—Fold the bandage narrow, lay the centre of it on the injured eye, and carry the ends backwards diagonally below the ear on the injured side, and above it on the sound side, and knot them at the back of the head.

Bandage for Wound or Fracture of Lower Jaw.—Fold the bandage narrow, place the centre of it on the chin, and carry the ends upwards, one on each side of the face, and tie them on the top of the head.

Bandage for the Forehead and Neck.—The bandage is folded narrow, and its centre placed over the wound; the ends are carried round, one on each side of the head, crossed at the back and knotted in front.

The Triangular Bandage in the Treatment of Bleeding.—There are two ways in which the bandage may be utilised in controlling severe bleeding from a wound:—

1. Local pressure by pad and bandage on the bleeding point.

2. Distant pressure on the main artery supplying the region in which the wound is situated.

Local Pressure.—Should pressure by the hand, raising the limb, &c., as described in the section which treats of the control of hæmorrhage, fail, it then becomes necessary to apply a firm pad over the wound, and to apply pressure on the open ends of the blood-vessels and occlude them by taking a bandage *folded narrow*, placing the centre of it over the pad and applying it firmly, according to the methods suitable to the region of the body in which the wound is situated, and which have been already fully described and illustrated, remembering always that the operator must assure himself, by watching the effects of the pressure which he has applied, that the bleeding *has* stopped, before he leaves the injured person.

Distant Pressure.—When the simpler methods, including local pressure by bandage, fail to control the bleeding, it becomes necessary

FIG. 77.—SHOULDER BANDAGE.

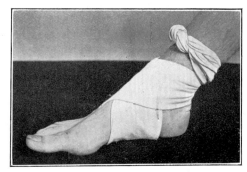

FIG. 78.—BANDAGE FOR SOLE OF FOOT.

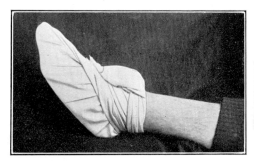

FIG. 79.—BANDAGE TO COVER THE
WHOLE FOOT.

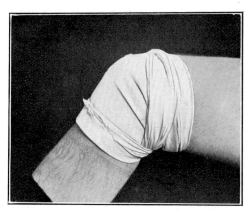

FIG. 80.—BANDAGE FOR THE KNEE.

FIG. 81.—BANDAGE FOR SCALP.

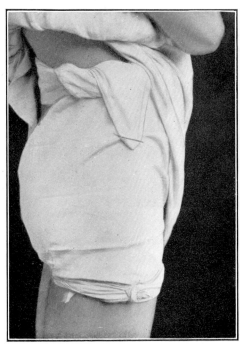

FIG. 82.—BANDAGE FOR THE HIP.

to go higher up the limb, to a point where the main artery which supplies blood to the limb *lies upon a bone,* and there, by pressing the blood-vessel firmly against the bone, prevent any blood flowing through it, and from being poured out at the wound.

The apparatus employed for the carrying out of this manœuvre is called a *tourniquet,* which consists of three essential parts :—

1. A pad.
2. A band to pass round the limb.
3. An apparatus for tightening the band in order to apply the necessary pressure.

There are many varieties of this instrument in use, that introduced by Petit, a French surgeon, in which a *screw* is used for regulating the pressure, being the most familiar. Professor Esmarch, of Kiel, recommended the elastic band tourniquet, which consists of an india-rubber band, which firmly encircles the limb several times, and is then fixed. A perfectly efficient instrument can, however, be *improvised* in the following manner :—

1. Take a round flat stone or a cork, and roll it up in a small handkerchief. This forms the pad.
2. Take a handkerchief folded diagonally to form a triangle, and then *folded narrow.* Tie this loosely round the limb with its centre over the spot where the pad is to be placed. This forms the *band.*
3. Hold the pad in position over the artery, adjust the bandage, so that it lies over the pad, and then take a key, or a closed penknife, or a bit of stick which is sufficiently strong, pass it through the bandage, and twist the bandage. This constitutes the apparatus for applying the pressure ; as the stick is twisted round, the bandage encircles the limb more tightly, and the pad presses the artery against the bone. When the desired amount of pressure has been obtained, the penknife or stick is fixed by taking one of the ends of the bandage, giving it a turn round the knife, and tying it to the other end. In the illustrations (Figs. 85 and 86) the knot of the bandage has been brought into requisition to act as the *pad* which presses the artery against the bone.

The Triangular Bandage for the Fixation of Splints.— In case of *fracture* the splints are retained in position by means of bandages which are folded narrow, and encircle the limb—including the splints—*above* and *below* the seat of fracture, the ends being invariably tied on the outer or more accessible end of the limb, the knots resting on the splint. In fractures of the lower extremity some difficulty may be experienced in passing the bandage under the limb, but may be overcome by folding one end of the bandage over the end of a flat, thin piece of wood, and pushing the bandage under the limb. If the bandages are placed in position before the splints are applied, the necessity for raising the limb to allow of the bandage being passed under it will not arise, which is a point of some importance.

It only remains to add, in conclusion, that all who are interested in the subject of First-Aid to the Injured—and who are not interested, for are not all liable to meet with accidents?—should practise the various methods of using the Triangular Bandage, for, simple though they be, it is only thus that they can perfect themselves in the art.

[*The reader is recommended to peruse the Section on the Skeleton (Vol. I.) as a preliminary to this portion of the work.*]

ON FRACTURES

When a bone in the body is *broken* it is said to be *fractured* (Latin, *frangere—fractum*, to break). Injuries to the bones and muscles, such as *fractures, dislocations*, and *sprains*, are commonly met with in every-day experience, and as the future usefulness of the limb depends largely on the manner in which it is treated at the outset, it is of the utmost importance that the nature of the accident, and the method of treating it, should be carefully considered, and the principles underlying its management thoroughly grasped.

Varieties of Fractures.—When a bone is broken, but the skin and soft parts covering it remain uninjured, the fracture is said to be *simple.* When, in addition to the broken bone, there exists a wound which *communicates with the ends of the broken bone*, whether this wound is caused by the force which produced the fracture, or by one of the sharp ends of the broken bone perforating the skin, the fracture is said to be *compound.* There are thus two great varieties of fracture—

1. Simple.
2. Compound.

It will be readily understood that simple fractures are much less serious than the compounds. They usually do well, whereas the latter are always serious, those of the upper extremity being less fatal than those of the leg, and these latter less so than those of the thigh. The importance of this fact will be borne in mind when treating a case of simple fracture, because the greatest danger to which the patient is exposed is that of the simple fracture being converted into a compound one, either by injudicious and

FIG. 83.—BANDAGE FOR CHEST (BACK).

FIG. 84.—BANDAGE FOR CHEST (FRONT).

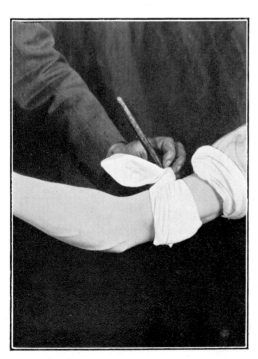

FIG. 85.—A TOURNIQUET (1).

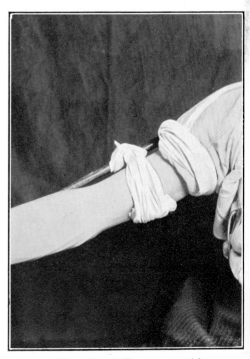

FIG. 86.—A TOURNIQUET (2).

FRONT VIEW OF ADULT MALE SKELETON

TO ILLUSTRATE SECTION ON FRACTURES

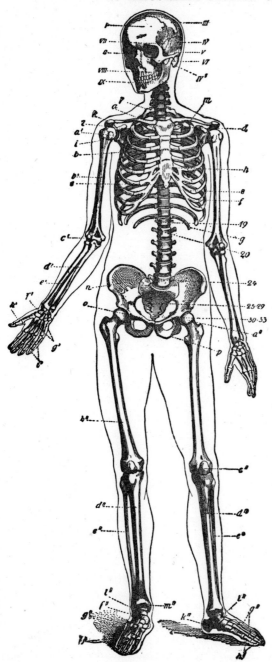

I. Frontal Bone.
II. Nasal Bones.
III. Parietal Bones.
IV. Temporal Bone.
IV'. Petrous part of Temporal.
V. Temporal Fossa.
VI. Cheek Arch.
VII. Temporal Bone
VIII. Upper Jaw.
IX. Lower Jaw.
7. Neck Vertebræ.
19. Last Dorsal Vertebra.
20. First Lumbar Vertebra.
24. Last Lumbar Vertebra.
25–29. Bones of Sacrum.
30–33. Bones of Coccyx.
a. Clavicle.
b. Scapula.
b'. Humerus.
c. Ribs.
c'. Elbow Joint.
d'. Ulna.
e'. Radius.
f'. Wrist.
g'. Metacarpus
h'. Thumb.
i'. Fingers.
d. Shoulder-joint.
e. Ribs.
f. Rib-cartilages.
g. Last Rib.
h. Ribs.
i. Scapula.
k. Acromion process.
l. Head of Humerus.
m. Clavicle.
n. Ilium.
o. Pubis.
p. Ischium.
a''. Head of Thigh or Femur.
b''. Femur.
c''. Knee-cap or Patella.
d''. Tibia.
e''. Fibula.
f''. Tarsus.
g''. Metatarsus.
h''. Toes.
i. Astragalus.
k. Calcaneum.
l''. Outer Projection of Ankle.
m''. Inner Projection of Ankle.

FIG. 86A

rough handling, or by the patient himself, in his efforts to move. He may be aided in these efforts by his friends or the bystanders who are ignorant of the danger to which he exposes himself, and it will be for the reader, should he witness such an accident, to insist on the patient lying still, till medical aid arrives, and in the event of this not being immediately available, to adopt the means hereafter to be described for *fixing* the broken ends of the bone in such a manner that no further injury can be inflicted, and further, to super-intend the careful removal of the patient to the hospital or his home.

In addition to the two great varieties into which fractures are divided, there are other methods of classifying them. Thus a simple or compound fracture is said to be *complete* when it is broken right through; *incomplete*, when it is only *cracked* or *bent*, as in "*green-*

| FIG. 87. | FIG. 88. | FIG. 89. | FIG. 90. |
| Impacted Fracture. | Transverse Fracture. | Oblique Fracture. | Longitudinal Fracture. |

stick" fracture, where, instead of the bone breaking, it bends, and the bone on the convex surface of the bend is split up, as happens when a green branch of a tree is bent—this form of fracture is frequent amongst children; *fissured*; *impacted*, when one end of the broken bone is driven into and fixed into the other. This form of fracture is most frequently seen in old people.

Then, again, *complete* fractures may be classified according to the direction of the line of fracture. They may be *transverse*, when the line of fracture lies at right angles to the long axis of the bone. These fractures are not very common, and are most frequently met with in children, and are then near one or other end of the bone. *Oblique*, when the fracture runs diagonally across the bone, and both broken ends have sharp points. This form is very common, and is the one in which there is the greatest risk of a simple being converted into a compound fracture. *Longitudinal*, when the line of fracture runs in the long axis of the bone; this form is usually met with in the vicinity of a joint (Figs. 87–90).

In a *Comminuted* fracture the bone is broken into several fragments. A *Multiple* is one where a bone is broken in more than one place. Finally, a fracture may be *complicated* by some other injury, as when one of the larger arteries in the vicinity of the injury is ruptured, giving rise to serious *bleeding*; or where a nerve is torn through, causing *paralysis*; or when an important organ, such as the *lung* in fracture of the ribs, or the *brain* in fracture of the skull, is damaged. The following table, which reduces the foregoing definitions to tabular form, may be of assistance to those who wish to convey to memory the different kinds of fractures :—

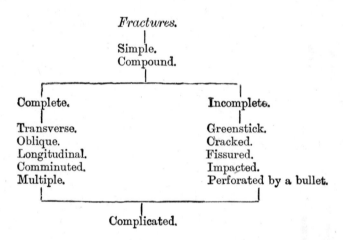

Causes of Fracture.—Fractures are met with at every period of life; in *infancy* they are generally incomplete, but complete fractures of the clavicle and bones of the forearm are common in childhood, about half the cases of the former occurring at this period of life. *Adults* are more liable to *complete* fractures, and men, on account of the nature of their work, are more frequently the victims than women. In *old age*, the *impacted fracture* is most frequently met with, as the bones at this period of life are brittle. The fracture being commonly situated at the upper end of the *thigh-bone*, or at the wrist, though it may be met with in other regions. Certain diseases predispose to fractures; thus *lunatics* are very prone to suffer from this accident, and this fact should be remembered by all who have to attend on such patients; and they must be most careful in applying any form of restraint which may be rendered necessary. *Rickets* is another disease in which the bones easily break. Whenever the bones are in a brittle condition, *muscular action* alone is sufficient to produce a fracture—thus snapping across of the knee-cap, the result of muscular exertion, is a very common accident. The collar-bone has been known to break as the result of attempting to lift a heavy weight. But apart from these constitutional causes of fracture, it may be taken as a fact that the cause of fracture is always *force* of some sort. This force may be applied from *within* the body itself in the form of *muscular action* or from without. Fractures, then, may be due to *internal violence* or *external violence*. The form that the external violence takes varies with almost every accident, but it may be divided into two great divisions—

1. Direct.
2. Indirect.

Direct violence may be due to a blow from a stick or the fist, the fall of a heavy mass on a part of the body, the passage of a wheel over a limb, a gunshot wound. Whatever the form of violence, the fracture invariably takes place at *the spot where the injury is received*, and, further, it is this form of violence which is apt to cause a *compound fracture*.

Indirect violence.—An individual stumbles, and in his endeavour to save himself from falling on his face strikes the ground with the palm of his hand, and fractures his *collar-bone*. Another, jumping down from a height, and landing on his feet, fractures the neck of his *thigh-bone*. It will be noticed that in these two accidents the fracture occurs, not at the point where the force was applied, viz., the hand or the foot, but at a point far removed from these regions, and on examination it is found that the fracture occurs at the *weakest point* in the column of bones through which the force has been transmitted, by a *bending* and subsequent *snapping* of the bone. A similar form of accident is met with in the *fibula* or outer bone of the leg. When the foot is forcibly pushed outwards, the lower end of the bone is also pushed outwards, the bone is bent and a fracture occurs not at the end of the bone, but a few inches higher up, where it is *thinnest* and *weakest*. The causes of fracture, then, may be tabulated as follows :—

Causes of Fracture.

| Direct violence: blows. Fracture at seat of injury. Serious, often *compound*. | Indirect violence: falls. Fracture at some distance from seat of injury. Usually *simple*. May be converted into compound by rough handling. | Muscular action. Some diseased condition of bones usually present. |

Symptoms of Fracture.—When a person complains of having received a blow or a fall, followed by a sensation of something giving way, and of *pain* when any attempt at movement is made, and when on examining the injured limb and comparing it with the sound one the former is found to be altered in shape or *deformed*, the presence of a fracture may be suspected. If, in addition to the above-mentioned symptoms, it is found that the patient is *unable to move the limb*, but that by manipulation it can be moved in abnormal directions, that during these manipulations a *grating sound* (*crepitus*) is produced, and finally that the limb is *shorter* than its neighbours, the presence of a fracture becomes certain.

The symptoms of fracture then are—

1. The history of a fall or blow, accompanied sometimes by a sensation of something giving way.

2. Pain on attempting to move the limb.

3. Inability to move the limb.

These three symptoms have to be elicited from the patient himself should he be conscious, and are called the *subjective symptoms*. Following on these there are—

4. Deformity.

5. Shortening.

6. Unnatural mobility.

7. Crepitus, or the grating sound produced by the broken ends of the bone rubbing against each other.

8. Swelling.

These are termed the *objective symptoms*, and have to be discovered by the person attending to the patient. Now, if all the symptoms mentioned were present in every fracture the discovery or diagnosis of the injury would be a simple matter; but, unfortunately, they are not all always present. For instance, when two bones lie side by side, as in the arm or the leg, and only one of them is fractured, the other bones prevent the *deformity* which is so important a sign. This state of matters is well illustrated in a transverse fracture of the tibia or inner bone of the leg, with no displacement, where the fibula or outer bone keeps the limb straight.

Then, again, in *impacted fractures* no abnormal mobility or crepitus exists, and, as a matter of fact, it is highly dangerous to try and get these symptoms in old people, the only symptoms present being a slight amount of shortening and a slight deformity. And, lastly, it is always difficult to discover a crack or *fissure* in the skull or any other bones, and often it is only possible to come to a decision by noting the symptoms produced in neighbouring organs. It will.

be seen then that, whilst ordinarily it is easy to discover the presence of a fracture, cases must frequently arise when it is very difficult to do so, nay, sometimes impossible to be quite sure, and in such cases it only remains for the unskilled attendant to treat the case as if it were a fracture.

In order that the treatment of fractures may be carried out in an intelligent manner, it becomes necessary to understand clearly how some of the symptoms already mentioned are produced, and of these the *deformity* is most important, so far as the future utility of the limb is concerned, for unless it is remedied the alteration in shape becomes permanent.

Fig. 91 shows a Röntgen-ray photograph of a fracture of the bones of the left leg. It was taken from the outer side of the limb through the temporary splints. The fibula shows darker than the tibia, which lies behind it, the faintest shadow being that of the soft parts. The points to be noted are (1) the shortening of the limb caused by the

FIG. 91.—Badly United Fracture of Femur Causing a Deformity.

lower fragments, with the foot, being pulled up by muscular action and by the direction of the force; (2) the deformity; (3) most important of all, the sharp ends of the broken tibia, which might so easily have pierced the skin and converted the simple fracture into a compound one had the patient been roughly handled.

Deformity is produced by *muscular action*. The muscles are attached to the bone. When the latter are intact the muscles contract and produce the various movements at the joints, but when a bone is broken the muscle in contracting pulls on one or other of the broken ends of the bones, and consequently gives rise to displacement (Fig. 92), and frequently shortening of the limb. The deformity may also be caused by the *weight of the limb*. In fractures of the lower extremity the foot is generally found lying on its outer side. The *direction of the fracture* is of importance, for, as has already been remarked, when the break is *transverse* there may be little or no displacement, whereas in *oblique* fractures there generally is a considerable amount, together with shortening. Lastly, the *direction in which the force* causing the fracture acted, influences the displacement. In the treatment of fracture the above-mentioned facts must be borne in mind, as its object must always be to combat the several causes of deformity.

Crepitus, or the grating sound produced by the broken ends of the bone rubbing against each other, is a conclusive sign of fracture when produced during the examination, but is not one that should be looked for when there are other signs evident; and indeed, in *impacted* fractures no attempt should be made to elicit it; the examination of such fractures being carried out with more than the usual amount of gentleness and care to be practised in the handling of every fracture.

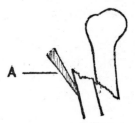

FIG. 92.—Fracture of Humerus. Deltoid Muscle A pulling lower fragment outwards and up-wards.

Unnatural mobility, too, is a symptom which should not be depended upon, when other equally distinctive symptoms are present. It entails unnecessary suffering on the patient, and in impacted fractures does irremediable harm. One shudders sometimes on hearing an ambulance pupil say that one of the symptoms of fracture is "unnatural mobility: that is to say, a joint where no joint should be," indicating an amount of roughness in manipulation truly appalling, and not to be imitated.

Swelling, following immediately after the receipt of injury, indicates the rupture of a large artery or vein, and consequent bleeding into the tissues round the fracture. In addition to the symptoms produced by the injury to the bone itself, there may be others, due to the effect of the accident on the general system. These are termed the *constitutional symptoms*, such as *shock* and *faintness*. In conclusion, it must be borne in mind that every fracture is to be examined with the utmost caution; it should be handled as little as possible, and when manipulations are absolutely necessary they must be carried out with the greatest *gentleness*. The *sound limb* should always be carefully examined in the first place, so as to familiarise oneself with the normal shape and the position of bony prominences. A comparison should then be made between it and the injured one, and a conclusion come to as to the nature of the injury, more by the *appearance* of the limb than by handling of it. Should it be necessary to remove part of the clothing, it should be cut off the injured side, if its removal in the ordinary way gives rise to discomfort or exposes the patient to any risk in the way of rough handling; and always, in removing the dress, begin doing so on the *uninjured* side.

Repair of Fracture.—Fractures heal more quickly in children than in adults. They heal more quickly if the ends of the broken bone are brought accurately together and kept *immobile*, just as in wounds involving the skin and soft parts, where, if the edges of the wound are brought together by stitches and the part kept at rest, it heals rapidly, leaving a very slight scar; whereas should nothing be done, it takes much longer to heal and leaves an ugly mark.

If the ends of the bone are not brought accurately together, or if, during the period of healing, the fragments are not kept absolutely steady, blood is poured out round the broken ends. This clots, becomes firm and organised, forming what is called the *callus;* it encircles the broken ends like a tube, and fixes them. Gradually *lime* salts are deposited in this organised material, and the ends of the bone are *cemented* together. But nature makes no attempt at neutralising the deformity, so that if nothing is done to help it the bones will unite in an unnatural position; and further, if the ends are not kept fixed, but considerable movement permitted, the lime salts may not be deposited at all, and the ends may be united by a cartilaginous band only, forming a *false joint*, and thus greatly impairing the utility of the limb, or indeed rendering it absolutely useless. It will thus be seen that the main object of treatment must always be to *aid nature* in her efforts at effecting a cure. If the broken ends of the bone are brought accurately together, if they are kept immovably fixed in this position for the requisite length of time, nature will do the rest; and in a longer or shorter period of time, depending on the age of the patient, his constitution, and the nature or severity of the injury, the bone will be restored to its original condition, and the limb be as useful as ever.

Treatment of Fractures.—To restore a bone to its normal position, and keep it there by means of surgical appliances, is the very simple principle which underlies the treatment of fractures, but the carrying out of this principle is often most difficult. Fortunately, however, the man who treats a fracture in an *emergency* is not concerned with the difficulties which beset the one who has to maintain this principle for some considerable time; all the former has to do is to convince himself of the presence of a fracture, or having reasonable grounds for *suspecting* the presence of one, to take such steps as will prevent any further injury being inflicted. Now as the larger proportion of fractures occur in the open air, in the street, in the country, or it may be in a workshop—at any rate at some distance from the patient's home or a hospital—the first point to be remembered is that he has to be *removed* from the spot where he was found lying, and that it is during the time of removal that the patient is exposed to the risk of further injury. In a simple fracture, the sharp end of a fragment piercing the skin, and converting it into the far more dangerous compound variety, it must then be the duty of the bystander, before he allows the patient to be removed, before he allows him to move—for often the further injury is self-inflicted by the patient's endeavouring to get up and walk—*to fix the broken ends* of the bone in such a way that they can inflict no further injury on the soft parts. In cases of *compound fracture* it is clearly his business—in addition to fixing the broken ends of the bone in some immovable apparatus—to *stop the bleeding*, and further, to *cleanse the wound* and apply a temporary dressing to it.

The temporary appliances requisite for fixing the two broken ends of the bone are *splints, pads,* and *triangular bandages,* or handkerchiefs.

Splints are pieces of wood, or other sufficiently firm material, which are fixed to a broken bone, and prevent movement of the ends; two are generally employed, one for each side of the broken bone. *Improvised splints* can be easily made, the material available depending on the locality in which the accident occurs; for instance, folded newspapers, covers of books, straw bottle-covers, thin boards, lids of boxes, walking-sticks, twigs, or branches cut from trees—it matters not what the material, so it be sufficiently *rigid* to keep the broken ends fixed.

Pads.—As the splints are hard, were they to be applied directly to the skin they would give rise to *pain*, and if the pressure were kept up long enough—more especially on the skin covering a bony prominence, such as is found at the *ankle* or the *elbow-joint*—they might cause *ulceration*. For this reason the splints must always be covered with some soft material, such as cotton wool, layers of flannel (in the country moss would make an admirable padding), and care must be taken that all the inequalities of the limb are carefully filled up by the padding, special attention being paid to the hollows above and below bony prominences. The padding should overlap the sides and ends of the splints.

The *triangular bandages,* which may be improvised by folding a handkerchief diagonally, are used to fix the splints in position, and are applied, one *above* and the other *below* the seat of injury, in the manner already described.

Having described the necessary apparatus, it now becomes necessary to consider the steps to be taken in treating the fracture. In the first place, the patient must be reassured and advised to lie very still. The crowd, which generally springs up all round, must be asked to stand back and give the patient room to breathe. Next a careful but gentle examination of the injury must be made, if necessary comparing it with the uninjured side. Having decided upon the nature of the fracture, it becomes necessary to improvise the splints that are required from whatever suitable material there may be at hand, and in order that they may fit properly, they are tried first on the uninjured limb. Some form of pads must next be provided, but it may be remarked that in simple fractures, where it is not necessary to remove the clothes, these form efficient padding, and no other need be provided. Finally, the bandages are prepared by folding handkerchiefs to the requisite breadth, and nothing now remains but to fix the splints firmly to the injured limb, and this is done in the following manner: Two assistants are called in to aid the operator, one grasps the limb above the seat of fracture and steadies the upper fragment; the other grasps it below the fracture and steadies the lower. If the deformity be great, and the danger of one of the sharp points of bone perforating the skin be imminent, gentle efforts may be made to rectify the displacement to some extent, and straighten the limb, by getting the man who is holding the lower fragment to pull upon it firmly and steadily without any jerking, the man who grasps the upper fragment keeping it steady all the time.

Whilst the extension on the lower fragment is being maintained, the operator takes the two splints and applies them to the limb, one on each side; he next fixes them by applying bandages firmly above and below the seat of injury, and it is only after the splint has been fixed that the two assistants relax their hold on the two portions of the fractured bone. But it must be clearly understood that it is only in exceptional cases that traction will need to be made on the limb, as part of the emergency treatment, in the large majority of cases; steadying the upper and lower fragments, and applying well-padded splints, being all that is necessary in cases of simple fracture. In compound fractures the procedure differs somewhat, because *before fixing* the fracture it is necessary, in the first place, to *stop the bleeding*, it may be by the application of a *tourniquet* to the main artery of the limb. Next the wound must be thoroughly cleaned and dressed. Washing it with clean cold water serves the double purpose of cleaning it, and also of allaying the bleeding from the surface of the wound. If it is considered desirable to add some *antiseptic* to the water, then it may be remembered that alcohol, which is as a rule readily obtainable, either pure or diluted with clean water, makes a very efficient antiseptic wash. For a dressing a piece of clean cloth soaked in clean water or alcohol, applied to the wound and retained in position by a bandage, does admirably. After the bleeding and the wound have been attended to, the broken bone is fixed in the same way as in a case of simple fracture in the same region.

When the fracture has been fixed, the last point to be considered is the removal of the patient. This subject will be considered fully in another chapter, and it is sufficient to say here that in fractures of the lower extremity the patient must always be carried on a stretcher, improvised or otherwise, or in an ambulance waggon. In no case must he be hustled into a cab or cart, and rattled off at a great speed to the nearest doctor, as invariably seems to be the desire of the onlookers. In fractures of the upper extremity, the patient may go in a cab, should he feel faint; but if in a condition to do so, it will be more comfortable and less painful for him to walk to his destination.

DISLOCATIONS

Before proceeding to a consideration of the management of special fractures, it will be useful to say a few words regarding dislocations. Many of the symptoms of this form of injury are similar to those of fracture—the difficulty of distinguishing the one from the other is sometimes very great—though as a rule it is easy to do so ; and the danger of meddlesome interference is as great, if not greater, than it is in fractures.

Definition.—A joint is said to be dislocated when the articular surface of one bone entering into the formation of the joint is displaced from that of the other.

The accompanying sketch of a dislocation of the shoulder-joint, where the head of the humerus A is displaced from the shallow cup or "glenoid cavity" B of the scapula or shoulder-blade, illustrates one of the varieties of dislocation at this joint.

Varieties.—A dislocation is said to be *complete* when the bone is wholly displaced, *incomplete* when the displacement is only partial. When a *wound* communicates with a dislocated joint it is called a *compound dislocation ;* when no wound exists, a *simple* one.

FIG. 93.—Dislocation of Shoulder.

Causes.—As in fractures, dislocations are caused by *external violence*, which may be *direct* or *indirect*, and they may also be produced by *muscular action*, as is frequently seen in dislocation of the *lower jaw*, due to yawning.

The *effects* of a dislocation are to tear the *ligaments* which bind the bones together, and to injure the muscles and soft parts surrounding the joint. Occasionally nerves are pressed upon or torn through, and the main artery injured, and it must always be borne in mind that all dislocations, and more especially those of the *ankle-joint*, may be complicated with fracture.

Symptoms.—In every case of suspected dislocation the injured side should be compared with the sound one, when the most important and obvious symptom of dislocation—*deformity*—will present itself. It will be at once seen that the *shape* of the joint is different from its fellow. Further, it will be noticed that the patient is unable to move the limb at the injured joint; and, lastly, the individual examining the injury will find that the mobility of the joint is greatly impaired, and that any attempt at movement causes severe pain. The symptoms then of dislocation are :—

1. Deformity.
2. Loss of the power of voluntary motion.
3. Fixation, or impaired mobility.

It will be observed that the symptoms of dislocation are in some respects similar to those of fracture. In both there is deformity, pain, and loss of voluntary power. They differ in that there is *no crepitus* in dislocation. There is fixation instead of abnormal mobility, as in fracture; and, lastly, a dislocation is *always* at a joint: a fracture usually some distance from it.

Treatment.—The "first-aid" treatment of dislocations consists *solely* in placing the injured joint in the most comfortable position possible, and sending for medical aid. Under no circumstances whatever should an unqualified person attempt to "reduce" or replace the dislocated bone. Should the injury be situated in the upper extremity he must content himself with putting the arm in a sling, if in the lower extremity of getting the patient to lie in the position he finds most comfortable, and supporting the limb on a pillow or cushion. In the event of the pain being very severe, and of delay arising in the arrival of the medical man, the clothes may be removed, with the same precautions as in cases of fracture, and warm applications made to the injured joint. In all cases dislocations should be reduced as soon as possible, and for this reason the medical man should be sent for at once, and the nature of the accident explained to him, to enable him to bring the necessary appliances.

SPRAINS

A sprain may be described as the first stage in the production of a dislocation ; that is to say, the bones forming the joint are forcibly separated from each other, but not permanently displaced, the ligaments which bind the bones together are stretched, and some of them lacerated. As a consequence there is *bleeding* into the joint from the small blood-vessels which have been torn across. The blood is poured out between the ends of the bones, and gives rise to the *swelling* which is such a marked symptom of the injury, and this distension causes the *severe pain* which is invariably present. The *causes* are very much the same as those of dislocation—a fall—forcibly moving the joint in an unnatural direction, as when the foot is twisted under one.

The Treatment of a sprain consists in relieving the pain, and stopping the bleeding which is going on within the joint. To relieve the pain the joint must be kept at *rest*, and. if necessary a splint applied to it to ensure this. The bleeding must be stopped by *cold applications*, by *pressure*, and by *raising the limb*. *Cold* may be employed in the form of ice applied in a bag, or cloths wrung out of cold water may be wrapped firmly round the joint.

To employ *pressure* the joint may be firmly wrapped up in a triangular bandage soaked in cold water, and applied according to the method described in the chapter on bandaging. Should the sprain be situated in the lower extremity the limb should be raised on a cushion or pillow, if in the upper extremity the arm should be placed in a sling. On no account should a sprained joint be allowed to hang down.

The after effects of a sprain are sometimes very serious. Should it have been neglected or improperly treated, and the limb not have been kept at rest for a sufficient length of time, the usefulness of the limb may possibly be permanently interfered with, or the apparently simple injury may become the starting point of serious joint disease.

From the foregoing remarks on dislocations and sprains it will be observed that the difficulties of distinguishing between them and fractures must sometimes be very great, more especially when a fracture is associated with one or other of them, as, for instance, when the tip of one of the bones forming the prominence of the ankle is snapped off in a severe sprain of that joint, and the object in introducing these two forms of accident at this stage, before the consideration of the treatment of special fractures, is to impress on the reader the care with which all such accidents should be handled, to let him see for himself the great danger that lies in meddlesome interference, and the risks that attach to treating an injury to a joint, however trifling, as of no importance.

Having considered the symptoms, treatment, &c., of fractures in general, it now becomes necessary to say a few words regarding the treatment of special fractures, as, whilst the *principles* are the same everywhere, the *methods* vary according to the region of the body in which the injury is situated. It will be convenient to take up the fractures in the following order :—

Fractures of the upper extremity.

Fractures of the lower extremity.

Fractures of the head and trunk.

SPECIAL FRACTURES

Fractures of the Upper Extremity. — *Fracture* of the *Collar-bone* or *Clavicle.*—The collar-bone is more frequently broken than any other single bone in the body, and the injury is very com-

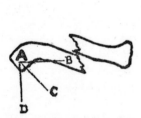

FIG. 94.—Fracture of Clavicle.

A. Point of shoulder drawn inwards, forwards, downwards, as indicated by lines B, C, D.

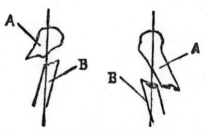

FIG. 95.—Fracture of Humerus.

monly met with in children; it is generally the result of *indirect violence*, such as a fall on the shoulder, though it may be produced by direct violence, such as a blow, in which case the fracture is usually compound. The fracture is most commonly situated in the *middle* of the bone, and is of the *oblique* variety.

As a result of *muscular action* and the *weight of the arm*, the outer fragment is pulled *downwards*, forwards, and inwards (Fig. 94), so that the inner fragment rides on the outer one.

Symptoms.—These are very characteristic. The patient is seen supporting the elbow on the injured side, and any attempt at movement of the arm is accompanied by *pain*. On comparing the two shoulders, that on the injured side is *lower* than the sound one ; it is also drawn *forwards* and *inwards* nearer to the middle line of the body (Fig. 94) ; on passing the finger along the broken bone, a depression will be felt, followed by a prominence caused by the inner fragment overlapping the outer one.

Crepitus may be felt, but it is not necessary to observe this symptom, as the other signs are sufficient aids to a correct diagnosis. Put shortly, the symptoms are

1. *Pain* on attempting to move arm.
2. *Deformity.*
3. *Drooping of the shoulder.*

The *treatment* consists in raising the shoulder and taking the weight of the arm off it by supporting the elbow in a sling, and in binding the arm to the body and thus preventing movement ; and is carried out in the following manner : Flex the forearm, and carry the hand to the opposite shoulder, and support the elbow in a sling as depicted in Figs. 71–73 in the chapter on bandaging ; next, take a bandage *folded broad*, and bind the arm firmly to the body (Fig. 96). It is sometimes advised to place a *pad* in the armpit, but this is unnecessary ; and if too large a one is used, may cause inconvenience to the patient.

Fracture of the *shoulder-blade* is a rare accident, and the result of severe direct violence, such as crushing, and is commonly associated with other severe injuries, as broken ribs. The *symptoms* are severe *pain*, inability to use the arm, and *bruising* over the site of injury ; and the *treatment* consists in supporting the elbow in a broad sling (Fig. 96), and binding the arm to the side with handkerchief folded broad, as in fracture of the clavicle.

Fractures of the Upper Arm are commonly met with, and may be the result of *direct violence* as a blow, *indirect violence* from a fall on the elbow, or muscular action as in throwing a ball. The fracture may be situated in any part of the bone, the most common site being at the junction of the middle and upper thirds, and is generally of the *oblique* variety.

Symptoms.—The main indication is *shortening* of the arm, the positions taken by the broken ends of the bone depending on the seat of injury and the several muscles which act on the two fragments, and also upon the line of fracture. When the fracture is situated high up, the upper fragment is drawn *outwards* (Fig. 95) and the lower fragment *inwards* (B) ; on the other hand, when the break is near the middle of the bone, the reverse state of affairs exists (Fig. 95). It addition to the shortening and consequent *deformity*, there is *inability to move the arm*, and *pain* at the seat of injury. *Crepitus* may be discovered during the necessary manipulations, but should not be looked for when the other symptoms indicated are present. The symptoms then are :—

1. Shortening of the upper arm.
2. Deformity.
3. Inability to use the limb.
4. Pain.

Treatment.—Consists in fixing the two fragments of the bone in splints and supporting the arm in a sling.

Two splints are sufficient as a rule—one applied to the *inner* side of the arm and extending from the *armpit* to the elbow, the other being applied to the outer side of the limb, extending from the shoulder to the elbow. The splints should be about the breadth of the arm, and must be carefully *padded*, special care being taken that they do not press directly on the bony prominences at the elbow-joint. Improvised splints may be made of the covers of books, newspapers, or brown paper folded to a suitable thickness, or straw bottle-covers, as seen in the illustration. Before the splints are applied, an assistant, standing behind the patient, who should be seated on a chair, fixes the fragments by grasping the injured arm at the shoulder and elbow ; he may apply a slight amount of *extension* by steadily and gently pulling the elbow downwards, to relieve the pressure of the sharp ends of the bones on the soft parts, and whilst this extension is being kept up, the splints are applied and firmly fixed to the arm by two bandages *folded narrow* and placed one *above* and the other *below* the seat of fracture. Finally, the forearm is bent at a right angle to the upper arm, and placed in a *lesser sling*, allowing the elbow to hang free, as any support afforded to this joint would tend to push the lower fragment upwards, and consequently accentuate the tendency to shortening which already exists (Figs. 97–99).

Fractures of the Forearm.—As there are two bones in the forearm, fractures may implicate both, or be confined to one or other of them. In the former case the symptoms are so marked that there is little, if any, difficulty in recognising the nature of the accident. In the latter, the uninjured bone acting as a splint often prevents deformity, and the symptoms may be masked ; the patient, however, should not be subjected to the pain and danger of a prolonged examination, the case being treated as one of fracture in all doubtful cases. All the *symptoms* of fracture, pain, inability to use the limb, and deformity are usually present.

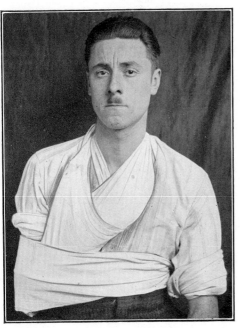

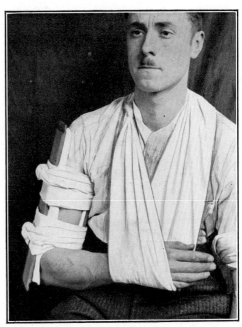

FIG. 96.—FRACTURE OF COLLAR-BONE.

FIG. 97.—FRACTURE OF UPPER ARM.

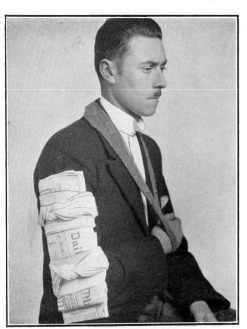

FIG. 98.—FRACTURE OF UPPER ARM
(IMPROVISED SPLINTS).

FIG. 99.—FRACTURE OF UPPER ARM
(IMPROVISED SPLINTS).

The *treatment* in an emergency is the same, whether both bones or one only is broken, and is as follows: Two splints are prepared, one to be applied to the *front* of the arm, extending from the bend of the elbow to the middle of the palm of the hand; the other to be applied to the *back* of the arm, and extending from the tip of the elbow to the tips of the fingers; they must be *broader* than the arm, because there are two bones in the arm, and were a narrow splint to be applied, the bandages which retain them in position would squeeze the bones which are lying side by side together, and increase the deformity. They must be well *padded*, and care must be taken that the upper end of the anterior splint does not press unduly against the front of the elbow when the arm is bent at a right angle to the forearm, nor the lower end on the ball of the thumb; the splints being fitted to the sound arm before being applied to the injured one. To apply the splints, the aid of an assistant is called in to fix the arm, which is bent at right angles to the upper arm with the *thumb pointing upwards*, and the assistant steadies the arm by grasping it by the hand and elbow, and by steadily pulling the hand applies slight extension. The splints are then applied, the posterior one first and then the anterior, and are fixed by two narrow folded bandages, one above and another below the seat of the fracture, and the arm is finally put into a broad sling, the elbow being supported (Figs. 100, 101).

A fracture which is apt to be overlooked, with disastrous results as regards the future utility of the arm, is that of the bony prominence forming the point of the elbow and called the *olecranon;* it is caused by a fall on the elbow, and is often mistaken for a sprain of the joint. A knowledge of the fact that such a mistake is often made should ensure the employment of skilled advice in all cases of injury to this joint. The emergency treatment consists in putting the arm in a sling supporting the elbow.

A fracture of a single bone of the forearm which occurs very commonly in old people is that of the *radius*, or outer bone of the arm at the *wrist*. It is caused by a fall on the palm of the hand, and may be mistaken for a *sprain of the wrist*. The *deformity* is well marked as a rule, the hand being drawn over to the thumb side of the arm. Sometimes, however, the only symptom is *pain;* with the history of a fall on the palm of the hand the pain is very severe, and is fixed just above the wrist. Such a case should be treated as a fracture, and whether deformity be present or not, the arm should be put up in splints as for fracture of both bones (Fig. 102).

Fracture of Bones of the Palm of the Hand.—There are five bones forming the palm of the hand, and any one of them may be broken as the result of a blow; those of the right hand being more liable to injury than the left. The chief symptoms are severe *pain*, and swelling of the hand. The *treatment* consists in applying a well-padded splint to the palm of the hand, extending from the middle of the forearm to the tips of the fingers, binding the hand firmly to the splint, and putting it in a sling.

Fractures of the Fingers are usually *compound*, though they may be *simple*. They are easily distinguished. The treatment is similar to that of fractures of the palm, and a splint extending from the tips of the fingers to the middle of the forearm, well padded, is applied to the palmar surface of the hand, the finger or fingers adjacent to the injured one being used as *lateral splints*, and all being bound to the splint. The hand is then placed in a sling, and kept slightly higher than the elbow. (See Fig. 103.)

Fractures of the Lower Extremity.—The *Thigh-bone*, or Femur may be fractured in three places—(1) at the upper end or neck; (2) at the shaft; (3) at the lower end. Fractures at the upper end occur most frequently in *old people*, and are divided into *impacted* and *non-impacted* fractures. *Non-impacted* fractures are usually caused by some slight *indirect violence*, such as tripping on the edge of a carpet: and the *symptoms* are (1) marked *shortening* of the limb, from one to two and a half inches; (2) *eversion* of the limb, so that the outside of the foot lies helplessly on the ground; (3) inability to *raise the limb* on the part of the patient; (4) *pain*; (5) *crepitus*; (6) *unnatural mobility*.

In *impacted fracture* there is a history of a blow or *fall on the side of the hip*, as often happens when the pavements are slippery in winter, so that the violence causing the fracture is *direct*. The *symptoms* are—(1) *slight shortening* of about one inch; (2) the foot is *fixed*, and may be turned outwards or inwards, and *gentle* efforts made to straighten it fail to do so (thus differing from the non-impacted variety where there is unnatural mobility); (3) inability to move the limb on the part of the patient; (4) pain; (5) there is *no crepitus, and no attempt should be made to elicit it*. The difference, then, in the symptoms of the two forms of fracture is that in the one the foot is everted, the limb is markedly shorter than the sound one, and there is unnatural mobility; in the other the foot may be everted or inverted, the shortening of the limb is hardly noticeable, and the limb is always fixed. The importance of remembering these facts when dealing with fractures at the upper end of the thigh-bone will be appreciated when it is understood (1) that a person with an impacted fracture has a much better chance of recovering with a useful limb than the one who has a non-impacted fracture; and (2) that

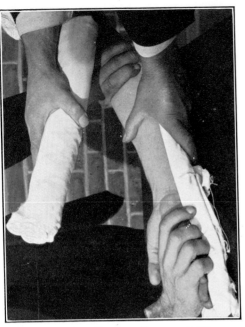

FIG. 100.—SETTING FRACTURE OF
FOREARM.

FIG. 101.—FRACTURE OF FOREARM.

FIG. 102.—FRACTURE AT WRIST.

FIG. 103.—FRACTURE OF FINGERS.

Impacted fractures are frequently converted into non-impacted ones by *rough handling* on the part of the examiner, and thus irreparable harm is done to the patient. In the *treatment* of these fractures, the handling must be of the gentlest and most careful. The patient must be advised to be very still, as he himself in his efforts to move may undo the impaction. The foot of the injured limb must be grasped and gentle efforts made to straighten it, so that the great toe points directly upwards; but should there be the least appearance of *fixation*, all further efforts in this direction must be discontinued. At the same time that the foot is being straightened, and when there is no fixation of the limb, steady extension should be made on the injured limb, and this must be kept up till the limb is the same length as the uninjured one, remembering that this is only to be done in cases of *non-impacted fracture*. Whilst the extension is being kept up, a *splint* must be applied, and this must always be a *long one*, extending from the *armpit* to the *sole of the foot*, the object being to keep the whole body rigid during the removal of the patient. Long splints can be bought, but improvised ones do equally well, and may be made from a broom-handle or a flat clothes-pole, a sufficient length being cut off. In the case of children—umbrellas, golf-clubs, the butt-end of a fishing-rod, the soldier's rifle—anything that is *long enough* and sufficiently *firm* to keep the body rigid. The splint is applied along the injured side of the body, and fixed with bandages folded broad (Figs. 104–107). Where bandages are not available, shawls, scarfs, towels may be used. One bandage is passed round the *chest*, a second round the *hips*, a third below the seat of fracture, a fourth below the knee, and a fifth binds the foot to the splint. The bandages can be applied under the body and leg with the help of a thin flat piece of wood, as has already been described, without raising the limb, which must be always avoided.

The splint having been firmly applied, it only remains to *bind the two limbs together*, the sound limb giving additional support to the injured one.

Fractures of the *shaft* of the thigh-bone are easily discovered. There is usually the history of a fall or blow, followed by loss of power. There is shortening and deformity, and the foot is everted. The *treatment* consists in applying *extension* till the limb is the same length as the sound one, holding the foot straight, with the toe pointing upwards. It is advisable to have two assistants to apply the extension—one grasping the thigh and fixing the upper fragment, whilst the other makes steady traction on the foot, applying a long splint in the manner already described, and binding the two limbs together. If considered necessary, a short splint may be applied to the inside of the thigh, extending from the knee to the groin, and another to the front of the thigh. And of the bandages fixing the long splint to the limb, two of them must always be placed, the one above and the other below the seat of fracture.

Fractures of the lower end of the femur often involve the knee-joint, and are then serious. The treatment is the same as for fractures in other regions of the bone.

Fracture of the patella or knee-cap is usually the result of muscular action which takes place when an effort is made to prevent the body falling backwards, and the fracture is transverse as a rule. The *symptoms* are sudden loss of power after muscular effort, and a separation of the two fragments. The *treatment* consists in bandaging the knee-joint with a triangular bandage, and applying a well-padded splint along the back of the leg, extending from the top of the thigh to the foot. Two of the four bandages which are required to fix the splint being applied, the one above and the other below the knee-joint.

Fractures of the Leg.—Both bones are usually broken, and when this is the case the nature of the injury is easily discovered; but when only one of the bones is fractured the diagnosis is not so easy, as the uninjured bone acts as a splint to the injured one, and prevents the deformity which is so marked a symptom when both bones are affected; but the existence of a fracture may always be suspected when, after a blow or fall, there is a *painful spot* at some point of the bone, and the accident is treated in the same manner as when both bones are broken.

The *cause* of fracture may be *direct violence*, as a wheel passing over the leg; or *indirect violence*, as when falling on the feet from a height. The *symptoms* when both bones are broken are the usual ones of fracture, together with *eversion* of the foot, which falls outwards by its own weight.

Treatment.—In the first place *extension* must be applied to the limb in the manner shown in the illustration (Fig. 104), one assistant grasping the upper fragments just below the knee and steadying them, whilst a second applies steady traction through the foot until the leg is the same length as the sound one, the foot being kept straight with the toe pointing upwards. Next well-padded splints extending from the knee to the sole of the foot are applied to the inner and outer side of the leg, and fixed with a bandage above and another below the seat of fracture. If available, a long splint should now be applied, as in fractures of the thigh, to keep the body rigid, and more especially to fix the *knee-joint;* and, finally, the two legs should be tied together. Whilst the necessary apparatus is

Fig. 104.—Applying Splints for Fracture of Leg.

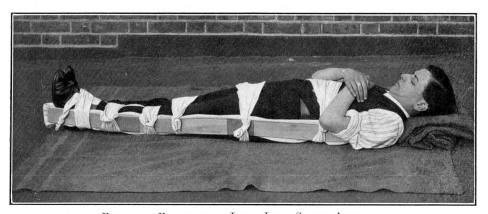

Fig. 105.—Fracture of Leg. Long Splint Applied.

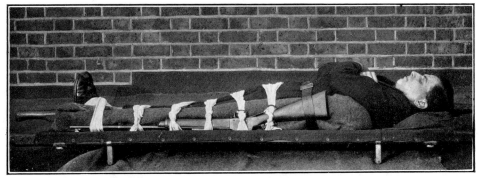

Fig. 106.—Fracture of Thigh. Rifle used as Long Splint.

being prepared the patient should be compelled to lie still, as any movement may result in a simple being converted into a compound fracture.

Fractures of the Foot are usually produced by some crushing force, such as a wheel passing over the foot, and are very serious from the severe injury to the soft parts.

Treatment.—The boot should be removed with the utmost care, cutting it off should there be any difficulty experienced in removing it in the ordinary way, the wound dressed, and the foot steadied by applying well-padded lateral splints. The subject of the removal of the injured is entered into fully in another chapter, but it might be well to remark here that in all cases of fracture situated in the lower extremity the patient should, if possible, be removed on a stretcher in the lying-down position.

Fracture of the Ribs.—This accident is less common amongst young people owing to the elasticity of the bones, but in old people, where the bones become very brittle, even a severe fit of coughing may cause it. The same condition of brittleness is common in insane people, so that fractured ribs are frequently met with in lunatic asylums.

Causes.—In the majority of cases the injury is the result of *direct violence*, such as falling against the sharp corner of a table or being struck a severe blow; the fracture occurs at the spot where the blow falls, and the sharp ends of the broken bone are driven in and may wound the *pleura* or covering of the lung, or even the lung itself. The injury may also be caused by *indirect violence*, such as a squeeze or a crush, in which case more than one rib is broken as a rule, and the fracture occurs about the middle of the bones.

The danger of the accident lies in the extent to which the organs contained in the chest are involved, as any injury to the lung may result in inflammation of that organ, or the patient may die from internal bleeding.

Symptoms.—There is generally the history of a blow or fall, and following this the patient complains of *pain* at the seat of injury, which is greatly aggravated by his attempting to take a deep breath or by pressing on the front of the chest. The breathing is shallow or catchy, as every breath causes pain, and the patient endeavours to keep the chest wall as quiet as possible. Sometimes the patient coughs up blood, which is a sure sign of the lung having been injured.

Treatment.—As the symptoms are produced by the movement of the chest-wall during breathing, the aim of treatment must largely lie in the direction of controlling these movements as far as possible, and this is done by applying a broad bandage round the chest; if necessary two or three bandages may be used, or a pillow-slip applied in the form of a binder. The bandage should be applied during expiration, and tightly enough to prevent his taking a deep breath, and to support his chest-wall when coughing, but not so tightly as to make him feel uncomfortable, the patient's own feelings being the best guide in this point. If, in addition, the arm is bound to the side, it will act as a splint, and further support the broken bones and control the movements of the chest (Fig. 109). Should the patient be in a *collapsed* condition this must be attended to, but stimulants must be administered with caution. Should he cough up blood he must be kept very quiet, lying down, and be given ice to suck or cold water to sip.

Fracture of the Spine.—All injuries to the spine are extremely grave, as there is always the possibility of the spinal cord being involved, and many accidents which appear trifling at the time of occurrence are followed by serious inflammatory changes in the cord later on. *Fractures* are caused by crushing, such as when the wheel of a heavy cart passes over the body, or by severe blows as from the buffer of a railway carriage. They may also be caused by falls from a height on the head. The *symptoms* will depend upon the extent to which the spinal cord contained within the spinal column is affected at the time of the accident. If the vertebræ are not displaced, and there is no crushing of the cord, there may be no other symptom than that of *pain* at the seat of injury, but should there be displacement of any of the bones then there will be, in addition to the local pain, irregularity in the shape of the spinal column, and the patient will have *lost the power of motion;* that is, he will be *paralysed* in all parts of the body that are below the seat of injury, so that if the soles of his feet are tickled he will not be able to draw up his legs; and the higher up in the spinal column the fracture lies the greater will be the extent of the paralysis, and should it be high up in the region of the neck the patient may die instantaneously. The symptoms then are—(1) pain; (2) paralysis; (3) deformity of the spine in a typical case. But, as has been remarked, *pain* may be the only immediate symptom present, and this, together with the history of an accident, should insure the patient being treated with the utmost care, and especially if it should be necessary to remove him. The treatment will consist in seeing that no further damage is done to the cord. He must be removed with great care, every possible effort being made to keep the *spine rigid*, and this may be best effected by carrying him on a door or shutter, supporting the spine both above and below and at the seat of injury when he is being lifted

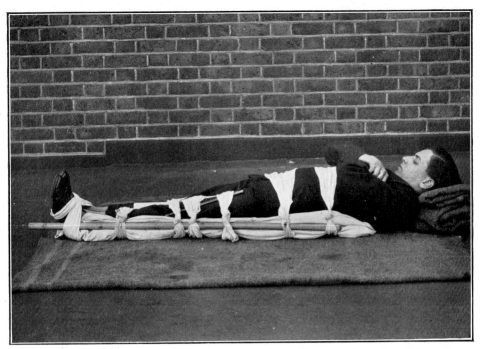

FIG. 107.—FRACTURE OF THIGH. IMPROVISED LONG SPLINT. AMBULANCE PILLOW.

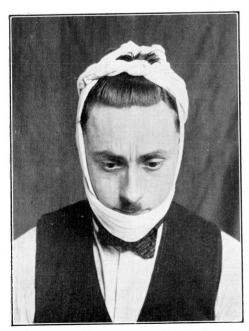

FIG. 108.—FRACTURE OF LOWER JAW.

FIG. 109.—FRACTURE OF RIBS (COMPLETE).

on to it. Should he be suffering from *shock* this must be treated, but stimulants are to be given with caution.

Fractures of the Pelvis, or haunch bones, are the result of a severe crushing force, such as the passage of a wheel over the body or a squeeze between the buffers of railway carriages, and the seriousness or otherwise of the accident depends upon whether or not the *bladder* or *intestines* are involved; should these have escaped the patient usually does well.

Symptoms.—The patient would probably be unable to sit up; he would complain of severe *pain*, or might show symptoms of *shock*.

Treatment.—A broad binder should be applied firmly round the injured region, and a long splint, applied as in fracture of the thigh, to keep the body rigid during removal. The shock must also be treated in the usual manner.

FRACTURES OF BONES OF THE FACE

A peculiarity of these fractures is that they are very frequently *compound;* so that attention has to be paid to the *bleeding*, which is sometimes severe. The wound is generally on the inner or mucous membrane side of the bone, as, for instance, in fracture of the lower jaw, where the bleeding comes from the mouth.

Fracture of Bones of the Nose is a common accident, and is the result of *direct violence*, such as a severe blow.

Symptoms.—*Bleeding* from the nose and great *swelling* of the face. Permanent *deformity* frequently results if the bones are not replaced in their natural position, and for this reason skilled advice should always be obtained.

The immediate *treatment* consists in applying cold water dressings to the bruised part, or ice, if this can be procured. Should the bleeding from the nose be profuse, this must also be attended to; but as a rule the cold applications both soothe the pain and arrest the hæmorrhage.

Fracture of the Lower Jaw is another common accident, the result of a blow or a kick, and is generally *compound* into the mouth, the mucous membrane being very thin. The fracture is commonly situated near the eye tooth, though other parts of the bone are also liable to be broken.

The *symptoms* of the injury are as a rule very characteristic; the patient endeavours to hold the fragments together, and is generally found supporting the jaw with his hand. He is unable to speak, and should he attempt to move the jaw he may feel the *crepitus* produced by the broken ends of the bones grating against each other. On passing a finger along the *teeth* an irregularity in their line will be detected, and there is bleeding from the mouth.

Treatment.—Take a bandage *folded broad*, place the centre of it under the chin; take the ends up one on each side of the face, and knot them on the top of the head; thus firmly fixing the lower jaw to the upper one, in addition, as there is sometimes a tendency for the *chin* to shoot forwards, a second bandage is folded narrow, the centre is placed on the chin, the ends are taken to the back of the head above the nape of the neck, crossed there, and brought forward again and tied on the forehead. If this bandage is not long enough to allow of its being knotted on the forehead, this may be done at the back of the head, and the tags of the two bandages tied together as in the figure (Fig. 108). To control the bleeding from the mouth the patient should be given ice to suck, or have sips of cold water frequently, and should not be allowed to talk.

Fractures of the Skull are caused by *direct violence*, such as blows or falls on the head : they may be situated on the *vault* or upper part of the head, or at the *base*, where the head rests on the spinal column. Those of the *vault* are usually *compound*, as they are the result of a fall on some sharp object, or of a direct blow.

The *symptoms* depend entirely upon the extent to which the *brain* has been injured. If it has been more or less severely *shaken* by the fall or blow, the patient is found in a state of *unconsciousness* more or less complete, and has lost all power of motion, and is said to be suffering from *concussion*, the *pulse* is slow and irregular, the *skin* cold, the *breathing* is shallow, the *pupils* or dark part of the eyes may be dilated or contracted, or one may be dilated and the other contracted.

Should the shaking have been not very severe, or should there be no more serious complications, after a longer or shorter period of time, the patient shows signs of improvement, his colour improves, he may move a limb, and can be roused if spoken to in a loud voice, the pulse becomes stronger, and he may *vomit*. (These signs of improvement are due to the *reaction* which follows an improvement in the circulation of the blood in the brain; and the great danger of giving *stimulants* in cases of head injury is that the reaction may be too great, too much blood being suddenly sent into the brain by the stimulating action of the alcohol on the heart, and inflammation of the brain may result; so that it must be taken as a fixed rule that stimulants are never to be administered in such accidents.) The signs of improvement become more apparent, and eventually, with the 'exception of a strong disinclination for mental or bodily exertion, the patient feels quite well. On the other hand, if in addition to the shaking of the brain, a blood-vessel in the brain has been ruptured, giving rise to *hæmorrhage*, or should a bit of bone have been driven into or be pressing upon the brain, as frequently happens in cases of fracture of the *base* of the skull, symptoms of *compression* supervene, and these are the same as those of *apoplexy* or *stroke*. The patient becomes absolutely insensible, and cannot be roused at all; the breathing is slow and *stertorous*, the pupils may be dilated or contracted, but they remain *fixed*, and light has no effect on them. In addition there may be *bleeding* from the *nose* and *mouth*, and blood and a watery discharge may be poured out from the *ear*. Whilst one or other of the above symptoms may be present, the most important guide after all, especially in an emergency, is the *nature of the injury*, so that, with the history of a fall from a height on to the head, or of a severe blow, followed by *unconsciousness* of longer or shorter duration, the case must be treated as one of *injury to the brain*, leaving the point as to whether or not a fracture exists to be decided by the surgeon, who should be sent for immediately. Much may be done, however, by the *intelligent* bystander to help the sufferer in his extremity during the time that elapses before the arrival of the medical man, all his efforts being in the direction of *preventing further injury to the brain*. The patient must be kept *lying down*, with his head slightly raised, *stimulants* in any form whatever must be kept from him at all costs—a difficult task sometimes, a glass of whisky being the one and only form of *emergency treatment* "the man on the street" has any faith in. Should there be a wound on the head it must be carefully and thoroughly *cleansed* with clean cold water, and protected by a piece of cloth dipped in cold water being applied to it, and kept in position by a handkerchief.

The removal of the patient to his home or the nearest hospital must be effected with the utmost care. The accident is serious enough, but any roughness or jolting would render the case hopeless. He must be removed on some form of *stretcher*, and this should be carried by hand rather than on an ambulance waggon. In lifting him on to the stretcher, special attention must be paid to the head, that it is kept steady. On arrival at his home, should that be his destination, he must be carefully laid in bed with his head slightly raised. The room must be darkened, and no talking allowed in it. *Cold applications* must be made to the head in the form of cloths wrung out of cold water, or a mixture of water and Eau de Cologne, or of ice, broken into small pieces and put into a sponge-bag, or tied up in a piece of flannel and applied to the head. Hot bottles are to be put to the patient's feet, care being taken that they are not too hot; for in cases where the patient is insensible the feet might be severely burned, as he himself cannot feel. The indications for treatment then are—

1. To prevent further injury by careful handling.
2. To keep the head cool.
3. To keep the feet warm.
4. To avoid all stimulants.
5. To see that the room is well ventilated, and that no loud talking is permitted in it.

In conclusion, it only remains to say that *gentleness* must be the watchword of those who are engaged in the emergency treatment of a fracture. In whatever region of the body it may be situated, they must bear in mind that the *dangers* of a fracture lie in the direction of a *simple* one being converted into a *compound*—of the sharp end of a broken bone being thrust into a large blood-vessel, causing serious bleeding, or of injuring important internal organs. That the risks of any of these calamities befalling a patient are greatly increased, nay, they are frequently brought about, by the rough handling of the anxious but ignorant friend. "Touch not, handle not, but look with all the eyes you've got," should be the motto in *examining* a fracture, and when the time comes for treatment and removal, be gentle! be careful!

SUFFOCATION

The term *suffocation*, medically known as *asphyxia*, is applied to that description of accident in which a greater or less degree of interference with the breathing functions is represented. As the main duty represented in breathing is that of getting rid of the waste products which accumulate in the blood as the result of our bodily work, and also the taking in of the oxygen gas which is a necessary part of our food—and without which all vital action would cease—it can readily be seen that when obstruction to breathing exists, grave results may be produced within a very short space of time.

Suffocation may be produced in various ways. Thus the case of choking represented by a mass of food becoming impacted at the top of the windpipe offers a typical illustration, and directions will be duly found in another Section regarding the relief of such cases. Suffocation, however, may be represented by *hanging*, which may be either the result of accident, or as is more usually the case, may be attempted for suicidal purposes. In a third class of cases we may meet with suffocation induced by *the breathing of poisonous gases.* In connection with this subject we have also to take into consideration *cases of drowning,* in which death undoubtedly takes place by a form of suffocation.

Hanging.—Dealing first with cases of *hanging,* we may note the difference between what may be termed "judicial hanging," as represented on the scaffold in expiation of the crime of murder, and that form of hanging represented in the suicide. In the former case the neck is broken by the introduction of the "long drop." In the latter case, where a man, say, suspends himself from the back of a door with his feet almost touching or actually on the ground, we find death to result from pure strangulation, that is from undue pressure on the windpipe preventing the entrance of air into the lungs.

It is a curious fact that when the public come face to face with a case of the latter kind, the tendency is at once to rush off to seek assistance. The duty of the ambulance student here is clear. Common sense alone should teach him that if the person is capable of being recovered at all, *the sooner he is cut down the better.* In severing the cord we must be careful that the body is not allowed to fall to the floor, so that cutting the cord with one hand we should support the body with the other, and thus allow it to reach the ground gently. Instantly, of course, any tight constriction around the neck must be removed, and all clothing likewise be taken away from the neck and chest. If it so happens that the body is warm, there will be the greater chance of reviving the individual. It will be necessary therefore for those attending the patient at once to commence the practice of *artificial respiration.* The various modes of carrying out this procedure will be fully described in the Section dealing with the recovery of apparently drowned persons. It may, however, be mentioned here that on the prompt and continued performance of artificial breathing will depend the chances of recovery of the individual. If additional assistance is at hand, cold water may be dashed on the chest at intervals. The legs also may be rubbed upwards with warm cloths to favour the return of blood to the heart and veins. In a desperate case, where the face is very much flushed and congested, the opening of a vein might be followed by favourable results. This procedure may be performed in one of the veins of the arm. A tight cord or ligature should be bound above the seat of the incision, and the blade of a clean penknife passed into the swollen vein in the long direction.

An accident which is of not unfrequent occurrence in the case of infants is that known as *smothering.* Through some carelessness or other on the part of the mother, a child sleeping with its parents may be overlain, or through some accident may be suffocated through the bed-clothes enveloping its nose and mouth. The same mode of treatment described in the case of suffocation by hanging is applicable in the case of the child.

Poisonous Gases.—In the case of *suffocation through breathing poisonous gases*, one of the chief examples of dangerous gases apt to be met with in ordinary life is *carbonic acid gas*, or as it is also called, *carbonic dioxide*. This gas is met with in deep mines and wells. It is the "choke damp" of the miner, and the practice of a man who is engaged to clean out a well of lowering a lighted candle before he descends is a wise one, inasmuch as carbonic acid gas does not support combustion or flame. The extinction of the light indicates that it is unsafe for the man to proceed further. This gas, it may be added, is present naturally in the air we breathe. It is the gas given off from our lungs, and which is found in the air of hot, ill-ventilated rooms. It caused the death of the persons in the Black Hole of Calcutta, and also acted fatally in certain cases of steamships where passengers have had the hatches battened down upon them during a storm without proper precaution being taken to provide a supply of fresh air. The vapour of burned charcoal represents another gas called by the chemist *carbonic oxide*. The breathing of this gas in an apartment all apertures of which have been closed, is a favourite mode of suicide in France. Carbonic acid gas and other gases are also found in the neighbourhood of lime and brick kilns, and accidents have sometimes happened to tramps and others who have lain down to sleep in the near vicinity of such places. Ordinary coal gas may also exercise fatal effects when a sufficient quantity of it has been breathed. In sewers and cesspools, occasionally, a gas known as *sulphuretted hydrogen* is developed. This gas gives off the characteristic smell of rotten eggs. If breathed in any great quantity, it may be fatal to life.

The proper mode of treatment in any such case is of course the immediate removal of the patient from the vicinity of his accident. He must be taken at once into a pure fresh atmosphere. Following out the rule applying to all cases of unconsciousness, all clothing must be removed from the neck and chest, whilst the limbs may be rubbed upwards and friction applied to the body generally. Cold water should be dashed on the face and the chest. It will, however, be understood that here, as in the case of ordinary suffocation, our mainstay is the *prompt performance of artificial respiration*, by way of exciting the lungs to perform their work and to secure the admission to and expulsion of air from the chest.

Rescue from Suffocation.—Certain directions might also here be given as to the best mode of rescuing persons who have been overcome by poisonous gases. Naturally this procedure is one not unattended with danger to those who rush to the rescue. In the case of a room filled with the vapour of burning charcoal, it is only to be entered under the condition, first, of the rescuer taking in a very deep breath, and of placing over his mouth and nose a cloth which has been soaked in vinegar and water. His next move must be made to the window, which should either be thrown open or the glass broken. In this way fresh air can be obtained for the rescuer and for the patient. In rescuing a person from a well or similar situation the same precaution should be observed. The mouth should be protected by a cloth dipped in vinegar and water, and careful precautions must be taken so that on the slightest appearance of danger to the rescuer he may be at once pulled up into the outer air.

It is proper also to point out the danger which attends the practice of those persons who in popular language " go to look for an escape of gas with a naked light." The mixture of gas and air in a room is a highly inflammable and explosive compound. Where an escape of gas is found the windows should be widely thrown open and no lights be used.

BURNS AND SCALDS

The difference between a burn and scald is rather a matter of distinction of the particular kind of heat causing the injury than of different effects produced by the application of intense heat. The burn is an injury produced by ordinary dry heat, as by fire, whereas a scald is the result of exposure of the body to moist heat or to the action of hot fluids. Viewing the burn as an accident, it may be noted that first of all it is an extremely painful form of injury, and it is important to note, therefore, in connection with this remark, that what is called *shock* is apt to be present in a very severe character, even in what is an apparently trivial injury of the kind noted. *Shock* is a term that is applied to the state of more or less pronounced collapse which follows the receipt of an injury. Its symptoms are marked by paleness of the skin and lips, by faintness, sometimes accompanied by nausea (or a tendency to vomit), by weakened heart action, enfeebled respiration, and a cold and clammy condition of the skin. All these symptoms indicate the effect of the injury upon the nervous system. As " shock " is a condition which follows injuries at large, it may be well to remind readers here of the general treatment applicable to all cases of this kind. The first indication in shock *is to keep the patient warm;* hence, after an injury of any kind sustained, even in hot weather, the patient may shiver and complain of cold. He must therefore be carefully covered up, and hot water bottles applied to his feet. It may be necessary also to administer stimulants in the shape of a little brandy or whisky, preferably given hot. The patient should be kept perfectly quiet, in a recumbent position, and with the head fairly low.

After burns, shock is the condition which is specially noticeable in children, and therefore in their case strict attention to the condition in question is even more necessary than in the case of adults. There are various degrees noted in the case of burning, ranging from a mere scorching of the skin onwards to the stage where blisters form, and finally including a third stage, where there is a greater or less amount of actual destruction of the tissues involved. In the treatment of a burn or scald, the main idea which should animate us is that of *excluding the air* from the injured surface as quickly and as completely as possible. The burn of course requires to be dressed, and if in the course of the injury the clothing, as is very likely, will have also been burned, it is important to note the proper procedure to be followed in removing any fragments of clothing which may remain attached to the burned surface. The importance of removing all such foreign bodies from what is practically a wounded surface will be apparent in view of the fact that the healing of the injury can only take place when all extraneous matters or substances have been completely taken away. Therefore fragments of clothing must be carefully taken away from the burned surface. No roughness must be employed here. The clothing has not to be forcibly removed, and if any of it should remain adherent to the burned surface, place the burned part in tepid water, thus moistening the clothing, so that it may be removed without pain. In some cases, soaking such attached portions of clothing with olive oil has been recommended. This is a plan often pursued in cases of burns of the legs where the stockings are adherent.

Dressings for Burns.—It may be remembered in connection with burns that the placing of a burned limb in fairly warm water will frequently give relief. Supposing the burned surface has in this way been thoroughly cleansed, or at any rate having had removed from it all fragments of clothing, the question of the best dressing for a burn naturally crops up. *Carron oil*, already alluded to in connection with injuries of the eye (consisting of equal parts of linseed oil and lime water), forms a very admirable dressing. This should be freely applied on strips of lint, and then the whole covered with dry lint or cotton wool, so as to make the patient in every way comfortable. If blisters form, it is probably best to prick them to allow the escape of their contained fluid. This opinion has been disputed, but if we have regard to the fact that the mere act of pressing the blisters may suffice to burst them, and that their removal has to be effected sooner or later, forms a strong argument in favour of pricking them at once and dressing them with oil.

Other substances have been used for the dressing of burns. Where carron oil cannot be had, use ordinary pure oil such as olive oil, carbolic oil (of the strength of 1 to 40), vaseline, castor oil, or even fresh lard or butter. Occasionally dry remedies may be applied to burns, but these last are rather applicable to burns which are not of a high degree of severity. Such substances as flour, starch, oxide of zinc, carbonate of soda powder, and borax have been used in this way. A little turpentine added to the carron oil is a plan which is adopted in many ironworks where accidents by burning are apt to occur, and the advantage of this latter procedure is said to consist in the addition tending to cause the oil to allay the pain more perfectly.

Where burning accidents occur from the skin coming in contact with any acid of a corrosive nature (such as sulphuric acid, or vitriol, nitric acid, and the like), the treatment by means of dusting on the part powdered chalk or whiting is that which should be adopted. The chalk or whiting should be afterwards washed off with water after a short interval. If no other application is at hand, a free use of cold water may be employed in such cases.

Scalding the Throat.—It is important here to note a species of accident that is not at all uncommon in the case of very young children. If left at home unattended in a kitchen where a kettle has been placed on the fire, little children may be tempted for one reason or another to drink out of the spout of the kettle. In this way a severe scald of the throat is sustained, with the result that dangerous swelling and inflammation of the throat are liable to occur very speedily, and suffocation of the child may be thus brought about. Naturally, in the case of an accident of this kind, the services of the doctor must at once be requisitioned, but if medical aid cannot be procured at once, while the doctor is being sent for the child must be treated for shock, wrapped in a warm blanket, by the way of counteracting the chill and the shock. Hot sponges or flannels wrung out of hot water should be applied to the throat outside, and the atmosphere of the room in which the child remains should be kept moist by means of steam from a bronchitis kettle placed on the fire allowed to escape into the apartment. Small pieces of ice may be placed in the mouth, and in some cases very favourable results have been obtained by giving cod liver oil itself, or a mixture of equal parts of cod oil and lime water, in doses of a teaspoonful. If this can be swallowed at all, the application has not merely a soothing influence on the scalded parts, but also gives the child a certain amount of nourishment. It is in such cases that the aid of the surgeon may be requisitioned to perform an operation — that of opening the windpipe—by way of saving the child's life.

Clothing on Fire.—It is of some importance in connection with the treatment and prevention of burns to know specially *what should be done in cases in which the clothing of a person takes fire.* Here, as in many other affairs of life, there is a right and a wrong way of treating the person. When, say, the clothing of a woman takes fire, instead of rushing immediately from the room calling for assistance, a procedure tantamount to causing the flames to assume greater violence, the person ought at once to lie down on the floor. If assistance is immediately coming and she is standing, the bystander must insist upon the person assuming the recumbent position. In this way the flames get less play, and if the patient in the recumbent position is rolled over and over, a certain amount of power of extinguishing the flames is thus exercised. An additional measure of extreme value is that of seizing a rug, blanket, table-cloth, or anything else of the kind which may be at hand, and of enveloping the sufferer in its folds. Thus enveloped, she may be rolled from side to side by way of extinguishing the flames by means of pressure. Water should of course be obtained as quickly as possible, and the patient drenched therewith in order to extinguish the heat of the burned clothes, inasmuch as a certain amount of further injury might be sustained by the contact of the heated clothes with the skin, even after the flames have been subdued. The main point in connection with these directions is undoubtedly that of causing the patient at once to assume the flat position.

[*The Treatment for Foreign Bodies in the Eye, Ear, Nose, Throat, and Windpipe, Drowning, Fits, Bleeding, Wounds, Poisoning, &c., and the various methods of Carrying the Injured, are included in Volume III.*]

END OF VOL. II.

Made and Printed in Great Britain by
Hazell, Watson & Viney, Ld., London and Aylesbury.
5450